RIVER PROCESSES

RIVER PROCESSES

An Introduction to Fluvial Dynamics

André Robert

Department of Geography, York University, Toronto, Ontario, Canada

A member of the Hodder Headline Group
LONDON
Distributed in the United States of America by
Oxford University Press Inc., New York

First published in Great Britain in 2003 by
Arnold, a member of the Hodder Headline Group,
338 Euston Road, London NW1 3BH

http://www.arnoldpublishers.com

Distributed in the United States of America by
Oxford University Press Inc.,
198 Madison Avenue, New York, NY 10016

The advice and information in this book are believed to be true and
accurate at the date of going to press, but neither the author nor the publisher
can accept any legal responsibility or liability for any errors or omissions.

British Library Cataloguing in Publication Data
A catalogue record for this book is available from the British Library

Library of Congress Cataloging-in-Publication Data
A catalog record for this book is available from the Library of Congress

ISBN 0 340 76338 8 (hb)
ISBN 0 340 76339 6 (pb)

3 4 5 6 7 8 9 10

Typeset in 10 on 12pt Palatino by Dorchester Typesetting Group Ltd
Printed and bound in India by Replika Press Pvt. Ltd.

What do you think about this book? Or any other Arnold title?
Please send your comments to feedback.arnold@hodder.co.uk

For Josée, Myriam, Geneviève, and Mélissa

CONTENTS

LIST OF SYMBOLS

a	acceleration
A	cross-sectional area
A_a, A_b	tributary cross-sectional areas
A_c	cross-sectional area of receiving stream
A_h	cross-sectional area of hyporheic zone
B	bedform shape factor (section 3.5)
B	percentage of silt and clay (section 5.1)
c	cohesion
C_d	drag coefficient
c_s	local sediment concentration
d	flow depth
d_r	reference depth
d_s	scour depth
D	particle size
D_0	initial grain size
D_{50}	median particle size
DFM	drag force moment
D_r	reference particle size
e	void ratio (section 3.2.3.)
e	efficiency ratio
E_p	potential energy
E_{pg}	gravitational potential energy component
E_{pp}	pressure potential energy component
E_v	kinetic energy
f	frequency (section 2.6)
f	Darcy – Weisbach coefficient (section 2.5)
f'	grain friction factor
f''	form friction factor
F	force
F_d	driving force (Chapter 1)
F_d	form drag (Chapter 2)
Fr	Froude number
g	acceleration due to gravity
g_b	volumetric transport rate (per unit width)
h	bedform height
h_Δ	head loss

H	hole size
H_p	potential head
H_t	total head
H_v	kinetic energy head
HZ	hyporheic zone
I	input
I_b	bedload transport rate
I_{b*}	dimensionless bedload transport rate
k_s	equivalent sand roughness height
K	intrinsic permeability (section 6.4)
K	subsurface grain size (section 3.2)
K	ratio of grain to form roughness (section 3.5)
l	bedform length (spacing) (section 4.2.1)
l	length of separation zone (section 4.2.3)
L	distance
LRBW	low-relief bed wave
m	mass
n	Manning coefficient
N	number of observations
n_g	Manning particle roughness coefficient
O	output
p	porosity
P_a	atmospheric pressure
P_d	pressure downstream of obstacle
$P1_f$	percentage of bed material finer than 1 mm in spawning gravels
$P1_i$	initial percentage of bed material finer than 1 mm
P_u	pressure upstream of obstacle
P_w	water pressure
Q	discharge
Q_a, Q_b	tributary discharges
Q_b	bankfull discharge
Q_c	discharge of receiving stream
Q_m	discharge of main channel (at a confluence)
Q_r	discharge ratio
Q_s	rate of movement
Q_t	discharge of tributary (at a confluence)
Q_{tot}	total discharge (of receiving stream at a confluence)
r_c	radius of curvature
R	hydraulic radius
Re	Reynolds number
Re_p	particle Reynolds number
RMS	root-mean-square
s	sinuosity
S	slope
S_b	bed slope
S'	grain component of water surface slope

S''	form component of water surface slope
SSC	suspended sediment concentration
S_t	shear strength
Str	Strouhal number
S_w	water surface slope
SWM	submerged weight moment
TKE	turbulent kinetic energy
T	time
u	instantaneous downstream velocity
u'	deviation from average downstream velocity (instantaneous reading)
U	average velocity
U_b	bedform migration rate (section 3.5)
U_b	bedload velocity (section 6.2)
U_g	average velocity of grains
U_m	main channel average flow velocity (at a confluence)
U_s	water surface velocity
U_t	tributary average flow velocity (at a confluence)
U_y	average velocity at height y above bed surface
U_*	shear velocity
U_0	pore-water velocity
v	instantaneous vertical velocity
V	average vertical velocity
V	volume
v'	deviation from mean vertical velocity (instantaneous reading)
V_0	settling (terminal) velocity
V_p	volume of voids
V_s	volume of solid
V_t	total volume
w	channel width (sections 1.1 and 1.2)
w	instantaneous lateral velocity (section 2.6)
W	work (section 1.1)
W	average lateral velocity (section 2.6)
w'	deviation from average lateral velocity (instantaneous reading)
X	independent variable
y	height above bed surface
y_0	roughness length
Y	dependent variable
z	surface elevation
Z	water surface super-elevation
α	empirical coefficient (section 3.2)
α	junction angle (section 5.4)
β	empirical coefficient
γ	weight density
$\gamma(h)$	semi-variance at lag h
δ	thickness of laminar sublayer

ΔS	change in storage
ϵ	coefficient of eddy viscosity
ϵ_s	sediment mixing coefficient
η	packing density
θ	dimensionless shear stress (Shields parameter)
θ_c	critical dimensionless shear stress
θ'	grain dimensionless shear stress
θ''	form dimensionless shear stress
ι	mixing length
κ	von Karman's constant
λ	streak spacing (section 2.6)
λ	axial wavelength (section 5.1)
λ_{arc}	arc wavelength
λ_s	dimensionless streak spacing
μ	dynamic viscosity
μ	pore pressure
ν	kinematic viscosity
ρ	water density
ρ_s	sediment density
σ	normal stress
σ'	effective normal stress
τ	shear stress
τ_0	bed shear stress
τ_0'	grain shear stress
τ_0''	form shear stress
τ_c	critical shear stress
τ_R	Reynolds stress
ϕ	particle size (phi scale) (section 3.1)
ϕ	angle of internal friction (section 3.2)
Φ	pivoting angle
ω	stream power per unit bed area
ω_c	critical stream power
Ω	stream power per unit length

PREFACE

This represents a concise, up-to-date textbook on fluvial processes, emphasizing primarily flow and sedimentary processes in alluvial channels. In its approach and level of treatment, my contribution is aimed at complementing Knighton's book (1998) on forms and processes in rivers.

The book was developed over the years while teaching Fluvial Geomorphology in the Department of Geography at York University, Toronto, Ontario (to both arts and science students). It is intended primarily for senior undergraduate and graduate students in physical geography, but also for students in other disciplines such as Earth science, environmental science, process sedimentology, and ecology.

There are six chapters, starting with a brief introduction to basic principles underlying the study of physical processes in rivers (intended primarily for students with little background in physical sciences). The second part of Chapter 1 emphasizes the factors controlling river bed morphology (bedforms and channel patterns) and the complex interactions among numerous variables at work in alluvial channels. This introductory section leads on to Chapter 2, which deals with stream flow processes. In addition to introducing basic concepts on the properties of fluids, boundary layers, and flow resistance, this chapter emphasizes flow turbulence and its significance for the study of fluvial processes. The concepts presented in the subsection on turbulence are used later in the text when dealing with sediment transport processes and bedform dynamics. Chapter 3 deals with sediment properties, the processes of erosion and the processes of sediment transport. Only the transport of particulate grains is considered, and sediment sources from the stream channel are emphasized. Solute behaviour is omitted; the book does not address specifically catchment hydrology, which is critical to understanding solute delivery processes. To adequately address these questions would represent a task that is beyond the goals of this book, and a brief treatment of such an important topic would have been inappropriate.

The concepts presented in the two sections on water flow and sediment transport provide the foundation for the subsequent chapters on bedforms and channel patterns. Flow turbulence and its interactions with bed sediment have been the central theme of numerous research endeavours in the last decade or so. Flow-bed interactions are emphasized, and the focus of Chapter 4 is on bedforms, in both sand- and gravel-bed rivers (and in sand–gravel mixtures). Chapter 5 deals with channel patterns. Flow and sediment transport processes in curved channels are detailed, together with braiding mechanisms in coarse-grained channels and related physical processes. This chapter also includes a subsection on channel confluences (neglected in previous books). In addition to being the nodes of the channel networks, confluences are ubiquitous in braided rivers, and significant progress has been made recently in the study of alluvial flow dynamics at channel junctions. Chapter 6 is novel in a fluvial textbook; it emphasizes river channels (bed sediment and submerged vegetation), aquatic habitats, and the hyporheic zone.

While writing this book, I had to keep constantly in mind that my main goal was to produce a text for teaching at the senior undergraduate level and at the graduate level. In that respect, I tried to provide a level of detail in the treatment that will allow a proper understanding of the fluvial processes involved. The list of references presented is not exhaustive, but an attempt was made, however, to include references to numerous review articles, in order to allow the reader to pursue a particular topic in greater depth. I have also deliberately tried to focus on the literature published during approximately the last two decades, with only occasional references being prior to 1980.

I hope that this text will prove to be a useful addition to the literature on fluvial processes and that it will contribute somewhat to a greater collaboration among researchers sharing an interest in rivers.

A.R.
June 2002
Burnaby, Canada

ACKNOWLEDGEMENTS

This book was written while on a leave of absence from York University, Canada. From August 2001 to June 2002, I was Visiting Faculty at Simon Fraser University (Department of Geography), British Columbia. I am grateful for the support of the then-Chair of the Geography Department: Professor Alison Gill. Access to library and computing facilities was instrumental for this project and the office space provided (with its quiet environment and the view of the Coastal Mountains) proved to be the ideal environment for such a writing endeavour.

Financial assistance was provided by the Faculty of Arts, York University (Sabbatical Leave Fellowship). Carol Randall and Carolyn King (Cartography Office, Department of Geography, York University) drew the illustrations.

I am also most grateful to Mike Church (University of British Columbia) and Ted Hickin (Simon Fraser University), who provided constructive and helpful comments on the manuscript. I am, of course, solely responsible for any shortcomings or errors that may remain in the text.

1

FLUVIAL PROCESSES: AN INTRODUCTION

The word *fluvial* is a general term that refers to anything produced by the action of a river, and also to organisms that are found in rivers (i.e. fluvial forms, fluvial processes, fluvial sediments and freshwater organisms; Thomas and Goudie, 2000). *Dynamics*, in turn, is a branch of physical science (and a subdivision of mechanics) that is concerned with moving bodies and the physical factors that affect the motion: force, mass, momentum and energy. (*Kinematics*, in comparison, describes motion, without regard to its causes in terms of position, velocity, and acceleration.) The term *fluvial dynamics*, therefore, is generally used with reference to water flow, sediment movement, and to bedform features resulting from the interactions of flow and sediment transport in alluvial channels.

1.1.1 Physical quantities

A relatively small number of quantities are needed to explain fluvial geomorphic processes. One of these quantities therefore is *force*, which can be loosely defined as anything that changes or tends to change the state of motion in a body (Ritter *et al.*, 1995). Force is a vector quantity, which means that it has both magnitude and direction. A force balance relation is often used in fluvial geomorphology, where a driving force and a resistance force are investigated together. To paraphrase Ritter *et al.* (1995), fluvial geomorphology can then be examined by using physical concepts that revolve around the application of force on surface materials. All movement is the result of forces, and in the natural environment, several forces are generally involved in a particular situation.

In more specific terms, a force is defined in terms of moving a mass with a particular acceleration:

$$F = ma \qquad (1.1)$$

where F is force, m is the mass of a body and a is acceleration. Gravitational attraction is a basic force in Earth science. Acceleration due to gravity varies very little over the Earth's surface, and is considered constant at 9.81 m s^{-2}. The measure of force (F) is weight and the standard unit of force is the newton (or dyne). A newton is the force necessary to give a mass of 1 kg an acceleration of 1 m s^{-2}. When expressed as a force per unit area, this is referred to as *stress*, and expressed in newtons per square metre (N m^{-2}) or pascal (Pa). It is common in fluvial studies to employ dynes cm^{-2}, where 1 dyne $= 10^{-5}$ N (with 10 dyn cm^{-2} being equal to 1 N m^{-2}). The concept of *shear stress*, for instance, is absolutely crucial in fluvial studies, and this will be explained in detail later.

There are a number of additional quantities derived from force. *Work* (*W*) is determined from the product of force and distance. More specifically, the amount of work done is defined as the product of force and the displacement of the body in the direction of the force. For instance, in order for a stream to move a cobble from one point to another, an adequate force must be exerted over the required distance (and therefore work must be done). The unit of work is the joule (J), which is the work done when a force of 1 N acts over a distance of 1 metre.

Related to the concept of work is *energy*, which can be defined as the ability or capacity to do work. Work and energy possess the same units. Water flowing above a rough surface involves the expenditure of energy (see section 2.2 for a detailed account of energy principles). In simple terms, the potential energy of a body results from its position relative to some reference level, while the kinetic energy of a body results from its motion. The potential energy of water therefore decreases along the length of a stream as its elevation above sea-level decreases. On the other hand, average stream velocity increases along river segments of sufficient length and the kinetic energy of the flow increases as potential energy decreases and water flows down the channel. The flow of water downstream is obviously resisted by the alluvial channel sediment (which tends to significantly limit flow acceleration), and the energy expenditure is significantly affected by changes in bed material size and related depositional features in the downstream direction in rivers (see Chapters 3 and 4 in particular).

Finally, the concept of *power* is also directly related to force and work. Power is the rate of doing work, and is obtained by dividing the work done by the time period considered. In order to push a body from one point to another, a small force can be exerted over a long period of time or a large force over a short period of time. The net effect is the same but, in the second strategy, higher power must be developed. Stream power has been a dominant concept in fluvial geomorphology in relation to sediment transport processes (Bagnold, 1977, 1980).

1.1.2 Dimensional character

A number of rules can be formulated for the analysis and manipulation of physical quantities commonly encountered in fluvial studies (Dingman, 1984, pp. 7–11). Most of them are very simple but are sometimes neglected or overlooked.

- The numerical magnitude of a physical quantity has no meaning without complete information on the unit(s) of measurement.
- The dimensional character of a physical quantity is expressed as either some combination of length (L), mass (M), time (T) and temperature, or is dimensionless (although temperature is often neglected in fluvial studies, unless dealing with viscosity and Reynolds numbers, as explained later).
- The dimensional character of each physical quantity can be expressed as:

$$M^a \, L^b \, T^c$$

where a, b, and c are integers or a ratio of integers. For dimensionless numbers, $a = b = c = 0$, and the dimensional character is expressed as [1].
- An equation that completely and correctly describes a physical relation has the same dimensions on both sides of the equal sign.
- When the dimensions are different, such an equation is referred to as inhomogeneous. In an inhomogeneous equation, the units of each variable in the equation must be specified. In this type of equation, all constants must be changed if the equation is to be used in another system of units (and the equation expresses, at best, a correlation).

The basic physical quantities and their dimensional character used in fluvial studies are the following:

- **Velocity**, a vector quantity, is the rate at which the position of a given body changes with time ($L\,T^{-1}$).
- **Acceleration** is the rate of change of velocity with time and has the dimensions:

$$(L\,T^{-1})/T = L\,T^{-1}\,T^{-1} = L\,T^{-2}$$

Thus a body is said to have an acceleration when its velocity changes in magnitude as the motion proceeds.
- **Momentum** is a vector defined by the product of the mass of a given body and its velocity ($M\,L\,T^{-1}$). Momentum flux ($M\,L\,T^{-2}$) is also often used in fluvial studies. The momentum per unit time (or momentum flux; Chanson, 1999) of a water body passing a particular point in a stream can be determined from ρQU, where ρ is water density (usually assumed to be constant at 1000 kg m^{-3}), Q is discharge ($L^3\,T^{-1}$), and U is average velocity.
- **Force** is defined in terms of moving a mass with a particular acceleration, and hence has a dimension resulting from multiplying mass and acceleration, i.e. $M\,L\,T^{-2}$.
- **Stress** is force divided by area, and the dimensional character becomes

$(M\ L\ T^{-2})/L^2 = M\ L^{-1}\ T^{-2}$. Pressure also has dimensions resulting from dividing a force by an area. The measure *bar* (as often used, for instance, in meteorology) is taken to be equivalent to a pressure of $10^5\ N\ m^{-2}$.

- **Work** is defined as force times distance, which becomes $M\ L\ T^{-2}$. $L = M\ L^2\ T^{-2}$. The unit for work is the joule (J).
- **Energy** is defined as the ability or capacity to do work, and is dimensionally equivalent to work.
- **Power** is the rate of doing work. Rate of doing work is work divided by time: $(M\ L^2\ T^{-2})/T$, which becomes $M\ L^2\ T^{-3}$. The units for power are watts (W). This is achieved when one joule is being expended per second (1 watt = $1\ J\ s^{-1}$).

To conclude this subsection, let us consider two specific examples as they apply to river flows. These quantities will be used frequently throughout the text, and their overall significance in fluvial geomorphology will become clearer as we proceed.

Bed shear stress. This quantity is used in numerous equations to describe river flows, determine the resistance created by the bed on the flow, determine the force driving the flow downstream, estimate the volume of sediment transported on the river bed, etc. The force driving the flow (F_d) is equal to:

$$F_d = W \sin \theta \qquad (1.2)$$

where W is water weight and θ is the channel slope. Weight is equal to mass times acceleration due to gravity (mg), and $W \sin \theta$ represents the downslope component of mass acted on by acceleration. Mass, in turn, can be substituted by:

$$m = \rho\ V \qquad (1.3)$$

where ρ is mass density (density per unit volume) and V is the volume of water considered. Substituting equation 1.3 into 1.2, the force driving the flow can be defined as:

$$F_d = \rho\ g\ V \sin \theta. \qquad (1.4)$$

Since stress is defined as force per unit area (A), the average shear stress exerted by the flow on the bed (τ_0) can be defined as:

$$F_d/A = \rho\ g\ V/A \sin \theta \qquad (1.5)$$

and:

$$\tau_0 = \rho\ g\ d \sin \theta \qquad (1.6)$$

(where d is flow depth). For small slopes (which is the case for most alluvial channels), $\sin \theta$ is approximately equal to $\tan \theta$ (the rise over a run or the drop in elevation over a given distance) and in general, this quantity is simply referred to as slope (S). Equation 1.6 therefore becomes:

$$\tau_0 = \rho \, g \, d \, S \tag{1.7}$$

which is the basic equation used to estimate average bed shear stress in alluvial channels. In relatively narrow channels, the average flow depth, d, is frequently substituted by the hydraulic radius, R, defined as the ratio of the cross-section area of the channel to the wetter perimeter, P (where P = channel width + $2d$). Equation 1.7 has been extremely useful in numerous field research situations and is, strictly speaking, applicable under uniform flow conditions, i.e. when the average flow depth and the average velocity are constant along a given reach. Thus, the dimensional character of τ_0 is:

$$M \, L^{-3} \, L \, T^{-2} \, L = M \, L^{-1} \, T^{-2} \tag{1.8}$$

(as defined before).

Stream power is also a very significant quantity in sediment transport studies. Stream power represents the rate of doing work (in transporting water and sediment). It is commonly expressed either as stream power per unit length (Ω) or power per unit bed area (ω). Since work is force times distance and power is rate of doing work, it follows from equation 1.4 that:

$$\Omega = (F_d \times L)/t \tag{1.9}$$

and

$$\Omega = (\rho \, g \, V \, S \, L)/t \tag{1.10}$$

where L is distance over which work is being done and t is time period. Since discharge (Q) is volume of water per unit time (V/t), it follows from equation 1.10 that the stream power per unit length (L) is proportional to the product of discharge and channel slope and:

$$\Omega = \rho \, g \, Q \, S. \tag{1.11}$$

Considering that $Q = w \, d \, U$ (where w is channel width, d is flow depth and U is velocity; see section 2.1), the stream power per unit bed area (A) is equal to:

$$\omega = \rho \, g \, w \, d \, U \, S \, L/A. \tag{1.12}$$

Since the bed area is equal to the product of width (w) and distance (L), equation 1.12 can be rewritten as:

$$\omega = \rho \, g \, d \, S \, U = \tau_0 U. \tag{1.13}$$

The stream power per unit bed area is therefore the product of the average shear stress (τ_0) and the average flow velocity (U), and this is the quantity frequently used to predict the rate of sediment movement taking place in the vicinity of the stream bed.

1.1.3 Physical equations

Following Dingman (1984), equations used in fluvial studies can be grouped (broadly) into five major categories. *Regression (empirical)* equations represent a first major type of physical equation used frequently in fluvial studies. Traditionally, empirical regression equations have dominated the study of forms and processes in alluvial channels. A very wide range of field and laboratory studies have been conducted during the last 50 years or so, which have led to numerous equations summarizing these observations. Empirical research (where measurements and observations are obtained under specific field or laboratory conditions) has been used extensively in process-based fluvial studies, providing the framework for describing and understanding the links between river channel morphology on the one hand, and flow and sedimentary processes on the other hand (Richards, 1982; Knighton, 1998). Field and laboratory measurements are also sometimes described as semi-empirical if the general formulation of the equation is derived from theory but specific coefficients determined from experiments or observations. Numerous examples of empirical and semi-empirical equations will be used in this text. This approach has been used extensively, for instance, to estimate flow resistance in both sand- and gravel-bed rivers, under fixed and mobile bed conditions. Another well-known example is the use of empirical regression equations to distinguish between various channel patterns (e.g. straight vs. meandering or meandering vs. braided; see Chapter 5).

Numerous applications in fluvial studies involve the use of power functions, i.e. linear regression techniques applied to logarithmic transformations of field measurements (e.g. Church and Mark, 1980; Ferguson, 1986). Linear regression equations and related power functions may involve more than one independent (or controlling) variable. The general form of the equation is:

$$Y = a\,X^b \qquad (1.14)$$

for the simple case involving one independent variable (X) or:

$$Y = a\,X_1^{b1}\,X_2^{b2} \qquad (1.15)$$

where Y is the dependent variable of interest and X_1 and X_2 represent two statistically significant controlling variables. Most regression equations in fluvial studies involve one or two controlling variables, but more can be added to the general form of equation 1.15. The reason underlying the use of such equations is to 'explain' the observed variability of the variable Y_i from the variation of one (or more than one) independent controlling variable(s). The parameters a, b_1 and b_2 in equation 1.15 are determined from simple linear equations involving logarithmic transformations. For the case of Y vs. X_1 and X_2, the values of a, b_1 and b_2 in equation 1.15 are determined from a multiple regression where:

$$\log Y = \log a + b_1 \log X_1 + b_2 \log X_2. \qquad (1.16)$$

The values of b_1 and b_2 are called partial regression coefficients, and they represent the predicted increase in Y per unit increase in X_j, with the other X variable(s) held constant (or $\log Y$ and $\log X_j$ as in equation 1.16).

A second major group of physical equations consists of forces (description or definition of forces) and, more specifically, balance of forces involved in erosional and depositional processes in alluvial channels. Perhaps the most widely used example in the study of fluvial processes is that related to driving and resisting forces involved in the initial movement of sediment particles resting on a river bed. The analysis of the moment at which a coarse particle resting on a stream bed is entrained by the flow is based on a balance of forces between the weight of the sediment particle itself and the drag force exerted by the flow on the bed (details about this type of approach will be presented in Chapter 3 on sediment transport processes). Similarly, erosion of a river bank may occur when the strength of the bank material (or the force resisting erosion) is less than the shear force exerted by the flowing water against the river bank. Each force may be quantified and a force balance equation can be established to determine stability conditions.

Another major category of physical equations commonly used in fluvial studies consists of equations involving *fluxes*. In the context of river processes, fluxes usually refer to flow–sediment interactions, and therefore to momentum and/or sediment fluxes. Sediment fluxes can be considered for particles transported in suspension within the flow and/or in contact with the bed surface, at a range of spatial and temporal scales. Sediment fluxes can be considered, for instance, at the scale of individual bedforms migrating along a sand-bed channel, at the reach scale, or at the scale of the drainage basin. A range of semi-empirical sediment transport equations have been developed over the years, and some of the most widely used will be presented in section 3.5.

A fourth major approach in fluvial studies involves using *conservation* equations. The basic principles underlying *conservation* equations are fairly simple, yet these principles provide the framework for many equations used in fluvial geomorphology in general. Conservation equations refer to the fact that, in any process, mass (matter), momentum, and energy cannot be created or destroyed. The general statement that refers to conservation balances input (I) and output (O) of mass, momentum, or energy for a given time period and a given space with what is being 'stored' in a given system:

$$I - O = S_2 - S_1 \qquad (1.17)$$

where I is the quantity entering the space, O is the quantity leaving the space, and S_2 and S_1 are the quantities stored in the space (again mass, momentum, or energy) at the beginning and the end of the time period considered, respectively (Dingman, 1984). Another way of writing equation 1.17 above would be:

$$\Delta I - \Delta O = \Delta S \qquad (1.18)$$

where the symbol Δ refers to changes (in input, output or storage) over a given period of time (t).

Alternative names for equations of conservation of matter are continuity or mass-balance equations. Those applied to energy principles are energy-balance equations and, when applied to momentum, they are referred to as momentum equations. A number of simple examples can be provided to illustrate the principles underlying continuity equations. One simple case refers to the river discharge and changes in channel morphology over some short distances. Many rivers are characterized by large-scale bed undulations, i.e. a downstream succession of shallow and deep sections. If there is no tributary input along a given reach, then continuity principles dictate that in shallow cross-sections (smaller cross-section areas) the river must flow faster to preserve mass continuity (section 2.1). Therefore, there must be acceleration from the relatively deep sections to the high topographic points, and deceleration from the shallow to the deep part of the stream. This 'topographic forcing' has significant implications for flow and sediment dynamics, and will be discussed later in the context of bed undulations or bedforms. Further examples could be used in relation to sediment budgets at the scale of the river reach or at the scale of the drainage basin. For the former, a balance can be established between the input of sediment into a given reach (sediment supply) and the transport of sediment through that reach. The difference between the supply or input and the ability of the stream to transport the supplied load may result in changes in storage along the reach, in the form of sediment accumulations or bars (Church, 1992; Ashmore and Church, 1998). At the drainage basin scale, budget equations can be established to assess differences between overall sediment mobilization, storage along rivers in the form of bars and on floodplains, and what is leaving the basin at its downstream end.

Other examples of conservation principles can be provided that refer to flow turbulence in river channels and momentum exchange mechanisms. In particular, it will be shown (Chapter 2) that a 'bursting' process has been documented in turbulent flows – where water parcels may be ejected from the near-bed flow regions towards the water surface. To preserve continuity, this is accompanied by the inverse motions of water parcels from the upper regions in the flow fields towards the bed ('sweep' motions). Similar examples will be discussed later with a focus on turbulent transfer, momentum exchange, and interactions between the flow and the bed of alluvial channels.

Finally, a fifth important group of equations can be referred to as *diffusion equations*. Diffusion equations describe the movement of matter, momentum, or energy in a medium in response to a gradient. The general form of a diffusion equation is:

$$Q_s = -\epsilon_s ds/dx \qquad (1.19)$$

where Q_s is the rate of movement of matter (or momentum or energy) through a unit area, ds/dx represents the gradient of concentration (of mass, for instance), and ϵ_s is a diffusion coefficient. In open-channel flows, the principles underlying diffusion equations can be applied, for instance, to vertical gradients and turbulent mixing of suspended sediment in turbulent water flows (see Chapter 3).

1.2 ALLUVIAL CHANNELS: CONTROLLING FACTORS AND PROCESS-BASED CLASSIFICATION

1.2.1 Water and sediment supply

The term *alluvial channels* refers to channels that flow through sediments which they have previously deposited, and therefore, rivers that are competent to modify the morphology (shape and size) of their channel (Church, 1992). The ability of a river to modify the morphological characteristics of its channel in turn depends on the balance between the erosional force exerted by the river flow and the strength or resistance to erosion of the material forming the bed and the banks. This, in turn, is essentially (but not exclusively) dependent upon the river discharge and the sediment grain size.

Before dealing specifically with the properties of water flows in alluvial channels and the characteristics of bed sediments (see Chapters 2 and 3), it is important to specify the role of sediment size and flow depth (or discharge) in controlling channel morphology, as well as how a process-based classification of rivers can be established using those two controlling factors.

The physical processes in rivers (and therefore their morphology) are determined, generally speaking, by the following four factors (Church, 1992):

- the volume and time distribution of water supplied from upstream
- the volume, time distribution and character of sediment delivered to the channel
- the nature of the material through which the river flows
- the topographic gradient down which the river flows.

Stated differently, the independent channel controls can be described as being the stream discharge, the sediment load input, the bed material size and the bank material composition and strength, and the imposed local topography, i.e. the slope of the valley within which the river is flowing.

Water supply at a given point along a drainage basin obviously depends on the size of the drainage basin itself, with a near linear increase in stream discharge with drainage area being frequently observed. In turn, changes in discharge at a given point along a channel during and after a precipitation event are a function of dominant runoff processes and a range of environmental variables. As drainage area increases, bed material size usually decreases systematically within drainage basins (see section 3.5.5) together with a systematic variation in channel properties and a sharp increase in sediment storage (e.g. floodplain area) once drainage basins reach a 'critical' size (Figure 1.1). The decrease in channel gradient, decrease in particle size, increase in channel size, increase in sediment storage, and gradual but slow increase in average flow velocity represent the overall representation of complex interactions among numerous variables (Church, 1992; Knighton, 1998).

Well-known empirical equations can be used to characterize the relations

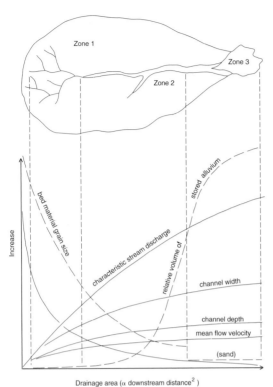

Drainage area (α downstream distance^2)

Figure 1.1 Schematic representation of the variation in channel properties within a drainage basin. After Church (1992), figure 6.3. Reproduced with the permission of the publishers, Blackwell Science Ltd, Oxford, UK. In broad terms, zones 1, 2, and 3 represent the sediment source area, the transfer zone, and the area of deposition, respectively (based on a concept of Schumm, 1977).

between channel characteristics and the downstream increase in discharge within drainage basins (these interrelations being schematically illustrated in Figure 1.1 in terms of rate of change for each individual variable with distance downstream). The empirical equations involving downstream increase in discharge and channel characteristics are known as *hydraulic geometry relationships* (Leopold and Maddock, 1953), and can be summarized as follows:

$$w = aQ^b \tag{1.20}$$

$$d = cQ^f \tag{1.21}$$

$$U = kQ^m \tag{1.22}$$

$$S = gQ^z \tag{1.23}$$

where w is width, d is depth, U is velocity, S is channel slope and Q is discharge (Leopold and Maddock, 1953). The coefficients a, c, k, and g and the exponents b, f, m, and z are empirically determined (see, for instance, Ferguson (1986) for a review of the hydraulic geometry relations). Since:

$$Q = w \times d \times v = aQ^b \times cQ^f \times kQ^m \tag{1.24}$$

it follows that the summation of the exponents b, f, and m in equations 1.20 to 1.22 must be equal to 1.0. Although the exponents of the hydraulic geometry relations vary from one empirical study to another, characteristic average values of $b = 0.50$, $f = 0.40$ and $m = 0.1$ are frequently reported (e.g. Knighton, 1998). These characteristic exponents, in turn, indicate that channel width tends to increase more rapidly than depth with distance downstream (cross-section shape or width–depth ratio changing with an increase in channel size), and the average velocity tends to increase with an increase in drainage basin area (a basic observation not always immediately recognized; Leopold, 1997). Slope, in turn, decreases steadily with distance downstream in drainage basins, and characteristic values of z in equation 1.23 vary between –0.10 and –0.30 (Knighton, 1998).

In addition to the volume of water supplied to a given river reach, the river morphology is affected by the volume and the character of the sediment delivered to the channel from upstream. Changes in the calibre of the sediment supplied to a given river reach and changes in the bed material size along the river channel are important factors controlling many physical processes occurring within alluvial channels (Powell, 1998). The very fine material tends to be transported in the flow itself, i.e. in suspension, and will be deposited during floods when overbank flows occur (i.e. floodplain deposition). Coarse sediment, because of its greater weight, will be transported near the bed of the river and locally deposited onto the channel in the form of 'bars'. These bar accumulations in turn affect the river flow characteristics, with local deflection and lateral activity (Church, 1992). The nature of the sediment over which the river flows is therefore influenced by the sediment supply conditions and, in turn, the characteristics of the river bed sediment will significantly influence the mean and turbulent properties of the water flow. Moreover, the organization of sediment movement down channel tends to vary significantly as a function of particle size. The type of *bedform* observed along a given river reach is directly a function of the bed material size and the flow strength (Chapter 4). A clear distinction is usually made between features observed along sand-bed channels and bed undulations frequently observed in coarse-grained or sand-bed mixtures (Best, 1996). The transition between fine- and coarse-grained channels depends to some extent on the energy of the stream, and can be placed within the range 0.3–1 mm (Church, 1992).

Based on sediment supply conditions and the capacity of streams to transport the supplied load, different channel types can be determined, with corresponding dominant bedform features (Figure 1.2). All the dominant types of bedforms in alluvial channels will be discussed at length in Chapter 4. Bedrock reaches (e.g. Wohl, 2000) and colluvial streams (hillslope erosion and formation of small depressions; e.g. Montgomery and Buffington, 1998) will not be discussed herein. As presented in Figure 1.2, the balance between the transport capacity of the stream (which can be viewed as being directly a function of flow discharge and channel slope) on the one hand, and the sediment supply condition on the other, is crucial in the determina-

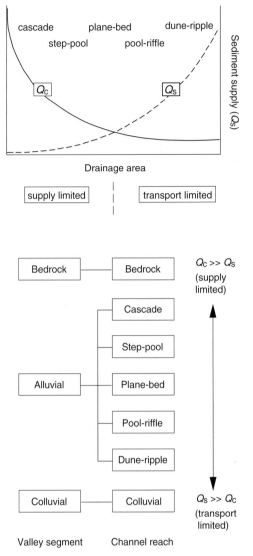

Figure 1.2 Schematic illustration of the transport capacities relative to sediment supply conditions for different channel types. After Montgomery and Buffington (1997), figures 10 and 11. Reproduced with the permission of the publishers, the Geological Society of America, Boulder, Colorado, USA.

tion of bedforms or 'reach-level channel types' (Montgomery and Buffington, 1998).

Along the same line, sediment calibre, sediment supply conditions, channel gradient, water supply characteristics and channel stability conditions all determine the type of channel pattern (channel configuration as seen from above – in plan view) that may occur under specific environmental conditions (Figure 1.3). The interactions between these variables are complex, and a range of configurations can result from spatial and temporal variations in the controlling variables. The flow and sediment transport processes associated with various channel patterns and related configurations will be discussed in Chapter 5.

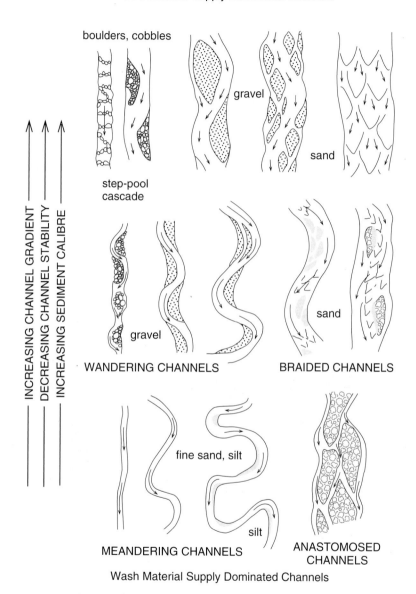

DECREASING CHANNEL STABILITY ⟶

INCREASING SEDIMENT SUPPLY ⟶

Bed Material Supply Dominated Channels

INCREASING CHANNEL GRADIENT
DECREASING CHANNEL STABILITY
INCREASING SEDIMENT CALIBRE

boulders, cobbles

gravel

sand

step-pool
cascade

gravel

WANDERING CHANNELS

sand

BRAIDED CHANNELS

fine sand, silt

silt

MEANDERING CHANNELS

ANASTOMOSED
CHANNELS

Wash Material Supply Dominated Channels

Figure 1.3 Patterns of morphological types of large channels. Sediment calibre is coarsest on the upper left and finest on the lower right of the diagram. After Church (1992), figure 6.8. Reproduced with the permission of the publishers, Blackwell Science Ltd, Oxford, UK.

1.2.2 Classifications

Various classification schemes for river channel morphology have been suggested (see, for instance, Montgomery and Buffington, 1998). Rosgen's classification of natural rivers (Rosgen, 1994) is well known and frequently used in river management studies. This classification involves seven major categories, based on variables such as channel patterns and channel slope. Rosgen's classification is not, however, process-based (Montgomery and Buffington, 1998), and this may limit its usefulness when assessing the response of stream channels to disturbances, for instance (Whiting and Bradley, 1993).

A process-based classification of rivers should involve bed material size, channel gradient, and channel depth (Whiting and Bradley, 1993). Following Church (1992), a relatively simple classification of stream channels based on channel size and sediment size can be established. This proposed classification is based on the ratio of flow depth (d) to a characteristic grain size index (D), with the grain size index being usually taken as the median size of the bed material. A broad range of channel gradients can also be associated with different categories of channels as determined by the ratio of flow depth to grain size (d/D). The flow depth (d) used in this classification should also be regarded as an average value (e.g. the flow depth corresponding with the mean annual discharge). The ratio d/D is used in numerous process-based equations in fluvial studies. This ratio controls overall flow resistance in channels, as well as related processes. As we will see in detail later, the ratio of flow depth to particle size is also of

Plate 1.1 Small channel (d/D <1), with large clasts protruding above the water surface (Maligne River, Alberta, Canada).

paramount importance in controlling the initiation of sediment movement on a stream bed and the volume of bed material transported in a given period of time.

Three categories of alluvial channels can, generally speaking, be defined based on the ratio d/D. *Small* channels can be defined as having a $d/D < 1$, where individual clasts (e.g. cobbles, greater in diameter than 64 mm) may protrude above the water surface and significantly affect local flow processes (Wiberg and Smith, 1991). Under these conditions, the bed is usually arranged in a sequence of steps and pools or cascades (Plate 1.1). These reaches are usually characterized by high gradients (greater than 1 per cent and maybe as much as 35 per cent; Church, 1992). Very often, the morphology of these channels can be locally controlled by the exposed bedrock (i.e. the sediment on the bed may be only one or a few grains thick and bedrock may be locally and sporadically exposed). Given the nature of the bed characteristics along these shallow headwater segments, the channels are rather stable. Bed sediment can be mobilized only during extreme flood events. The very steep slopes promote relatively high velocities that sometimes may be sufficient to dislodge even very large grains.

The second major category of channels (*intermediate* channels) can be defined by a d/D greater than 1 and smaller than 10 (the depth being as much as 10 times greater than the bed material size). As channel size increases and bed material size decreases downstream, channel gradient tends to decrease, and intermediate channels are usually associated with channel gradients varying between 0.1 and 1 per cent. These intermediate channels (Plate 1.2) are characterized by bed particles being fully

Plate 1.2 Example of an intermediate channel ($1 < d/D < 10$). Meandering, riffle-pool stream, Rouge River, Ontario, Canada (channel width ≈ 12 m).

Plate 1.3 Large channel; Squamish River, British Columbia, Canada – d/D >10; channel width approximately 35 m.

submerged in the water (even under base flow conditions) and by a channel width much in excess of the bed material size. An upper limit for channel width for intermediate channels cannot be determined precisely, but most rivers in this category are characterized by a channel width of up to 20–30 m (Church, 1992).

Intermediate channels can be associated with relatively straight reaches or meandering rivers of various degrees of sinuosity and with the presence of channel bars (or sediment accumulation zones). In the downstream direction, the beds of these rivers are often characterized by a succession of shallow and deep sections, referred to as riffle-pool sequences. The riffle-pool sequences often dominate morphology and processes in intermediate channels, and frequently form the major physical element in such channels. The pools are usually associated with meander bends (more specifically, with the scour zone often observed along the outer section of a meander bend). This again will be discussed in detail later (Chapter 5). The flow field along such intermediate channels is not as chaotic as above step-pool systems, for instance. Although highly variable locally, some definite and systematic variations in bed surface texture and flow properties can be described and explained at the reach scale (Clifford and Richards, 1992).

The third and last category can be defined as *large* channels characterized by a d/D ratio greater than 10 (Plate 1.3). As mentioned before, the transition between intermediate and large in many environments occurs at a channel widths of the order of 20–30 m, with a corresponding 'bankfull' discharges of the order of 30–50 m^3 s^{-1} (Church, 1992). The flow field above the bed along large channels often possesses well-defined characteristics. As illustrated in Figure 1.3, these rivers are either meandering or braiding and the actual pattern depends upon sediment supply (calibre and volume) as well as stream discharge, channel gradient and the degree of stability of the river banks. The resulting morphology is the result of complex interactions among numerous variables (e.g. Ferguson, 1987; Church, 1992; Knighton, 1998).

Large rivers are also usually characterized by a well-developed flood-plain (a floodplain being the result of sediment deposition during lateral migration of the channel and overbank flooding; Figure 1.1). The bed may still be dominated by riffles and pools (especially for channels where d/D is not much in excess of 10) or by macro-scale bar forms (e.g. braided rivers; section 5.3). Large channels are also often dominated by sandy bed material and, as such, are more likely to be characterized by relatively large sand bedforms (e.g. dunes; section 4.2). These rivers are deep and their morphology is controlled almost entirely by physical processes (as opposed to factors such as bank vegetation, bedrock exposures, etc). Large channels are also usually characterized by much smaller gradients (although this is significantly dependent upon the type of channel pattern).

There are obviously alternatives to this classification based on the ratio of flow depth to grain size. However, this approach does introduce some useful ideas and it integrates a number of important points about interactions between controlling and controlled variables, the role of channel gradient, channel size and bed material size. Many of the points raised in this first chapter will be reiterated throughout the book in relation to flow, bed sediment (and bedform), and sediment transport interactions at different spatial and temporal scales in alluvial channels.

2

WATER FLOW: BASIC PRINCIPLES AND CHARACTERIZATION

Stream discharge (Q) is the product of cross-sectional area (A) and mean velocity (U). Along a river channel and at successive cross-sections with areas A_1 and A_2, continuity is satisfied if the discharge $Q = A_1U_1 = A_2U_2$. It follows from this principle of mass continuity (or conservation of matter) that if the cross-sectional area of a channel locally decreases, the flow accelerates (or decelerates if the cross-sectional area locally increases).

Velocity, in turn, can be expressed at different time and spatial scales. This distinction between different measurements of velocities and their respective scale must be kept in mind in all applications. At the reach scale (or cross-sectional scale), the average velocity is usually estimated from a number of measurements across the channel (see Goudie (1994) for a detailed account of procedures for measurements). This cross-sectional average velocity, when estimated accurately, varies little along natural rivers, as long as there is no contraction and expansion of the flow due to bed undulations (i.e. as long as the cross-sectional area remains roughly constant along the channel). Cross-sectional average velocity values are often used in conjunction with discharge estimates in reconnaissance surveys of stream channels, gauging of stream flows, and in flow resistance equations.

Alternatively, an average velocity can be estimated at a specific vertical (local average), i.e. at a specific location across the channel and along a given river reach. This is usually determined from velocity profile measurements. Profiles of velocities are often taken at selected verticals to illustrate changes in flow velocity with position above the bed surface (velocity gradients), the forces acting on the bed (and related flow fields) and the flow structure above a given surface. The properties of these velocity profiles also change significantly from place to place in relation to changes in bed material size and bed undulations. Finally, average velocity may refer to a single point in the flow field. This approach is frequently used for a multitude of points both vertically and along a longitudinal transect, in order to illustrate complete flow fields above bed features (with flow velocity interpolated between the measured points).

Moreover, flow velocities can be estimated for a range of time scales (e.g. Clifford *et al.*, 1995), with averaging being done over periods ranging from a few seconds to a few hours. In turbulent flow studies, we also often seek to determine the velocity of a parcel of water at any given instant of time (*instantaneous velocity*). High-frequency fluctuations in velocities are emphasized, usually in conjunction with sediment transport processes and bed surface characteristics. Studies of instantaneous velocity fluctuations, although not novel, have been dominant in fluvial geomorphology recently (e.g. Clifford *et al.*, 1993a; Ashworth *et al.*, 1996), partly because of the rapid development of the technological means to measure turbulence and process the data. Turbulence and its links with sediment transport and bedform development will be a significant part of this text, and details are presented in most sections of the book.

The force exerted by the flow on the bed can also be estimated at different spatial and temporal scales. There are numerous examples of studies using bed shear stress estimates in investigations relating bedform development, flow turbulence, and the movement of bed material. At the reach scale, the average bed shear stress (as determined from the depth–slope product; equation 1.7) is commonly used to estimate the average flow force exerted by the flow on the bed along a given river section. This requires the accurate determination of a water surface slope, which can be difficult to obtain in the field. At the local scale, the average bed shear stress can be determined from the measured vertical velocity profiles (i.e. from the near-bed velocity gradients). The theoretical and practical aspects of this approach will be presented later in this chapter (section 2.4 on the boundary layer). Finally, at-a-point fluid stresses can be determined from velocity fluctuations (Middleton and Southard, 1984). Fluid stresses are frequently determined from measured series of horizontal and vertical velocity fluctuations, either from a time average perspective or from instantaneous variations. Vertical profiles of measured average turbulent stresses can also be used to estimate local values of bed shear stresses (e.g. Bennett and Best, 1995; Horton, 2001). These questions will also be addressed later when dealing with flow turbulence (section 2.6).

2.2 MECHANICAL POTENTIAL ENERGY

Motion occurs when a fluid is subjected to a gradient of mechanical potential energy (MPE). Mechanical potential energy is due to the forces of gravity and hydrostatic pressure. These forces are always present in moving fluids. Total potential energy at any given point (E_p) is given by:

$$E_p = E_{pp} + E_{pg} \tag{2.1}$$

where E_{pp} is the pressure potential energy component and E_{pg} is the gravitational potential energy component. The gravitational potential energy component can be defined as:

$$E_{pg} = \gamma \, V \, z \tag{2.2}$$

where γ is weight density (Dingman, 1984), V is volume (e.g. of a parcel of water), and z is surface elevation (above a given datum). Weight density is the weight per unit volume of a substance, and is defined from the product of mass density (i.e. mass per unit volume – ρ) and acceleration due to gravity (g). The dimensional character of E_{pg} in equation 2.2 is therefore $M \, L^2 \, T^{-2}$ (as specified before).

As specified in equation 2.1, pressure is also important when you consider the flow of water, because pressure is a component of potential energy. The water pressure exerted on a given surface (e.g. bed surface area) is simply defined by:

$$P_w = \gamma \, y \tag{2.3}$$

where γ is as defined before (weight density) and y is the height of the water column above a given bed surface (or local flow depth). The total pressure P above that plane is actually given by:

$$P = P_w + P_a \tag{2.4}$$

where P_a is the atmospheric pressure. Atmospheric pressure is usually left out because it can be considered a constant for any given problem in the fluvial environment (a free-water surface being always at atmospheric pressure). Moreover, in most circumstances, we are actually dealing with pressure differences rather than actual pressures. Hydrostatic pressure therefore is due to the weight of the water and the atmosphere right above it, and the non-gravitational component of potential energy at any point depends only on the pressure γy at that point. When expressed in terms of energy, this component is therefore the pressure potential energy, E_{pp}, and:

$$E_{pp} = \gamma \, V \, y \tag{2.5}$$

where, as before, γ is weight density, V is the volume of the water parcel considered and y is the distance measured vertically downward from the water surface to the point of interest. Therefore, the total potential energy at any point (E_p) is given by:

$$E_p = E_{pp} + E_{pg} = \gamma \, V \, y + \gamma \, V \, z. \tag{2.6}$$

This last expression can be generalized by dividing each term by the weight of the parcel (γV), which yields:

$$H_p = y + z \tag{2.7}$$

where H_p is simply called the potential head and has the dimensions [L].

The vertical distance z above a datum in a liquid is referred to as the elevation head, and y is the pressure head (i.e. the distance y as measured from the water surface to a specific point below the water surface is the pressure head at that point). If the water surface is horizontal, then H_p is the same at all points in a waterbody. Under these conditions, no gradients of potential energy would exist and hence no motion would occur in such a body. The concept of head, although not often used by fluvial geomorphologists, is frequently employed in hydraulics and groundwater studies.

In open channel flows, equation 2.7 becomes:

$$H_p = z + y \cos \theta \qquad (2.8)$$

where θ is as defined before, i.e. channel slope. Note then that equation 2.7 becomes a special case of equation 2.8 where $\theta = 0°$ and $\cos \theta = 1$.

Flow occurs only if there is a gradient of potential energy, and flow is obviously from higher to lower potential energy. This means that potential energy along a 'streamline' must decrease downstream in any flow. Since energy is conserved, it cannot be created or destroyed, but only converted to other forms. The downstream decrease in potential energy in a flow therefore represents the conversion of potential energy to the kinetic energy of the flow. The kinetic energy, in turn, is ultimately transformed to heat energy, due to friction between parcels of water moving at different speeds (e.g. 'eddies' in turbulent flows).

Kinetic energy (E_v) at any point in the flow is:

$$E_v = \rho \, V \, U^2 / 2 \qquad (2.9)$$

where ρ is water density, V is volume and U is velocity. Kinetic energy head, H_v, can be defined analogously to potential head by dividing E_v by the weight of the parcel of water:

$$H_v = E_v/(\rho g V) = 0.5 U^2/g. \qquad (2.10)$$

The quantity H_v is commonly called the velocity head and has the dimensions [L].

The total mechanical energy at any point along the channel is represented by the total head, H_t, which is the sum of potential head and velocity head:

$$H_t = z + y \cos \theta + 0.5 \, U^2/g. \qquad (2.11)$$

This equation is often refereed to as the Bernoulli equation. As mentioned before, the conversion of energy from one form to another inevitably includes an irreversible conversion of at least some of the energy to heat (due to friction). Therefore, the conversion of E_p to E_v in a flow is accompanied by a downstream decrease in the total mechanical energy of the flow and the total head, H_t, must decrease downstream. Consequently,

$$z_1 + y_1 \cos \theta + U_1^2/2g = z_2 + y_2 \cos \theta + U_2^2/2g + h_\Delta \qquad (2.12)$$

where the subscripts 1 and 2 refer to upstream and downstream sections respectively, and h_Δ is the 'head loss' between two sections. Under conditions of constant flow depth (represented here by y_1 and y_2) and constant velocity (U) along a given reach, the head loss becomes a function of the drop in elevation (z) along the channel. Under uniform flow conditions, the slope of the channel therefore represents a measure of the rate at which energy is dissipated as heat due to frictional resistance.

2.3 TYPES OF FLOW

Viscosity represents the resistance of a fluid to deformation. The molecular (or dynamic) viscosity therefore can be defined as the internal friction of a fluid that resists forces tending to cause flow. The dimensional character of dynamic viscosity is $[M\ L^{-1}\ T^{-1}]$. The relationship between the applied force, the shear rate, and the resistance to deformation (or molecular viscosity) can be summarized by the following relationship:

$$\tau = \mu\ du/dy \qquad (2.13)$$

where τ is shear stress, μ is dynamic viscosity, du is change in velocity and dy is change in height. The shear stress (τ) can therefore be regarded as the force that produces a change in velocity relative to height above the boundary. For a given force applied, the greater the dynamic viscosity, the smaller the deformation within the fluid (or velocity gradient du/dy). Dynamic viscosity of water is very sensitive to changes of temperature (see Table 2.1).

Viscosity can also be expressed in kinematic terms derived from length and time units. Kinematic viscosity (v) is defined as the ratio of molecular viscosity to fluid density where:

$$v = \mu/\rho. \qquad (2.14)$$

By definition, it also fluctuates significantly with temperature (in the case of water) and is expressed in $cm^2\ s^{-1}$.

This introduction of the property of viscosity leads to a distinction between laminar and turbulent flows. This distinction between turbulent and laminar flows is important to establish as it provides the conceptual framework needed to better understand flow and bedform dynamics. We have already seen that when a force (F) is applied over a given area (A), a velocity gradient du/dy is developed. In viscous (laminar) flows, the relationship between the shearing force within the fluid (F/A), the dynamic

Table 2.1 Dynamic viscosity of water

T (°C)	μ (g cm^{-1} s^{-1})
0	0.018
10	0.0131
20	0.00998

viscosity of the fluid and the induced velocity gradient is given by equation 2.13. Laminar flows can be represented by a series of parallel layers, without any mixing between the layers. In turbulent flows, however, the relationship between the shearing force and the velocity gradient is defined by:

$$\tau = (\mu + \epsilon)\, du/dy \tag{2.15}$$

where ϵ is called the coefficient of eddy viscosity. Eddy viscosity is a friction within the flow that results from the vertical circulation of turbulent eddies (rather than from the sliding of layers). Eddy viscosity expresses the vertical transfer of momentum, where slower-moving parcels of water are transferred to regions where the flow is faster, and vice versa (Chanson, 1999). Stated differently, ϵ represents a momentum exchange coefficient or turbulent mixing coefficient. Because of eddies, properties carried by the flow, such as dissolved material and suspended solids, tend to be spread throughout the flow field.

Reynolds numbers are used to differentiate between laminar and turbulent flows. Reynolds numbers are defined as:

$$Re = Ud/v \tag{2.16}$$

or:

$$Re = \rho Ud/\mu \tag{2.17}$$

where, as before, ρ is water density, μ is dynamic viscosity, v is kinematic viscosity, U is velocity and d is depth. When Re numbers are small (e.g. smaller than 500), viscous forces dominate and the flow is laminar. When Reynolds numbers are relatively high (e.g. greater than 2000), turbulent forces are dominant and the flow is fully turbulent (with intermediate conditions – or 'transitional stages' – corresponding with Re numbers between 500 and 2000). Most natural flows of interest in fluvial studies, both in the field and in laboratory channels, have Reynolds numbers well in excess of 2000. To illustrate this, let us consider the following example with values of U and d that are commonly seen in field situations. For an average flow velocity of 50 cm s^{-1} and a flow depth of 50 cm, the Reynolds number as determined from equation 2.16 and Table 2.1 (for a water temperature of 10°C) is equal to 1.9×10^5 (Reynolds numbers are dimensionless numbers).

The term *open-channel flow* is applied to the flow of water confined in a channel and with a free surface exposed to the atmosphere. Open-channel flows are driven by gravity, i.e. by the weight of the water contained in the channel. Opposing the motion is the frictional effect exerted on the flow by the bed and banks. There are four broad categories of open-channel flows based on the Reynolds number (equation 2.16) and the Froude number (Fr), which is defined as:

$$Fr = U/(gd)^{1/2}. \tag{2.18}$$

The Reynolds number allows distinctions between laminar, transitional and turbulent flows. The Froude number, in turn, can be used to distinguish between subcritical flows (where Fr < 1) and supercritical flows (where Fr > 1). In nature, most river flows are fully turbulent and subcritical.

Also of great significance in fluvial dynamics are *separated flows*. These occur when there is a sudden change in the boundary condition or orientation. When this occurs, the flow cannot remain attached to the boundary, and there is 'flow separation' (Figure 2.1). There are numerous flow and bedform dynamics phenomena that are directly related to flow separation in alluvial channels. The flow characteristics in these zones (average flow properties and turbulent flow characteristics) are important, because they control many sediment transport processes (erosion–deposition). Within a separation zone, there is basically no downstream flow. The separation zone is usually separated from the much faster external flow by a zone of rapid velocity change called a *shear layer*, in which there is normally intense mixing in the water column. Perhaps the best examples of flow separation in rivers are those schematically illustrated in Figure 2.1, i.e. at river confluences, downstream from the junction 'corner' and immediately downstream from transverse steps (e.g. bedform crests or obstacles). These phenomena will be described and explained in detail later. Finally, *secondary flows*, as the

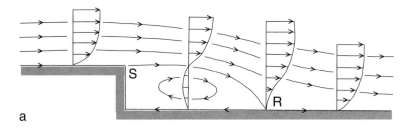

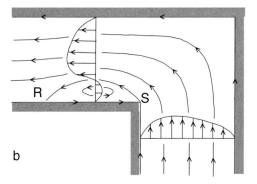

Figure 2.1 Examples of flow separation (S: separation point; R: reattachment point), illustrated by time-averaged streamline patterns at (a) a downward transverse step and (b) a sharp bend in an open channel. After Allen (1994), figure 2.24. Reproduced with the permission of the publishers, Blackwell Science Ltd, Oxford, UK.

name implies, are flow components that are superimposed upon the main downstream flow component. Secondary flows are commonly observed, for instance, in river meanders and at channel confluences (as summarized for instance in Allen (1994) and Powell (1998)).

2.4 BOUNDARY LAYER

Generally speaking, friction arises between a fluid and a solid with which it is in relative motion. This friction is restricted to a zone or a layer adjacent to the solid called the boundary layer (Allen, 1994). Stated differently, the boundary layer is therefore the flow region next to a solid boundary where the flow field is affected by the presence of the boundary and where friction plays an essential part. The velocities across the boundary layer vary from zero at the boundary to the 'free-stream' velocity at the outer edge of the boundary layer (Chanson, 1999). In practice and because most rivers are relatively shallow and characterized by relatively small relative roughness d/D, the boundary layer extends to the water surface (although the increase in velocity is much more rapid in the near-bed region, as will be seen later). The flow depth therefore represents the boundary layer thickness in most natural streams, and the free-stream velocity is often estimated from the water surface (or near-surface) velocity. Boundary layer thickness and free-stream velocities are often used in diagrams expressing empirical or theoretical relationships between dimensionless numbers.

To reiterate, the boundary layer is the zone within which there is a velocity gradient due to the friction exerted by the solid boundary on the moving fluid. The velocity characteristics of the boundary layer are of great interest in fluvial studies. The shape of the velocity profiles, especially in the near-bed region, the rate of increase in velocity with height above the bed surface, the turbulent flow characteristics within this layer, and their links with sediment movement and bed surface features have all been the central themes of numerous investigations in the last few decades.

The shear stress at any point within a turbulent velocity profile is given by equation 2.15. The dynamic viscosity (v) can, however, be neglected, as it is insignificant relative to eddy viscosity ϵ. The shear stress at any point within the turbulent profile thus becomes:

$$\tau = \epsilon\, \rho\; du/dy. \tag{2.19}$$

Eddy viscosity, in turn, is not a constant and varies with position above the bed. More specifically:

$$\epsilon = \iota^2\, du/dy \tag{2.20}$$

where ι is defined as the mixing length, i.e. the characteristic distance travelled by a particle of fluid before its momentum is changed by the new environment (Chanson, 1999). The mixing length therefore measures the degree of penetration of vortices within the flow (see section 2.6.1 for a further

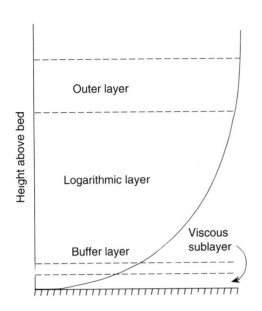

Figure 2.2 Velocity profile and boundary layer for turbulent flow. Illustration of how the average velocity (on the horizontal axis) varies with the position above the bed surface (the thicknesses of the layers are not to scale).

discussion of vortices and related definitions). The degree of momentum exchange is dependent upon the mixing length. The mixing length depends on the distance from the boundary and is generally assumed to be equal to:

$$\iota = \kappa y \tag{2.21}$$

where κ is known as 'von Karman's universal constant' and is generally assumed to be equal to 0.41 (in clear water flows). Under mobile bed conditions, the determination of the von Karman's constant is still a matter of debate, and experimental research is still being pursued on this question (e.g. Horton, 2001).

A complete turbulent velocity profile consists of three distinct layers (Figure 2.2). Very close to the bed, a thin layer of laminar flows can prevail. The thickness of this laminar sublayer (δ) is defined by:

$$\delta = 11.6 \, \nu / U_* \tag{2.22}$$

where U_* is a quantity known as shear velocity. Shear velocity has dimensions of velocity and is determined from shear stress:

$$U_* = \sqrt{(\tau_0/\rho)}. \tag{2.23}$$

Therefore, it can be seen from equation 2.22 that the thickness of the laminar sublayer decreases with an increase in shear stress as turbulence penetrates closer to the bed (Richards, 1982). Above the laminar sublayer, a transitional 'buffer' layer can be observed, and, immediately above it, a fully turbulent flow zone (represented in Figure 2.2 as the logarithmic layer). It is the latter that is of most interest in fluvial studies. It is within the fully turbulent layer that flow measurements are made, shear stresses estimated, and links with sediment transport processes usually established.

Moreover, if we define k as the boundary roughness height (determined from the height of roughness features on the bed), the flow is said to be 'hydrodynamically smooth' when $k < \delta$ (where all the roughness features are within the laminar sublayer). Under these conditions, the bed is 'protected' from the overlying turbulence. This is a rather unlikely situation in natural alluvial channels, because of the presence of coarse sediment, bedforms, or other obstructions (e.g. vegetation). In most cases in natural rivers, $k > 5\delta$, and the flow is said to be 'hydrodynamically rough'. Under those conditions, the laminar sublayer is disrupted by the presence of vortices, both from above the top of the roughness elements and from those generated at or near the bed from the individual particles and/or from the bedforms themselves.

In fully turbulent flows, the velocity is often observed to increase with height above the bed surface, according to:

$$U_y = b \ln (y/y_0) \tag{2.24}$$

where U_y is the mean velocity at a given height y above the bed surface. There are two parameters of interest in this equation: b and y_0. The value of b is the gradient in velocity and y_0 represents the (projected) height above the bed at which the velocity is zero. From experiments above uniform bed particles, it has been shown that an expected value of roughness length y_0 under uniform bed sediment conditions is $y_0 = D/30.1$ (where D is particle size). The value b, on the other hand, is a measure of the gradient in velocity. It is used therefore to estimate the shear stress exerted by the flow on the bed surface. More specifically, it can be shown (e.g. Richards, 1982; Middleton and Southard, 1984) that:

$$b = 2.5 \sqrt{(\tau_0/\rho)} = 2.5U_*. \tag{2.25}$$

Equation 2.24 can therefore be rewritten as:

$$U_y = 2.5 \, U_* \ln (y/y_0). \tag{2.26}$$

The constant 2.5 in equation 2.26 is equal to $1/\kappa$ (where κ is as defined before, i.e. the von Karman's constant). Equation 2.26 is also often referred to as the *law of the wall* for the variation of velocity with height above the bed surface. Equation 2.26 is generally considered applicable in the bottom 20 per cent of the flow.

The law of the wall has been used extensively in empirical studies to derive shear stress and roughness length from measured velocity profiles, i.e. from measured values of U_y at various predetermined heights (y) above a given bed surface. Equation 2.24 can be rewritten as:

$$U_y = b \ln y - b \ln y_0. \tag{2.27}$$

When plotting measurements of U_y against elevation (y) above the bed, one can therefore expect to observe a linear relationship between U_y and y (on a semi-log scale). That is,

$$U_y = a + b \ln y \tag{2.28}$$

where both a and b can be estimated from liner regression (a being the intercept of the linear regression equation and b the slope). It follows from equations 2.27 and 2.28 that:

$$a = -b \ln y_0 \tag{2.29}$$

$$-a/b = \ln y_0 \tag{2.30}$$

and:

$$y_0 = e^{-a/b}. \tag{2.31}$$

It also follows from equations 2.25 and 2.28 that the bed shear stress can be estimated from the slope b of the regression line, and:

$$\rho(b/2.5)^2 = \tau_0. \tag{2.32}$$

Roughness length and bed shear stress estimates determined from empirical measurements at a given vertical are highly variable (Wilcock *et al.*, 1996). The standard error of such estimates (see Wilkinson, 1984) can also be quite significant (Robert *et al.*, 1992), and care must be taken when interpreting the results (Wilcock, 1996; Biron *et al.*, 1998). The spatial variability clearly is controlled by the local bed material conditions and the presence of bed-forms (and the position in relation to that bedform). Spatially averaged velocity profiles (e.g. Smith and McLean, 1977) are often reported (from which a more representative and accurate estimate of the average local bed shear stress and roughness length can usually be determined). It is also worth noting that velocity profiles are often plotted with the height above the bed on a vertical logarithmic axis (since it represents the vertical dimension) with velocity on the horizontal axis (while, clearly, it is the velocity U_y that is regressed against the logarithm of the height above the bed; Bergeron and Abrahams, 1992).

Numerous and accurate velocity measurements are also needed in the near-bed region (e.g. the bottom 20 per cent), in order to obtain an accurate and reliable estimate of bed shear stress and roughness length (Biron *et al.*, 1998). At greater distances above the bed surface, velocity profiles and cor-responding velocity gradients reflect the roughness exerted by the bed at increasingly larger spatial scales (e.g. Lawless and Robert, 2001a).

A 'velocity defect-wake law' is also sometimes used to describe average velocity profiles in turbulent boundary layers (e.g. Kirkgöz, 1989). A dimen-sionless approach is used where $(U_{max} - U)/U_*$ is plotted against $\ln (y/d)$ (where U_{max} is the maximum average velocity observed at a given vertical – usually the near-surface or 'free-stream' velocity). Measurements of $(U_{max} - U)/U_*$ usually vary from zero near the water surface to a maximum of 10–12 in the very near-bed region. Relatively few empirical studies suggest, however, that the velocity defect-wake law generally poorly describes velocity distributions above rough surfaces, especially in the bottom portion of the boundary layer (e.g. $y/d < 0.4$; Kirkgöz, 1989; Horton, 2001).

EXAMPLE

The following velocity profile measurements (average velocity U_y at various heights y above the bed surface) were made at a specific location along a coarse-grained channel (median bed material size: 18 mm).

y (cm)	U_y (cm s^{-1})	ln y
3	39.8	1.0986
4.5	44.2	1.5041
6	52.1	1.7918
10	55.1	2.3026
15	64.3	2.7080
20	65.2	2.9957
30	74.2	3.4012

A linear regression was performed on the measured values of U_y and ln y (listed above). The following empirical linear regression was obtained:

$$U_y = 23.5 + 14.6 \ln y. \tag{2.33}$$

(where $R^2 = 0.979$). From equations 2.32 and 2.33, the estimated shear stress exerted by the flow on the bed at that particular location is equal to 34.1 dyn cm^{-2} or 3.41 Nm^{-2} (since 1 dyne is equal to 10^{-5} N). Similarly, the roughness length y_0 can be estimated from the regression coefficients in equation 2.33 and from equation 2.31. The estimated y_0 is therefore equal to 2.0 mm. It is worth noting that under most natural conditions, y_0 is much larger than the expected 0.033 D_{50} (where D_{50} is the median size of the bed material; Robert, 1990; Whiting and Dietrich, 1990). The irregularities created by heterogeneous bed material and bedforms at various spatial scales act to increase the roughness length of the bed (e.g. Heathershaw and Langhorne, 1988).

Considerable scatter is usually observed as a result of varying boundary conditions, and this prevents the identification of a generally applicable empirical description.

2.5 FLOW RESISTANCE EQUATIONS

As illustrated in Figure 2.2, water flowing in river channels is retarded by the resistance exerted by the bed. With distance away from the boundary, the friction exerted by the bed becomes less effective and retardation diminishes. External boundary conditions (especially the range of particle sizes and the shape and size of bedforms) control the magnitude of the resistance exerted by the bed on flow. Resistance is also affected by other types of obstruction, such as aquatic vegetation (Hickin, 1984) and abrupt changes in cross-section geometry.

2.5.1 Keulegan equation

The average velocity at a given vertical is affected by the magnitude of the resistance exerted by the bed on the flow. In order to estimate the average velocity at a vertical, the law of the wall (equation 2.26) can be integrated from $y = y_0$ to $y = d$ (where d is flow depth) and:

$$U = 2.5 \; U_* \left[\ln \left(d / k_s \right) + 2.40 \right] \tag{2.34}$$

or·

$$U/U_* = 2.5 \ln \left(d / k_s \right) + 6.0 \tag{2.35}$$

where U is the average velocity at a vertical (or a cross-section), U_* is shear velocity and k_s is referred to as the *equivalent sand roughness height* and is equal to $30.1 y_0$.

Equation 2.35 constitutes the basic theoretical equation used to estimate flow resistance in straight uniform open channels (two-dimensional flow). In practice, it is also often applied to channels with heterogeneous bed material and with bed undulations. Semi-logarithmic flow resistance equations have therefore been used extensively in both natural and laboratory streams in order to estimate flow resistance and its relationship with grain sizes and bed configurations (U/U_* being commonly used as a measure of flow resistance). The main problem, however, remains the determination of k_s, the effective roughness height. For experimental conditions with densely packed grains of uniform size and shape (and for a flat immobile bed), the value of k_s can be approximated by the median diameter of the bed material. When applied to natural coarse-grained channels with heterogeneous bed material, numerous studies have showed that k_s could be as high as 6–7 D_{50} (e.g. Bray, 1982; Robert, 1990). These observed values of k_s under natural conditions in coarse-grained channels are usually associated with the presence of bedforms, and with a range of grain sizes and shapes (Clifford *et al.*, 1992a, b; Robert, 1993). The empirical coefficients most frequently observed from field measurements are 3.5 D_{84} (where D_{84} is the size for which 84 per cent of the bed material is finer) or 6.8 D_{50} (e.g. Robert, 1990; Clifford *et al.*, 1992b).

At the reach scale, $U_* = \sqrt{(\tau_0 / \rho)} = (gdS)^{1/2}$ and equation 2.35 can be rewritten as:

$$U/\sqrt{(gdS)} = 6.0 + 2.5 \ln \left(d/k_s \right). \tag{2.36}$$

The average velocity U (and therefore discharge) for a given flow depth can be estimated or predicted from equation 2.36. That is, for a known or assumed flow depth (d) and channel slope (S), and by setting k_s equal to a given multiplier grain size index that corresponds with widely observed empirical observations (e.g. 6.8 D_{50} for coarse-grained channels; Bray, 1982; Robert, 1990), the average velocity can be calculated from equation 2.36 and the discharge per unit width predicted. This represents a widely used application of equation 2.36 for engineering purposes (e.g. estimation of depth–discharge curves in ungauged catchments; Bray, 1982).

Finally, it should be noted that Reynolds numbers can be calculated based on the shear velocity and particle size (or k_s). These values are referred to as the *boundary, grain* or *shear Reynolds number* (Re_*) and are defined as:

$$Re_* = U_* k_s / v \qquad (2.37)$$

or:

$$Re_* = U_* D / v \qquad (2.38)$$

where U_* is shear velocity, D is particle size, v is kinematic viscosity and k_s is the equivalent sand roughness as described above. Fully turbulent flows (which characterize most open-channel flows) have boundary Reynolds numbers (Re_*) in excess of 100.

2.5.2 Friction factors (or flow resistance coefficients)

It is clear from the previous discussion that the resistance to flow affects three main flow variables: mean velocity, average flow depth, and average slope (usually taken as the average water surface slope). In addition to the ratio U/U_*, there are two other commonly used flow resistance coefficients in alluvial channels. These are the Darcy–Weisbach and the Manning friction factors. The Manning coefficient has been used for decades in engineering. It is an empirical coefficient that is defined as follows:

$$n = (d^{2/3} S^{1/2})/U \qquad (2.39)$$

(with d expressed in metres and U in metres per second). Photographs of river reaches (or charts) covering a range Manning's n values can then be used to determine which specific value should be employed in equation 2.39 to predict the average velocity for a given depth and slope (see, for instance, Dingman, 1984, pp. 143–147). Alternatives to this basic expression of the Manning coefficient (equation 2.39) have been suggested in the literature (see, for instance, Wohl (2000) for a review of those various expressions for the Manning's n). The value of n in equation 2.39 expresses the total roughness of the channel. In a straight, flat bed channel with roughly uniform bed material, n can be estimated only from particle size and:

$$n_g = 0.048\, D_{50}^{1/6} \qquad (2.40)$$

(for D_{50} in metre units; Carson and Griffiths, 1987). The value of n_g therefore represents a particle roughness coefficient.

Perhaps more useful, however, is the Darcy–Weisbach friction factor. This coefficient has a sound theoretical basis, and is dimensionless. The Darcy–Weisbach friction factor (f) is defined as:

$$f = 8gdS/U^2. \qquad (2.41)$$

It follows from the definition of shear velocity U_* (equation 2.23) and from equations 2.36 and 2.41, that $f = 8U_*^2/U^2$, and that:

$$1/\sqrt{f} = 2.11 + 2.03 \log_{10} (d/k_s) \qquad (2.42)$$

(using $\ln x = 2.303 \log_{10} x$). Equation 2.42 therefore implies that, as flow stage increases (and d/k_s increases), the value of the friction factor f decreases (as long as k_s remains roughly constant, which may not be always the case if there is sediment movement).

EXAMPLE OF APPLICATION OF EQUATIONS 2.41 AND 2.42

$d = 0.32$ m
$S = 0.0005$
$D_{50} = 5.2$ mm and $k_s \approx 6.8D_{50} = 35.4$ mm
$U_* = 0.040$ m s^{-1}
$1/\sqrt{f} = 4.05$
$f = 0.061$
Predicted average reach velocity: 0.45 m s^{-1}
Predicted discharge per unit width is 0.144 m^2 s^{-1}.
For an increase in flow depth from 0.32 to 0.52 m (same water surface slope and same value of k_s),
$f = 0.050$
U (predicted) = 0.64
Q per unit width (predicted) = 0.33 m^2 s^{-1}.

There are two main difficulties with the application of equation 2.42 to natural stream channels. Even under stable conditions (no bed material transport), k_s is difficult to determine in the presence of bedforms and/or heterogeneous bed sediments (the roughness height k_s being a function of the size, shape and spacing of bedforms). Under mobile bed conditions, the value of k_s may vary significantly with discharge. This is due to the fact that the bed configuration may change considerably with flow rate (see Chapter 4 on bedforms). Changes in the roughness height (k_s) in turn affect the rate of change of velocity and depth with discharge.

In addition to bed material size and bedforms, vegetation can significantly alter the rate of change of velocity with increasing discharge (e.g. Sand-Jensen *et al.*, 1989). The effects of aquatic vegetation on the flow characteristics will be further discussed in Chapter 6.

2.5.3 Flow resistance (and shear stress) components

Most, if not all, natural alluvial channels do not have a flat, uniform bed surface. Most rivers are characterized by heterogeneous bed material and by the presence of bedforms. The total flow resistance measured from the mean flow properties is a function of both the friction created by the grains on the flow and the additional roughness introduced by the bed undulations (Li,

1994). The former component is usually referred to as grain roughness (or skin or grain friction) and the latter as form roughness or form resistance (or form drag; Raupack, 1992).

The concept of roughness or shear stress components was first explicitly elaborated by Einstein and Banks (1950). By adding pegs to cubic roughness elements (which simulate grain friction and form drag), Einstein and Banks (1950) found their effects on the flow resistance to be additive. That is, the total flow resistance can be divided into two components:

$$f = f' + f''$$ (2.43)

where f' is that component of f pertaining to grain roughness, and f'' represents the additional resistance created by the presence of bedforms in rivers (Vanoni and Hwang, 1967). Since f is determined from the ratio of U_*^2/U^2 (equation 2.41), the shear velocity term can be further subdivided into a grain and a form component and:

$$U_* = (g\ d\ S)^{1/2} = (g\ d\ S')^{1/2} + (g\ d\ S'')^{1/2}$$ (2.44)

(where $S = S' + S''$). Since the gradient of the channel can be interpreted as a measure of the amount of energy loss per unit distance downstream, it is appropriate to divide it into components associated with grain resistance and form roughness. As for shear velocity (equation 2.44) and considering that the average bed shear stress at the reach scale is also determined from the product of depth and slope (equation 1.7), the total mean boundary shear stress in uniform flow can also be divided into two components, and:

$$\tau_0 = \tau_0' + \tau_0''.$$ (2.45)

Among these components, only τ_0' is an 'effective' shear stress acting on a river bed (Einstein and Barbarossa, 1952), i.e. only the grain stress is responsible for bedload transport (i.e. moving sediment particles in contact with the bed surface; e.g. Carson, 1987; Petit, 1989).

By selecting an appropriate value of k_s for grain roughness only, and by using it in equation 2.42 (i.e. the approximate value of k_s that would be observed in the absence of bedforms and with a relatively flat and uniform surface), the grain roughness f' can be estimated. With an estimated value of f' determined from equation 2.42, the grain component of total shear velocity (U_*) can also be determined from $f = 8U_*^2/U^2$ and the grain stress calculated (since $\tau_0 = \rho U_*^2$). The form roughness or the form drag component can then be estimated by simply subtracting the grain component from the total value of f or τ_0.

Alternatively, form stress or form resistance can be estimated separately from the flow and the bed morphological characteristics. Following the pioneering work of Vanoni and Hwang (1967), numerous attempts have been made to present empirical or semi-empirical equations for form roughness (e.g. Smith and McLean, 1977; Prestegaard, 1983; McLean et al., 1999). In particular, it is useful to approach this question using an equation based on the definition of pressure or form drag. The form drag, F_d, sometimes called profile drag, of a bed with undulations of height, h, and of unit width, may have the form:

$$F_d = 0.5 \, C_d \, h \, \rho \, U^2 \tag{2.46}$$

where C_d is a drag coefficient (e.g. Vittal *et al.*, 1977; Griffiths, 1989). From equation 2.46, the average shear stress, τ_0'', due to form drag induced by the presence of bedforms is therefore:

$$\tau_0'' = 0.5 \, C_d \, (h/l) \, \rho \, U^2 \tag{2.47}$$

(where l is bedform spacing). To determine the value of C_d in the above equation is problematic. Form drag is a function of the pressure field above the bedforms and, as such, the use of a constant for C_d in equation 2.47 is difficult to determine. From experiments on rigid roughness elements, Vittal *et al.* (1977), for instance, proposed:

$$C_d = (P_u - P_d)/(0.5 \, \rho \, U_c^2) \tag{2.48}$$

where P_u is the average pressure on the upstream face of the obstacle, P_d is the downstream pressure, and U_c was defined in the laboratory investigation as the average velocity determined from velocity profiles measured along the centre-line of the flume (Vittal *et al.*, 1977). Research is still ongoing into these questions (e.g. McLean *et al.*, 1999), and further details will be provided in Chapter 4.

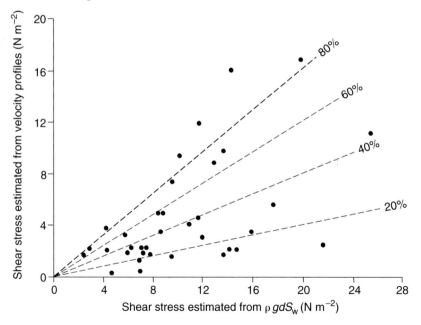

Figure 2.3 Differences between bed shear stresses estimated from vertical velocity profiles and averaged reach-scale values determined from depth–slope products. After Robert (1990), figure 10. Reproduced by permission of Arnold Publishers, London, UK.

The magnitude of the form roughness component may vary significantly from place to place along a channel, and also from one river reach to another as a function of numerous factors (controlled by bed sediment properties and related bedform characteristics). It is important to bear in mind that the method used to estimate the bed shear stress must be related to the spatial scale of the investigation and, therefore, to the corresponding scale of the roughness features. A reach average bed shear stress determined from the depth–slope product may include grain and form resistance at various spatial scales and may be much larger than that determined from local velocity profiles (Figure 2.3; Robert, 1990). On the other hand, bed shear stress from near-bed local velocity gradients reflects local friction phenomena in the immediate vicinity of the measurements (upstream from them), i.e. local 'skin' friction and potentially small-scale form drag effects.

2.6 FLOW TURBULENCE

2.6.1 Description

Numerous studies of flow turbulence in alluvial channels have been conducted recently (as emphasized, for instance, in Clifford et al., 1993a and Ashworth et al., 1996), above both sand- and gravel-bed rivers (e.g. Kostaschuk, 2000 and Nikora and Smart, 1997).

Turbulence is generated when a fluid flows past a solid surface or past an adjacent stream of the same fluid with a different velocity (Middleton and Southard, 1984; Clifford and French, 1993a,b). In turbulent flows, the fluid particles move in irregular paths, causing an exchange of momentum from one portion of the fluid to another (Bradshaw, 1985; Chanson, 1999).

The turbulent characteristics of the flow in boundary layers were originally considered as stochastic (random) entities. Significant progress since the early 1960s has provided considerable evidence that turbulent boundary layers exhibit a deterministic structure of irregular, but repetitive spatial–temporal flow patterns described as *coherent flow structures* (Robinson, 1991; Smith, 1996). Furthermore, it has been determined that such structures are self-perpetuating and thus can be considered cyclical phenomena. They are important, as they are responsible for most of the turbulent energy production within a stream (Grass et al., 1991).

Two terms are very commonly used in the analysis of turbulent flows and turbulent boundary layers in rivers: turbulent eddies and vortices. Both terms will be used frequently throughout this book, and are worth defining from the outset. Following Middleton and Southard (1984, pp. 3–13), *eddies* can be defined as swirls of fluid with highly irregular shapes and a wide range of sizes, that are in a continual state of development and decay. *Vorticity*, in turn, can be loosely defined as the property of solid-body-like rotation of fluid at a given point in the flow. The remainder of this chapter will focus on the nature of this turbulence by examining the approaches used to study turbulence in rivers, the statistical treatment of turbulent flow fluctuations, vortices, coherent flow structures above smooth and rough surfaces, and modern instrumentation used to measure turbulence and display turbulent flow fields (e.g. Levi, 1991; Clifford and French, 1993a; Best, 1996).

2.6.2 Approaches

Velocities measured at a fixed point are referred to as *Eulerian velocities* (Eulerian analysis of velocity fluctuations). The velocity at any point in the flow can be measured in three mutually perpendicular directions: the downstream flow (u), the vertical flow (normal to the boundary; v) and the lateral flow (w), the latter being parallel to the boundary and normal to the downstream flow. Because the flow is turbulent, the velocity (in any of the three directions) is not constant, but varies continuously through time.

The quantitative analysis of turbulent flows is based on measurements of velocity fluctuations at a single point in the flow (or a multitude of points from which flow fields can be inferred). Velocity fluctuations can be defined as:

$$u' = U - u \tag{2.49}$$

where u' is the deviation (the fluctuation) from the mean velocity U, and u is the 'instantaneous' velocity. Fluctuations for the vertical (v) and lateral (w) flow components can similarly be defined from:

$$v' = V - v \tag{2.50}$$

and:

$$w' = W - w. \tag{2.51}$$

Deviations from the mean are either positive or negative. The average magnitude of the deviation from the mean for a given velocity signal or series (i.e. series of measurements of u, v and w over a given period of time) reveals the 'intensity' of the turbulence for any specific velocity component. Variability around the average for a normal or near-normal distribution is best characterized by the standard deviation of the velocity distribution (also referred to as the root-mean-square value – RMS). Root-mean-square values are considered measures of turbulence intensity. For the downstream flow component, RMS is defined as:

$$RMS_u = \sqrt{((\Sigma u'^2)/N)} \tag{2.52}$$

where N is the total number of observations in a given series. Similar expressions can be defined for the vertical and lateral flow components, with:

$$RMS_v = \sqrt{((\Sigma v'^2)/N)} \tag{2.53}$$

and:

$$RMS_w = \sqrt{(\Sigma w'^2)/N}. \tag{2.54}$$

The three expressions can be combined to provide an index of 'total turbulence intensity'. More specifically, the turbulent kinetic energy of the flow (per unit volume) is defined from:

$$TKE = 0.5\rho(RMS_u^2 + RMS_v^2 + RMS_v^2) \tag{2.55}$$

(where ρ is water density; Clifford and French, 1993a). Turbulent kinetic energy represents the energy extracted from the mean flow by turbulent eddies (Bradshaw, 1985). The dimensional character of TKE is therefore $M\,L^{-1}\,T^{-2}$ (energy per unit volume). When the turbulence intensity is the same for each velocity component (i.e. in all directions), the turbulence is said to be *isotropic*. Otherwise, the turbulence flow field is *anisotropic*. Measurements in alluvial channels show turbulent fields that are usually strongly anisotropic (with RMS_u being dominant). Turbulence intensity measurements are frequently made dimensionless by dividing the RMS by the average velocity U or the shear velocity U_*. This in turn allows comparisons between flow fields, while taking into account the average velocity or the shear stress (via the inclusion of U_*).

A second major way to look at velocity fluctuations consists of following trajectories of fluid points or markers as they travel with the flow (Figure 2.4; Middleton and Southard, 1984), measuring the velocity components as a function of time ('Lagrangian velocities'), and tracing the path of parcels of water (flow visualization). This type of analysis can be done, for instance, with video or photo images of the three-dimensional motion of some fluid

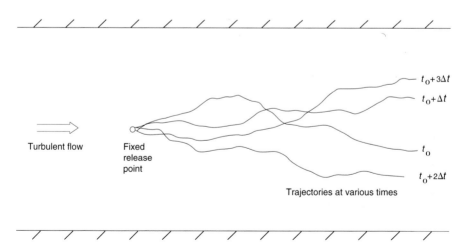

Figure 2.4 Trajectories of fluid markers released at the same point, but at various times in a turbulent flow. After Middleton and Southard (1984), figure 3.11. Reproduced with the permission of the publishers, SEPM (Society for Sedimentary Geology), Oklahoma, USA.

marker introduced into the flow (e.g. Roy *et al.*, 1999), and how it dissipates within the flow field (past the point where it is introduced into the flow). The trajectories of the fluid markers that one would observe in such an experiment would be very sinuous in three dimensions and highly irregular (Figure 2.4). There would be a succession of different trajectories at different times, with each trajectory being different in detail. The use of markers within the flow allows the visualization of eddies and vortices. Numerous recent visualization studies of flow–sediment transport interactions have added significantly to our knowledge of fluvial processes (e.g. Drake *et al.*, 1988; Thorne *et al.*, 1989; Best, 1992). Both approaches (at-a-point measurements and flow visualization) have been instrumental in the development of our knowledge on coherent flow structures in turbulent boundary layers (Roy *et al.*, 1999).

2.6.3 Instrumentation

During the past ten to fifteen years, three main devices have been used to measure turbulence in rivers: electromagnetic current meters, acoustic Doppler velocimeters, and laser Doppler velocimeters. A brief overview of each type of instrument is provided below.

The first widely used instrument was a two-dimensional electromagnetic current meter (Plate 2.1). With these current meters, a magnetic field is generated from within the probe. When water moves through that field, a voltage is produced that is linearly proportional to the water velocity. High-frequency measurements are obtained, and the sampling rate is usually under the control of the researcher. Electromagnetic current meters are still used in many instances (e.g. Williams *et al.*, 1989; Clifford and French, 1993b; Buffin-Bélanger and Roy, 1998; Buffin-Bélanger *et al.*, 2000). The two velocity components measured depend on the orientation of the probe (Plate 2.1). Different sensor sizes and shapes exist, with the most commonly

Plate 2.1 Flow sensor of an electromagnetic current meter (EMCM); field version – diameter of probe: 40 mm.

used being either spherical (as illustrated in Plate 2.1) or discoidal (Lane *et al.*, 1993). For spherical sensors, sampling volume is about 2.5 times the volume of the sensor itself. Small sensors are more suitable for laboratory or shallow flows, while larger ones are more robust and can be used in field situations while the bed is mobile (such as that shown on Plate 2.1). The different shapes may also significantly affect the measurements and their interpretation, since these instruments are intrusive. Care must therefore be taken in the data interpretation (Lane *et al.*, 1993). Particular attention must also be paid to the frequency with which measurements are taken, the duration of the sampling period (or series length), and the filter characteristics of each type of current meter (Soulsby, 1980; Clifford and French, 1993a, b; Roy *et al.*, 1997).

Acoustic Doppler velocimeters (ADV; Plate 2.2) are more recent, and have been used with success in both laboratory and field settings. These instruments are now readily available from various manufacturers, with different versions that can be used either in a laboratory setting or for field-based studies (Lane *et al.*, 1998). The two main advantages over the electromagnetic meters are that the ADV is non-intrusive and most probes are three-dimensional. In most cases, the volume of water that is being sampled is also very small (e.g. 0.25 cm^3) and the small volume sampled is located at a given distance (e.g. 5 cm) below the sensor tip. This allows measurements of the three orthogonal velocity components as close as a few millimetres above the bed of a given river (e.g. Lawless and Robert, 2001a, b). The probe consists of a transmitter and three receivers (Plate 2.2). The transmitter generates a short pulse of sound at a known frequency, which propagates to the sampling volume and is scattered from particulate matter in transport there. A proportion of the transmitted signal is returned to the receivers, from which the velocity of the particulate matter in the flow may be calculated (Sontek Inc, 1997). There are numerous other technical matters that may need to be addressed when dealing with the specifics of ADV measurements, and the reader is referred to the detailed reports of Nikora and Goring (1998) and McLelland and Nicholas (2000) for further information.

The third major type of instrumentation used recently for the study of turbulence is the laser Doppler velocimeter. This instrument has allowed significant advances in data acquisition, since it allows very refined and

Plate 2.2 Flow sensor; acoustic Doppler velocimeter (ADV).

detailed measurements of tiny volumes of water in laboratory settings (e.g. Bennett and Best, 1995, 1996). These devices provide very high-frequency measurements (e.g. up to 100 Hz; Bennett and Best, 1994). Their main advantages then are the non-intrusive measurements at a high spatial and temporal resolution. They do not, however, provide measurements at a constant time interval (Biron *et al.*, 1995), and most applications have been two-dimensional. As the name implies, these instruments utilize the Doppler effect to sense subtle shifts in the frequency of light scattered by fine particles conveyed by the fluid (Clifford and French, 1993a, p.15). Also using laser technology, particle image velocimetry (PIV) systems are now available to visualize complete flow fields instantaneously and with a very high spatial resolution. This promises to be of great value in studying flow dynamics in laboratory settings in the very near future. There are other types of instruments that can be used for the sampling of turbulent flow fluctuations (e.g. the hot-wire anemometers used, for instance, by Sand-Jensen and Pedersen, 1999), but the devices described herein have been the most widely used instruments for flow turbulence measurements in both laboratories and natural streams during the past decade.

2.6.4 Reynolds stresses and quadrant analysis

Reynolds stresses (turbulent stresses) represent the degree of momentum exchange at a given point in the flow. Reynolds stresses defined from the horizontal and vertical flow fluctuations will be emphasized herein (because of their relevance for the study of flow–bed–sediment transport interactions). In a turbulent boundary layer, particles moving towards the bed or away from the boundary in the turbulent mixing process retain most of their horizontal momentum. Particles moving upward into the flow are characterized by a positive velocity fluctuation (positive v' in equation 2.50). Since they tend to preserve most of their momentum, these upward-moving water parcels create a negative u' in the upper faster layer (Clifford and French, 1993a, p.8). Conversely, water particles moving downward (towards the bed surface) give rise to a positive fluctuation in the horizontal velocity in the slower bottom layers. Therefore, on average, positive v' is associated with negative u' and vice versa and, for most of the time, the product $u'v'$ is expected to be negative.

This product $u'v'$ is a quantity of great interest in fluvial dynamics studies. This quantity is related to the exchange of momentum across a plane parallel to the mean flow direction. This momentum exchange gives rise to the shear stress, τ_R, acting on the plane. The exact definition of Reynolds stress thus becomes:

$$\tau_R = -\rho\, u'v' \qquad (2.56)$$

and the average product $-\rho u'v'$, as determined over a given period of time, is the average Reynolds stress acting at a given point in the flow field. An example of a Reynolds stress 'signal' is presented in Figure 2.5. This signal

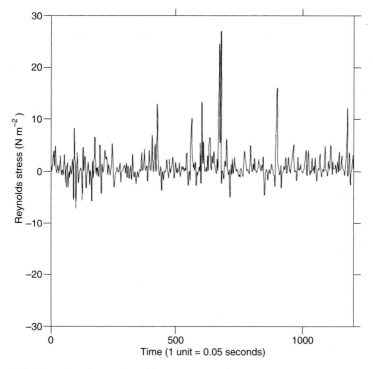

Figure 2.5 Example of a series of instantaneous Reynolds stress measurements (one-minute sampling at a rate of 20 measurements per second).

(and therefore the original series of u and v fluctuations from which it is derived) was measured in the near-bed region above a coarse-grained channel. The following observations are particularly noteworthy:

(a) the very significant temporal variability of the instantaneous values of $u'v'$;
(b) the sporadic, intermittent and short duration appearance of relatively high instantaneous values of Reynolds stresses; and
(c) the fact that most observations of instantaneous Reynolds stresses are positive, as explained above (i.e. the instantaneous product of $u'v'$ is negative; see equation 2.56).

Quadrant analysis of the instantaneous u and v velocity signals allows a quantitative understanding and description of the turbulence structure. This approach was developed by Lu and Willmarth (1973) and Luchik and Tiederman (1987), among others. It has been used frequently in the last decade or so to illustrate changes in turbulent flow fields above different bed surfaces (e.g. Bennett and Best, 1995, 1996; Buffin-Bélanger and Roy, 1998; Buffin-Bélanger *et al.*, 2000). The instantaneous horizontal and vertical velocities can be classified into four quadrants according to their deviation from the mean (Table 2.2).

Table 2.2 Instantaneous velocity fluctuations and quadrant analysis

Quadrant	u' deviation from mean	v' deviation from mean
Quadrant I	Positive	Positive
Quadrant II	Negative	Positive
Quadrant III	Negative	Negative
Quadrant IV	Positive	Negative

Quadrant analysis can be applied to the entire Reynolds stress signal, or to values above a specific threshold. These thresholds are sometimes referred to as 'hole size' (H) and defined by comparing the instantaneous $u'v'$ product with the product of the component RMS values:

$$H = |u'v'| / (RMS_u \times RMS_v) \tag{2.57}$$

(where $|u'v'|$ represents the absolute value of the instantaneous product). Significant turbulent flow 'events' are sometimes associated with specific thresholds. The specification of thresholds is arbitrary, but H values from 1 to 5 are frequently used. Illustrated in Figure 2.6 is a field example of quadrant divisions of instantaneous u and v signals (measured again above a

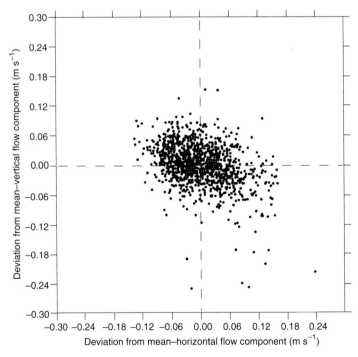

Figure 2.6 Example of quadrant representation of instantaneous horizontal and vertical velocity fluctuations (deviations from mean value; one-minute sampling at rate of 20 measurements per second).

coarse-grained channel in the near-bed region). In Figure 2.6, the entire velocity signal was taken into account (and velocities were sampled at a rate of 20 measurements per second – or 20 Hz – over one minute). The shape of the scattergram is of interest in Figure 2.6, as this illustrates the relative concentration of observations in each of the quadrants.

From quadrant analysis, it is possible to categorize turbulent motions in the u–v space, and to identify each quadrant with a particular type of event (Figure 2.7). Two quadrants are particularly important: quadrant II and quadrant IV. Quadrant II events are characterized by slower than average downstream flow and positive vertical flows (i.e. away from the boundary). In a broad sense, these types of event can be refereed to as *ejection* events. These events therefore refer to ejection of fluid from near the bed upward into the outer flow. The fluid incorporated in the ejection (or burst) events is of lower downstream (longitudinal) velocity than the flow around it. In quadrant IV, on the other hand, the downstream flow component is greater than average while the vertical velocity component is negative (fluid motion towards the bed surface). These events are called *sweep* events. Sweep events therefore refer to the movement of fluid towards the bed in the lower regions of the boundary layer (the origin of ejections and sweeps will be discussed separately; see below).

Ejection and sweep motions of significant magnitude are generally active a small fraction of the time (Grass, 1971; Gordon, 1974; Drake *et al.*, 1988; Lapointe, 1992) but are responsible for most of the momentum exchange (the momentum exchange process being described as 'intermittent'). Bursting motions (sweeps and ejections) may also have significant impacts on sediment transport processes. Although discussed in detail later, ejection events (fluid motions away from the boundary) may be important to maintain particles in suspension within the flow and there appears to be a direct link between the presence and the intensity of ejection events and the

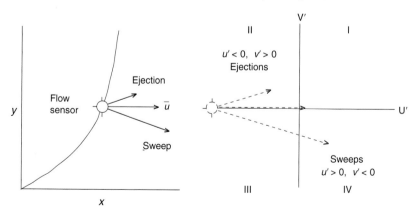

Figure 2.7 Illustration of the different quadrants and related definitions of sweep and ejection events. After Robert (1993), figure 1. Reproduced by permission of Arnold Publishers, London, UK.

concentration of sediment in suspension (Lapointe, 1992). Sweeps, on the other hand, represent faster downward fluid motions (localized in space and in time). These events may significantly impact the movement of sediment on the bed surface (bedload transport mechanisms; Drake *et al.*, 1988; Thorne *et al.*, 1989; Williams, 1996).

2.6.5 Vortices and coherent flow structures

Turbulent boundary layers are dominated by the presence of various types of vortices. A first category of vortices correspond to features that have been observed over smooth surfaces originating from alternate zones of low and high fluid speeds in the very near-bed region. *Low-speed streaks* represent a key component of turbulent boundary layers. They are known to be persistent features of the near-bed flow above smooth surfaces in fully developed turbulent flows (Smith and Metzler, 1983; Smith *et al.*, 1991; Best, 1993). Initially observed through the work of Kline *et al.* (1967), streaks can be defined as relatively narrow zones of low-speed fluid in the near-bed region. Their spanwise spacing λ (across the stream) is determined by the shear velocity (U_*) and the fluid kinematic viscosity (v) and, in dimensionless terms:

$$\lambda_s = \lambda U_* / v \qquad (2.58)$$

(where λ_s is the dimensionless spanwise spacing; Best, 1993). Away from the boundary, streak-like patterns persist for some distance but their degree of coherence and organization decreases gradually. Streak spacing may also increase with distance away from the bed. In plan view, elongated zones defined as low-speed streaks do not usually present a straight downstream orientation but tend to be characterized by some degree of meandering (Best, 1993).

These elongated zones of low velocity alternate with zones of high-speed fluid. The alternate zones of low-speed streaks and high-speed fluids across the flow in a turbulent boundary layer are considered to give rise to coherent flow structures such as horseshoe vortices (Figure 2.8). More specifically, visualization work from Head and Bandyopadhyay (1981) and Smith *et al.* (1991), among others, has shown that low-speed streaks have some degree of streamwise vorticity in the form of a hairpin or horseshoe vortex (Best, 1993; Williams, 1996). The low-speed streaks characteristically form the 'legs' of such horseshoe or hairpin vortices that may become elongated and stretched as they develop and are gradually lifted away from the bed (Figure 2.8). These vortices observed in the near-bed region over smooth surfaces therefore represent three-dimensional objects predominantly oriented in the streamwise flow direction with closed 'loop heads' extending downstream and away from the surface and two 'legs' extending upstream. As illustrated in Figure 2.8, these features are advected upward and uplifted at an angle that may be of the order of 40–45° to the mean flow (Best, 1993). Once formed, grouping of vortices may be observed. If relatively weak, they

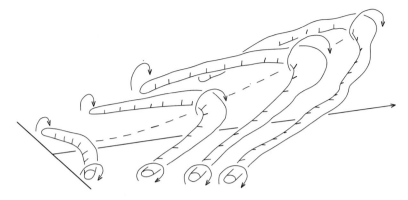

Figure 2.8 Schematic representation of the development, lifting, and stretching of a horseshoe vortex. After Dyer (1986), *Coastal and Estuarine Sediment Dynamics*, figure 3.20. Reproduced by permission of John Wiley & Sons Ltd, Chichester, UK.

may also dissipate while being uplifted.

Flow visualization studies therefore have shown that low-speed streaks culminate in ejections of fluid from the bed outward. Ejections represent a component of the bursting process documented above smooth walls in turbulent boundary layers. To preserve continuity, the fluid motions known as ejections are followed by high-speed outer layer fluid penetrating the near-bed flow. These motions represent the sweep component of the bursting process (Figure 2.9). These inrushes of higher than average downstream velocity fluid have a width (in the spanwise direction) somewhat larger then the preceding streak. They lose momentum with impact with the bed and diffuse laterally (Best, 1993).

It has also been suggested that the periodicity of these ejection and sweep events scales with outer boundary layer variables (Rao *et al.*, 1971), i.e. boundary layer thickness and free-stream velocity (approximated in natural channels by the flow depth and water surface velocity, respectively). There is no general consensus, however, on the scaling of these features and what controls their periodicity (Best, 1996). The scaling of sweep and ejection-like events has been empirically investigated above the beds of alluvial channels (e.g. Lapointe, 1992; Kostaschuk and Church, 1993; Babakaiff and Hickin, 1996), and this will be further discussed in Chapter 4.

This type of bursting process has been suggested as the dominant process responsible for the formation of sand ripples (Best, 1992; see Chapter 4). Sweep fluid motions have also been reported as being instrumental in controlling local bedload transport initiation and magnitude (e.g. Drake *et al.*, 1988; Thorne *et al.*, 1989; Williams, 1996). Although there is field and laboratory evidence to support the existence of a busting process (as described above) over coarse sand and fine gravels, for instance (e.g. Drake *et al.*, 1988), questions remain unanswered about the origin of burst-sweep mechanisms above rough surfaces. Implicit in the model presented above is the

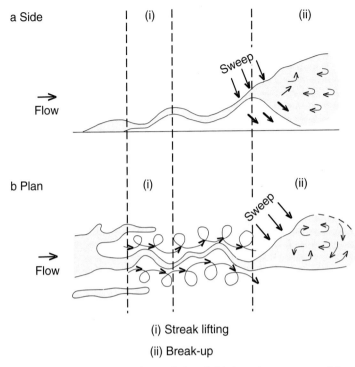

(i) Streak lifting

(ii) Break-up

Figure 2.9 Schematic representation of the fluid bursting process. After Williams (1996), figure 1.5. Reproduced with the permission of the publishers, John Wiley & Sons Ltd, Chichester, UK.

presence of a viscous sublayer in which streaks are formed and uplifted. In the presence of coarse bed sediments and/or the presence of bedforms, this sublayer may be absent or disrupted, and the implications of this on the bursting model remain to be elucidated.

A second major group of vortices and coherent flow structures has been observed over coarse-grained surfaces. Coherent flow structures above coarse surfaces in natural rivers may be dominated by vortices induced by the presence of large particles on the bed and/or the presence of bedforms (e.g. Kirkbride, 1993, 1994; Bennett and Best, 1995; Roy *et al.*, 1999). These represent the second major group of coherent structures that will be described herein. This group of flow structures around and above obstacles and bed undulations can be summarized as *eddy shedding* phenomena. That is, eddies are shed off from behind obstacles and from the shear layer observed along the lee-side flow separation zone downstream from obstacles or downstream from the bedform crest (i.e. whenever the downstream flow cannot remain in contact with the bed surface because of the sudden change in bed elevation).

The presence of large particles and grain protrusions into the flow therefore creates vortices similar in shape but genetically different from the

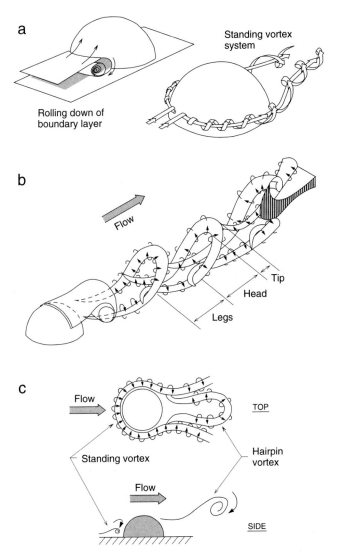

Figure 2.10 Vortices associated with isolated particles. (a) 'Rolling down' of boundary layer in front of clasts, and generation of a standing vortex system; (b) horseshoe vortices generated from flow separation downstream of an obstacle; and (c) standing and hairpin vortices developing around isolated clasts. After Acarlar and Smith (1987) and Best (1996), figure 3.9. Reproduced by permission of John Wiley & Sons Ltd, Chichester, UK.

horseshoe or hairpin vortices of the turbulent boundary layers described before. Figure 2.10 illustrates some of the most common phenomena observed around, above, and downstream from protruding particles. Firstly, there is the development of a 'standing' vortex (Figure 2.10a) upstream of an isolated large grain (due to the 'rolling up' of the boundary layer; Best,

1993). In addition to the standing vortex system and the diversion of the flow around the particles, flow separation occurs downstream from large isolated grains. The separation zone downstream of isolated obstacles therefore produces horseshoe-shaped vortices (Figure 2.10b,c) that propagate downstream into the outer flow (Acarlar and Smith, 1987; Best, 1993). The process of eddy shedding from a shear layer is perhaps best exemplified by the schematic illustration presented in Figure 2.11, downstream from a transverse downward step (which is analogous to a bedform or obstacle crest). It is seen from Figure 2.11a that vortices are developed along the zone separating the main stream and separation 'bubble' (in the immediate lee of the transverse step) by the 'rolling up' of the shear layer, and that this zone corresponds with locations where turbulence intensity is maximized. The turbulent stresses (determined by the product $-u'v'$) are also maximized along the shear layer, as illustrated in Figure 2.11c. Under natural conditions, these simple models (as illustrated in Figure 2.10) are complicated by the heterogeneous nature of the bed material (Lawless and Robert, 2001b). This will be further discussed in detail when dealing with bedforms in coarse-grained channels.

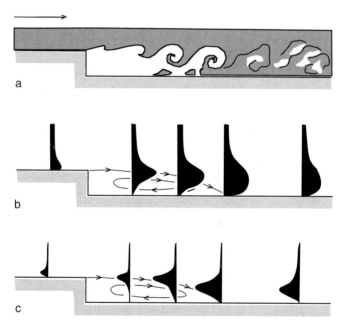

Figure 2.11 Schematic illustration of the properties of a separated flow and related shear layer at a transverse downward step. (a) Vortices developing by the rolling up of the shear layer between the external flow and the separation zone; (b) variation in the relative intensity of turbulence for the downstream flow component, and (c) variations in the $(u'v')$ product (normalized by average velocity). After Allen (1994), figure 2.25. Reproduced with the permission of the publishers, Blackwell Science Ltd, Oxford, UK.

The frequency of the eddy shedding process downstream from isolated obstacles can be determined. This is usually expressed by the dimensionless Strouhal number (Str) where:

$$\text{Str} = (f \times D)/U \qquad (2.59)$$

where f is the frequency at which eddies are shed from such obstacles, D is

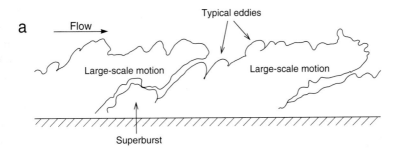

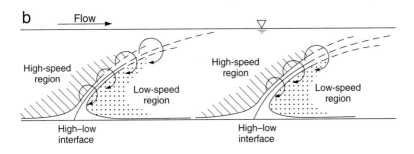

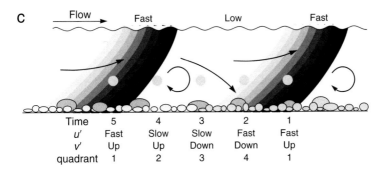

Figure 2.12 (a) Large-scale flow motions with the presence of typical eddies at their boundaries; (b) representation of high- and low-speed regions within the flow; (c) representation of a sequence of turbulent flow events associated with the passage of high- and low-speed wedges. After Buffin-Bélanger *et al.* (2000), figure 1. Reproduced by permission of Elsevier Science Publishers, Oxford, UK.

obstacle size, and U is average flow velocity. Although difficult to measure from velocity records sampled above heterogeneous bed sediments, this process of eddy shedding has been presented as the dominant energy dissipation mechanism in coarse-grained channels. This mechanism has been considered responsible for the greater than expected flow resistance generally observed in coarse-grained channels (Clifford *et al.*, 1992a, b). It has also been suggested that the periodicity of this eddy shedding process may be reflected in measured time series of velocity fluctuations in the form of *pseudo-periodic oscillations* (Clifford *et al.*, 1992b; Robert *et al.*, 1993).

Although the origin of sweep-like fluid motions above coarse-grained surfaces remains to be fully explored, numerous recent investigations suggest that vortex shedding from behind obstacles and from the shear layer on the lee-side of large particles and downstream from bedform crests represents the dominant mechanism by which bursting takes place in alluvial channels and energy is dissipated. Large-scale flow motions have also been investigated to some extent in coarse-grained channels (e.g. Ferguson *et al.*, 1996b; Buffin-Bélanger *et al.*, 2000). These large-scale (macroturbulent) coherent flow structures may also show a periodicity that is controlled by the channel size (e.g. flow depth; Carling and Orr, 2000). Recent measurements in coarse-grained channels (Buffin-Bélanger *et al.*, 2000), for instance, suggest the presence of spatially differentiated zones of relatively fast and slow flows (Figure 2.12). A downstream succession of high- and low-speed wedges has been observed, superimposed upon smaller and more 'typical' eddies. Much research remains to be conducted, however, on the occurrence of large-scale turbulent flow structures in coarse-grained channels, their generative mechanisms, their temporal characteristics, and their interactions with other vortices and flow structures within turbulent boundary layers (Kirkbride, 1993; Ferguson *et al.*, 1996b).

3

FLUVIAL SEDIMENT: PROCESSES OF EROSION AND TRANSPORT

3.1 GRAIN CHARACTERISTICS

The processes of erosion (entrainment), transport, and deposition of sediment particles by water are controlled essentially by the characteristics of those particles and by the characteristics of the moving fluid. Properties of sediment particles and processes of sediment transport will therefore be the focus of this chapter. I will address sediment characteristics from two perspectives: individual grain characteristics and bulk properties.

3.1.1 Size

Grain size is the most important parameter to consider when dealing with sediment transport processes. The mode of sediment movement and the mechanisms involved in the initial displacement of a sediment grain (i.e. how and when a given sediment particle moves, over which distances and at what speed) are, at least in part, dependent upon the size of the sediment grain(s) involved.

Grain size can be specified in a number of different ways. The most widely used measurement of size in geomorphology (and sedimentology) is simply based on external diameter. There are three different ways of measuring external diameters: external 'caliper' diameter, sieve diameter, and equivalent spherical diameter. The choice of the method varies essentially with the particle size(s) involved (see Goudie, 1994 for details).

The Wentworth grain size scale is commonly used in fluvial geomorphology to classify particle size. The Wentworth scale is based on a geometric sequence with ratio 2. The most common categories (and corresponding grain sizes) of the Wentworth scale are provided below (Table 3.1). Particle size can be expressed in mm, microns (1 μm being equal to 0.001 mm), or in logarithmic units 'phi' (φ). In order to facilitate data presentation

Table 3.1 Grain-size categories

mm	phi	class terminology
0.002–004	>8	Clay
0.004–062	8 to 4	Silt
0.062–0.25	4 to 2	Fine sand
0.25–1	2 to 0	Medium sand
1–2	0 to –1	Coarse sand
2–4	–1 to –2	Granules
4–64	–2 to –6	Pebbles
64–256	–6 to –8	Cobbles
>256	< –8	Boulders

and statistical analysis of grain size distributions, the logarithmic phi scale is often used. Phi units are determined as:

$$\phi = -\log_2 D \qquad (3.1)$$

where D is particle size in mm (the minus sign was introduced so that the sand sizes would have positive ϕ-numbers).

With sediment particles being three-dimensional objects, the 'external caliper' diameter of coarse particles can be determined from any of the three orthogonal axes: the small axis (or c-axis), the intermediate (b) axis or the longest diameter (a-axis). Since most, if not all, natural sediment particles are not perfect spheres, the three dimensions will differ, and their ratios can be used to refer to various shape indices. In most studies of sediment transport processes, the intermediate axis is the dimension that is measured and reported. This is partly because it is easier to measure directly, and partly because it is the dimension that is equivalent to the sieve diameter for sand particles determined from laboratory analysis. Most grain size measurements used for instance in flow resistance studies are intermediate diameters, even though it is usually the small axis that lies at the vertical (Limerinos, 1970).

As mentioned before, size controls mass, which in turn controls mode of sediment movement and rates of transport. More specifically, the behaviour of a grain, when subjected to the force exerted by a moving fluid, is controlled in part by its mass. Mass increases very rapidly with diameter (it varies with the third power of the radius). Mass represents a measure of the inertia of a body, i.e. the resistance that the body offers to having its velocity or position changed by an applied force (Pye, 1994, p. 2).

In the field, the coarse material (e.g. coarser than about 5 to 10 mm; Rice and Church, 1996a) at the surface of river beds is frequently sampled by a systematic sampling strategy referred to as the grid-by-number sampling method. This method, first introduced in the 1950s (Wolman, 1954) and widely used to characterize exposed fluvial gravels, consists of measuring the axial diameters of a number of particles randomly selected from the exposed material. In practice, a grid is laid out on the surface, and particles beneath the grid intersections are sampled and measured or sorted using phi templates. The grid dimensions must be of sufficient size to ensure independence of measurements (e.g. twice the maximum particle diameter; Rice and Church, 1998). The number of particles sampled varies from one study to another. Previous assessments (e.g. Hey and Thorne, 1983; Mosley and Tindale, 1985) suggested that 60 to 100 particles are needed to obtain reliable estimates of the median size of bed material. Recent studies by Rice and Church (1996a, 1998) suggest the sampling of 400 particles to obtain sufficiently accurate grain size indices for the entire distribution (samples where 95 per cent confidence limits of $\pm 0.1\phi$ are required).

Photographic techniques have also been used. These are often utilized to collect a larger volume of summary grain size information (Church *et al.*, 1987; Rice and Church, 1996b). In this method, quadrats of a given size (e.g. 0.25 m^2) are photographed, and the number of grains exposed within each photographed quadrat is counted. A 'photo calibration curve' is then established between the number of particles in a given quadrat and the corresponding surface D_{50} (where clearly the number of exposed particles increases as surface D_{50} decreases; e.g. Rice and Church, 1996b, p. 6). This calibration curve can then be used at various locations to estimate changes in median bed material size from field pictures of exposed material. Bulk samples of surface and/or subsurface material can also be collected in the field and analysed in the laboratory using traditional sieving methods (e.g. size distribution established using, for instance, the half-phi size class). Bulk samples must be of sufficient size to provide accurate estimates of grain size distributions (Church *et al.*, 1987). The weight of a given sample can be estimated from that of the largest clast that can be collected. Ferguson *et al.* (1996a), for instance, used bulk samples where the heaviest clast was normally 1 per cent of the total and never more than 3 per cent (with bulk samples of up to 1000 kg). Bulk sampling of surficial material must be used for particles smaller than about 8 mm, and, clearly, for the characterization of subsurface bed material. It should also be noted that grid-by-number sampling methods and bulk sieve analysis are frequently used together in many field situations (e.g. Ferguson *et al.*, 1996a).

3.1.2 Grain shape and density

Density represents the mass per unit volume of a substance, and is expressed in kg per cubic metre. In the case of natural sediments in rivers, it is usually assumed to be constant at 2650 kg m^{-3}. This, however, is the density of quartz, and the actual density of a sediment grain varies with its mineral composition. For most common 'light' minerals, the difference is fairly small and is usually neglected in sediment transport investigations. Grain density affects the settling or fall velocity of a sediment particle (i.e. how fast a grain moves down a water column), together with other factors such as grain shape and fluid viscosity.

The term *specific gravity* (s) is also used sometimes. The specific gravity of a solid or fluid is its density relative to that of water. In fluvial studies, the term specific gravity is therefore used to refer to the ratio of sediment density (ρ_s) to that of water density (ρ), i.e.:

$$\rho_s/\rho = 2650 \text{ kg m}^{-3}/1000 \text{ kg m}^{-3} = 2.65 \tag{3.2}$$

Grain shape also affects sediment movement. Shape here refers to both the actual form of the grain and the surface texture. Shape affects fall velocity (see below): the greater the departure from a spherical shape, the smaller the settling velocity (with other factors being equal). In other words, very flat particles will settle much more slowly when compared with a sphere of the same weight and density (Pye, 1994). Shapes of relatively large particles can be qualitatively described, for instance, as spheres, discoids, blades, or rods. Moreover, a number of shape factors can also be determined to classify sediments (based on the length of the three axes of coarse sediments). Grain 'elongation', for instance, may be represented by the ratio a/b (the ratio of the long to intermediate axes) and a measure of grain 'flatness' determined from the ratio c/b (with c, again, being the shortest diameter).

Grain shape is also a significant factor to consider when assessing the initial movement of sediment grains resting on a bed surface. The determination of thresholds of initial movement in natural environments is a complex question that will be specifically addressed later in this chapter. The shape of a grain essentially affects the surface area exposed to the flow and the 'rollability' (Pye, 1994) of a given particle and, as such, the ease with which a grain will be entrained and kept in motion. If you consider, for instance, a flat surface with isolated particles of various shapes, spherical particles will be entrained, and will be kept in motion more easily than particles of other shapes (with other factors being constant, such as size and density).

3.1.3 Settling velocity

In still water, a particle in suspension has a downward vertical motion (since it is heavier than water). This is called the fall velocity or settling velocity (V_0) of sediment particles. The magnitude of this settling velocity depends on a balance of forces: the downward force, which is a function of the submerged weight of the material, and the opposing viscous and inertial resistance forces. We need first to define a particle Reynolds number (Re_p):

$$Re_p = V_0 D/\nu \tag{3.3}$$

where, as before, D is particle diameter and ν is kinematic viscosity. The terminal velocity of spherical particles in still water equals:

$$V_0 = \sqrt{\{[(4gD)/(3C_d)] (s - 1)\}} \tag{3.4}$$

where C_d is a drag coefficient and $s = \rho_s/\rho$ (Chanson, 1999). The drag coefficient in turn is a function of the particle Reynolds number, as defined by equation 3.3, and it also depends on particle shape. For spherical particles and for $Re_p < 0.1$, the drag coefficient is inversely proportional to Re_p, and the fall velocity varies as the square of the grain diameter. For gravels, on the other hand, the particle Reynolds number Re_p exceeds 1000, and high fall velocities induce a turbulent boundary layer, flow separation, and a turbulent wake (Richards, 1982). For coarse material and $Re_p > 10^3$, fall velocity varies as the square root of the particle diameter. For large Reynolds numbers (Re_p) and for spherical particles, the drag coefficient C_d is nearly a constant at 0.5 (Chanson, 1999).

When expressed in terms of grain diameter, submerged weight and viscosity, the fall velocity for silt and clays (Stoke's Law) is:

$$V_0 = (1/18) D^2 (\rho_s - \rho)g/\mu \tag{3.5}$$

where μ is dynamic viscosity. The fall velocity therefore varies significantly with water temperature (as the fluid viscosity changes with temperature). Particles coarser than 2 mm, on the other hand, experience resistance from the inertia of the water (and viscosity is unimportant), and the fall velocity for coarse material (>2 mm) can be determined from:

$$V_0 = \sqrt{[2/3D\, g\, (\rho_s - \rho)/\rho]} \tag{3.6}$$

Sand particles (0.063–2 mm) are affected by a combination of viscous and inertial forces, and a composite law can be derived to express fall velocities (with particle shape becoming a predominant factor). Fall velocity curves can be drawn for particle sizes within the sand range, and for various shapes. Observed terminal velocities can also be considered and compared with computations. Examples of terminal fall velocities are presented in Table 3.2.

Table 3.2 Terminal settling velocity of sediment particles (within the sand size range) in still water (at 20°C) (from Chanson, 1999)

D (mm)	V_0 (m s^{-1})	Re_p	C_d
0.089	0.005	0.44	55
0.147	0.013	1.9	15
0.25	0.028	7.0	6
0.42	0.050	21	3
0.76	0.10	75	1.8
1.8	0.17	304	1.5

3.2 BULK SEDIMENT PROPERTIES

3.2.1 Grain size distribution

Bulk sediment characteristics refer to the properties of a volume of hetero-geneous material on the bed or the banks of a given river. Most natural bed sediments are highly heterogeneous, i.e. characterized by a fairly wide range of grain sizes. The frequencies of various particle sizes usually differ from the characteristics of a normal distribution, i.e. grain size distributions are usually asymmetrical (positively skewed or right-skewed distributions). For that reason, the use of a logarithmic unit (phi) is useful in the sense that it transforms the frequency distribution of grain sizes into a normal (or near-normal) distribution. However, the assumption of a log-normal distri-bution of grain sizes is frequently only a rough approximation (Rice and Church, 1996a). Some natural rivers are also characterized by a bimodal dis-tribution of particle sizes, with fine 'matrix' material infiltrating into or being deposited above a coarse 'framework' of gravel-size material (Lisle, 1989). Fine sediment can also be segregated from the coarse fraction during the waning stages of bed material transport events and be deposited in areas along the channel where shear stresses and near-bed velocities are reduced (Lisle, 1979, 1989; Jackson and Beschta, 1982: see section 4.4 on riffles and pools).

A normal distribution in turn can be characterized by its mean and stan-dard deviation. These two indices are frequently used in fluvial geo-morphology. That is, the mean of a log-normal distribution is equivalent to the median of the original distribution of grain sizes. The median grain size of a sample of bed sediments is commonly identified by D_{50}, where the subscript 50 simply refers to the size for which 50 per cent of the sampled material is finer. Similarly, D_{84} is frequently utilized, and that refers to the size for which 84 per cent is smaller (and it is also one standard deviation above the mean for a normal distribution).

Sorting refers to the range of particle sizes observed in a distribution. The degree of sorting of a given frequency distribution of grain sizes can be con-veniently expressed by the standard deviation of the distribution. Well-sorted sediments will therefore be characterized by a narrow range of particle sizes and a small standard deviation (e.g. in phi units) and vice versa for poorly sorted bed material. Various sorting indices can be deter-mined. Given the fact that D_{84} and D_{16} refer to, respectively, one standard deviation above the mean and one standard deviation below the mean of a (log-)normal distribution, the ratio D_{84}/D_{16} (or its square root) can be con-veniently used as a sorting index (e.g. Robert, 1990). The degree of sorting increases with a decrease in the ratio D_{84}/D_{16}.

As will be emphasized later in various contexts, systematic spatial varia-tions in grain size exist in coarse-grained channels (Whiting, 1996; Powell,

1998). Segregation patterns in sediment size resulting from sediment transport processes and sorting patterns can be observed vertically (from the bed surface downwards), longitudinally (at different spatial scales) and laterally (e.g. across stream in curved channels).

3.2.2 Packing arrangement and friction angle

The packing arrangement of sediment grains is also a significant bulk sediment property. Frequent qualitative observations are reported on the packing arrangement of coarse grains, and how this may affect sediment transport. Packing arrangement is, to some extent, self-explanatory. It refers to the organization of the particles on the stream bed. This is especially important with coarse gravels, irregular particles, and poorly sorted sediment. Some qualitative broad categorization of stream beds can be used, based on the arrangement of the particles (e.g. imbricated, interlocked, 'open' bed positions, etc.) and how it affects sediment movement (e.g. Brayshaw, 1985).

In addition to inertia, the forces opposing the motion of dry, cohesionless material are frictional. Loosely defined, frictional forces can be described as

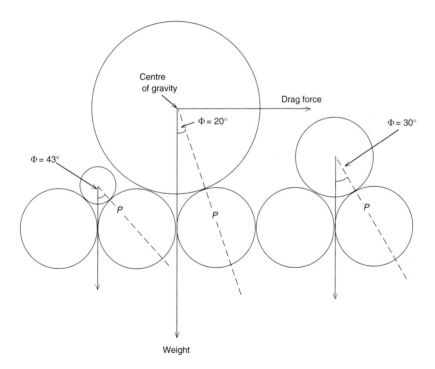

Figure 3.1 Schematic diagram showing the dependence of the pivoting angle (Φ) on the relationship between the diameter of the grain considered and that of the grain upon which it rests. After Pye (1994), figure 1.1; reproduced with permission of the publisher, Blackwell Science Ltd, Oxford, UK.

a measure of the ability of a grain to resist failure. In the context of sediment transport, it refers to the contact angle between superimposed particles and, again, the 'rollability' of a given grain or how easily it can be moved from its resting position. This frictional angle is illustrated in Figure 3.1. In uniform sediments, this angle would be of the order of 30–32°. In heterogeneous sediments, it varies tremendously with the particle sizes involved. Figure 3.1 clearly shows that, for the simple case of spheres, the pivoting angle varies with the ratio of the size of the spherical grain to the size of the grain upon which it rests. More specifically, pivoting angles decrease significantly as the ratio D/K increases (where D is the diameter of the grain considered and K is the diameter of the grain upon which it rests, or the base grain). It has been shown, for instance, that:

$$\Phi = \alpha(D/K)^{-\beta} \tag{3.7}$$

where Φ is the pivoting angle, D and K are as defined before, and the two coefficients α and β are determined from empirical regression equations (linear regression on log-transformed values). It has also been shown that β increases with the degree of sorting of the bed material (Kirchner *et al.*, 1990), which means that the angle of repose (or pivoting angle Φ) decreases more rapidly with the ratio D/K on a well-sorted bed surface than on a poorly sorted one. A wide range of coefficients α and β in equation 3.7 can be observed as a function of size and shape (Figure 3.2), as shown in studies on both fixed-bed features and water-worked sediment surfaces (Li and Komar, 1986; Komar and Li, 1986, 1988; Kirchner *et al.*, 1990). Under natural conditions, pivoting angles vary tremendously and individual values can hardly be determined in field situations.

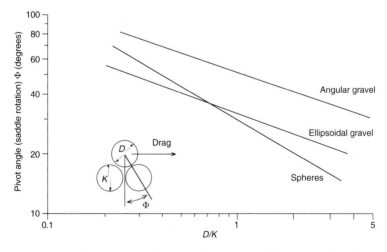

Figure 3.2 Relationship between the pivoting angles and the ratio of particle diameter and the size of particle underneath (for different particle shape categories). After Li and Komar (1986), and Reid and Frostick (1994). Reproduced with the permission of the publisher, Blackwell Science Ltd, Oxford, UK.

3.2.3 Porosity, permeability, and shear strength

Porosity, moisture content, and cohesion are also important bulk sediment characteristics to consider in alluvial channels. In contrast to friction angle and grain shape, these characteristics are of greater importance for particle sizes smaller than gravel. These properties may play a significant role in, for instance, bank erosion and in the movement or exchange of water within the zone immediately beneath the bed surface (the hyporheic zone; see Chapter 6).

Moisture content is usually defined as the mass of water that can be removed from a sediment sample by heating. This is usually expressed as a percentage of the dry mass, i.e. the ratio of loss of moisture to dry mass times 100 per cent (Pye, 1994).

Cohesion can be defined as the intermolecular attractive force acting between grains. The importance of this force varies widely with particle size. It is a very significant force for clay-size particles, while it has essentially no significance for sands (and, obviously, grains coarser than sands). Therefore, a distinction is often made between cohesive material and cohesionless sediment, with the former usually containing a significant proportion of clay-sized sediment.

River sediment is a porous medium, i.e. it contains a series of interconnecting void spaces or pores. Porosity (p) of the sediment is defined as the ratio of pore volume or volume of voids (V_p) to the total (bulk) volume (V_t), with the bulk volume being the sum of the pore volume (V_p) and the volume of solids (V_s). As the porosity of a given volume of sediment increases, the volume of voids in that sample increases. Stated differently, a void ratio (e) can be defined as:

$$e = V_p/V_s \qquad (3.8)$$

and as the void ratio e increases, so does porosity p. Since $V_t = V_p + V_s$, void ratio (e) and porosity (p) are related, and:

$$e = p/(p-1) \qquad (3.9)$$

or

$$p = e/(e+1) \qquad (3.10)$$

Both p and e are obviously dimensionless and can take any value between 0 and 1 (although e can even exceed 1; Dingman, 1984; Pye, 1994). Table 3.3

Table 3.3 Range of porosities and void ratios (from Dingman, 1984)

Materials	p	e
Gravel	0.25–0.40	0.33–0.67
Sand	0.25–0.50	0.33–1
Silt	0.35–0.50	0.54–1
Clay	0.40–0.70	0.67–2.3

provides some characteristic ranges of porosities and void ratios for various sediment sizes. Porosity may therefore affect moisture content, which in turn may exert a significant control on the strength of the sediment or its resistance to erosion.

Porosity is reduced when interstices in heterogeneous bed sediments are filled with fine material (Carling and Reader, 1982; Lisle and Lewis, 1992). Porosity is therefore a function of the fine-sediment accumulation rate (or infiltration rate expressed for instance in grams per minute per square metre) and removal. In natural heterogeneous coarse-grained channels, porosity values as low as (approximately) 0.10 have been observed (Carling and Reader, 1982). The low porosities observed in the sediments reported by Carling and Reader (1982) were attributed to very poor sorting and closed packing, with porosities generally decreasing with an increase in bed material size. Fine sediment is introduced into gravel void spaces by gravitational settling and turbulent flow fluctuations (Carling, 1984). Sedimentation rates or ('siltation' rates) are dependent on turbulence activity and suspended sediment at the sediment–water interface (Carling, 1984). Infiltration is highly variable, and also depends on the size characteristics of the infiltrating sediments and those of the gravel framework within which infiltration takes place (Kondolf *et al.*, 1993). If there is sufficient supply of fine sediment and little scouring from turbulent flows, coarse bed surfaces become embedded by fine material (Klingeman and MacArthur, 1990). Deposition of fine sediment into an open framework of heterogeneous bed sediment (and its effects on bulk sediment properties such as porosity) is of concern to fisheries biologists, and this will be further discussed in Chapter 6.

Permeability, on the other hand, is essentially the ease with which a material can transmit a fluid. This depends on the fluid viscosity, the hydrostatic pressure, the size of void spaces, and the degree to which the void spaces are interconnected. Porosity and permeability do not refer to the same bulk properties of materials; porosity refers to how much water a given soil volume can hold, while permeability is how easily water can be transmitted (Easterbrook, 1999).

The *shear strength* of a given soil volume is essentially what controls the resistance to erosion of river banks or their stability with respect to mass failure. Shear strength depends on cohesion, friction angle and the normal stress exerted on a given planar surface covered by unconsolidated soil material (the component of the weight acting perpendicular to a sloping surface). This perpendicular component of the total stress (normal stress) is usually represented by the symbol σ (as opposed to τ for shear stress, which is that component of the weight that promotes downslope movement). More specifically, shear strength is defined by the Coulomb equation:

$$S_t = c + \sigma' \tan \phi \qquad (3.11)$$

where S_t is shear strength, c is cohesion, ϕ is the angle of internal friction, and σ' is the effective normal stress. The importance of normal stress is its capacity to hold material together (Ritter *et al.*, 1995, p. 100), therefore increasing the internal resistance to erosion. In reality, soil volumes are occupied by openings filled with air and water, and pore pressure exists in these interstitial voids. Pore pressure tends to support part of the normal stress exerted by overlying debris on a given surface. The total normal stress is therefore the summation of two elements: the effective normal stress σ' and the pore pressure (μ) and:

$$\sigma = \sigma' + \mu. \tag{3.12}$$

Under saturated conditions (e.g. poorly drained river banks), pore pressure is positive, causing the effective normal stress to be lower (since $\sigma' = \sigma - \mu$; see equation 3.12), while, in partially saturated soils, effective normal stress is increased (or it is the same as normal stress for dry conditions). Under saturated conditions, shear strength is therefore reduced, and material is more susceptible to instabilities and mass failure. This will be further discussed below in the context of bank erosion and sediment sources.

3.2.4 Characteristics of coarse bed surfaces

In addition to grain characteristics and bulk sediment properties, it is useful to consider properties of sediment surfaces (Gomez, 1993). Recent work on such surfaces with a high degree of spatial resolution has allowed the identification of some valuable features. Microtopographic profiles (Robert, 1988) and subsequent analyses of surfaces show the complexity of natural gravel-bed surfaces (Kirchner et al., 1990; Gomez, 1993; Nikora et al., 1998; Butler et al., 2001), especially at the grain size scale and related small-scale sedimentary structures (Robert, 1988).

Butler et al. (2001) also clearly showed that the surface irregularity varies with the direction of measurement. From digital photogrammetric methods and digital elevation models, they clearly observed that micro-scale irregularities are more pronounced in the downstream direction, indicating that the effect of water working on natural surfaces is to increase surface irregularity, and therefore surface roughness. The use of digital photogrammetric methods (e.g. Butler et al., 1998; Lane, 2000) provides opportunities for characterization of river bed topography at various spatial scales and the characterization of its irregularity in ways that were not possible until very recently.

3.3 EROSIONAL PROCESSES

In this chapter, the emphasis is solely on the transport of particulate matter, i.e. the transport of individual grains or sediment particles, either in contact with the bed surface (bedload transport) or in suspension within the flow (suspended sediment, when the weight of the particle is 'supported' by the upward component of turbulence). The transport of particles in suspension or in contact with the bed surface (bedload) obviously depends heavily on the particle size and the local flow conditions. As the flow conditions vary at a given cross-section during and after a precipitation event, particles making up the bedload (or transported in contact with the bed) may at any given instant become suspended if the vertical velocity exceeds settling velocity (with flow turbulence generating the strong positive vertical velocity fluctuations necessary to maintain particles in suspension).

The suspended sediment is usually divided into two components: the wash load and the bed material load. The wash load refers to the fine material transported in suspension and which originates from the drainage basin (hillslope erosion). The bed material load, as the name implies, refers to material originating from the stream channel itself, i.e. the lower bank and/or the bed material. The wash load component is usually composed of exceedingly small particles that are maintained in suspension within the flow over long distances. As such, it is usually considered that they have little influence on the channel morphology (Leopold *et al.*, 1964).

3.3.1 Bank erosion

Bank material can represent a very significant source of sediment or a significant component of the bed material load (e.g. Saint-Laurent and Guimont, 1999). Bank erosion varies significantly along river channels. This spatial variability in erosion rates is in turn controlled by the longitudinal and/or vertical variation in grain size, moisture content, organic content, bank vegetation, channel curvature, bank angle, and related variations in shear stress applied on a given bank (Thorne, 1982; Hickin, 1984).

There are two broad categories of bank erosion processes: flow erosion and mass failure (Richards 1982; Knighton, 1998; Thorne, 1998). Water flowing in the channel exerts a drag force on the river banks, which may lead to detachment and entrainment of surface particles. This in turn is balanced by the shear strength of the bank material or the internally derived force capable of resisting the shear force applied by the flow. Bank materials are often stratified, becoming gradually finer upwards (because they are formed primarily by fluvial deposition). As mentioned above, the bank material properties may also vary significantly over relatively short distances along river channels. Similarly, the spatial distribution of shear forces exerted on the banks of a channel may also vary tremendously with position along stream channels, as a function of bank material properties, channel curvature, and bank geometry. Near-bank velocity gradients may for instance be maximized along the outer bank of meander bends where high bank erosion rates are commonly observed. These spatial distributions also vary temporally with changes in discharge. Most channel banks possess some fine material and therefore some degree of cohesion (Knighton, 1998; Thorne, 1998). Packing and cohesion of bank materials and the likely presence of vegetation and root systems may increase the strength of the bank material and its resistance to erosion (Hickin, 1984). The effects of root systems will clearly vary with the type of vegetation and its density, and their effects can be more significant in the upper layers of the river banks. For these reasons, it is usually not possible to simply define bank erosion in terms of a balance of forces between the shear force exerted by the flow, and the weight of particles involved.

Most river banks contain significant amounts of silt and clay, i.e. they can be categorized as fine grained. They possess some degree of cohesion and they resist erosion essentially through inter-particle, electrochemical bonding. When erosion does take place, it is often aggregates of grains that are detached (Thorne, 1998, p. 892). The strength of such soil characteristics is also highly dependent upon recent antecedent conditions of wetting and drying. For all these reasons, the critical conditions for erosion of cohesive banks are complex and difficult to define accurately, and are usually higher than for non-cohesive banks (Thorne, 1998).

The second major category of bank erosion processes is referred to as mass failure. The susceptibility of the banks to erosion, or their susceptibility to mass failure, depends on the processes of weathering and weakening. Mass bank failure reflects the bulk mechanical properties of the bank materials, where the shear resistance or shear strength is a function of cohesion, friction, and effective normal stress, as defined by equation 3.11. As explained before, the effective normal stress is a function of pore-water pressure. In poorly drained soils, the pore-water pressure is usually positive, and positive pore-water pressures act to reduce bank stability. Soil moisture conditions at and beneath the bank surface can therefore be very significant in controlling bank stability (as are previous flow and precipitation conditions). Rapid immersion of dry banks and repeated wetting and drying cycles can contribute to cracking (Plate 3.1), which will in turn reduce the shear strength of the bank materials and increase its susceptibility to erosion. Intense drying and shrinkage of the bank in particular may lead to 'desiccation' cracking (Thorne, 1998). Mass failure is also related to flow erosion, in the sense that the flow scours the bed and the bottom portion of the bank. This may increase the bank height and the bank angle (by undercutting). It is the cause of bank retreat, which may also trigger instability and mass failure.

As mentioned before, there tends to be a gradual fining of the bank material upwards (especially in the presence of a well-developed floodplain), where cohesive material may overlie non-cohesive sand or gravel (bank material with a smaller percentage of silt and clay). This vertical stratification will tend to induce further erosion of the bottom layers of the bank, undercutting, and eventually collapse of the bank (or the upper portions of the bank) in a gravity-induced mass failure. In banks made of composite materials and some level of vertical stratification, the stability of the entire bank is to some extent controlled by the strength of its 'weakest' component, since its removal may lead to the mass bank failure. There also appears to be a tendency for mass failure to be more dominant in the downstream reaches of rivers, because of the increase in bank height and a tendency (overall) for bank cohesion to increase in the downstream reaches

Plate 3.1 Bank erosion (cracking and mass failure) along a coarse-grained channel (southern Ontario).

(Lawler, 1992). The role of vegetation in mass failure is difficult to assess, and may be either positive or negative, i.e. it may enhance or reduce susceptibility to bank mass failure (Thorne, 1998). Roots reinforce the soil, but this effect is negated when bank height far exceeds the depth of the root system. Moreover, soil moisture levels decrease with the presence of high-density vegetation (increased interception by vegetation and evapotranspiration), which reduces the frequency of occurrence of saturated conditions leading to mass failure. On the other hand, a well-developed root system may invade cracks or fissures in a soil, which may lead to instability. Therefore, depending on the local context, and the dominance of either mass failure or fluvial erosion, the presence of vegetation may accelerate or reduce significantly bank erosion and the supply of sediment to the stream.

3.3.2 Bed erosion

Most river beds are composed of cohesionless sediment particles. Few silt-bed streams exist, because fine material delivered to the stream from hill-slopes or from bank erosion will pass through the drainage system as wash load (ASCE, 1992). Clay-bed streams may not be uncommon, but are restricted to specific areas (e.g. proglacial marine deposits) and, as such, are not discussed here in the context of bed erosion in alluvial channels.

Various approaches have been used in the past to determine when particles resting on a stream bed are entrained by the flow, i.e. when erosion of a bed made up of particles of various sizes is actually taking place (e.g. critical velocity or critical discharge). The most widely used modern approach is based on a balance of forces between the immersed weight of the grains and the flow force. This force balance approach is usually referred to as the threshold shear stress for initial motion (e.g. Buffington and Montgomery, 1997).

The bed shear stress estimate to be used in analyses of the thresholds of initial motion can be derived from the average flow conditions at the reach scale, from the local flow conditions (as determined for instance from the law of the wall), or from the turbulent stresses. The choice of the particular bed shear stress estimate to use in incipient motion studies depends on the scale and the goals of a given investigation.

For the sake of simplicity, let us consider that the flow along a given river reach is quasi-uniform (average flow depth constant along the channel), the bed surface is flat, and the bed material is of approximately the same size and shape. Under these conditions, bed material will start moving when the force driving the flow is equal to or just exceeds the submerged weight of the sediment. More specifically, the critical shear stress is defined by balancing the 'drag force moment' (DFM) and the 'submerged weight moment' (SWM). The drag force moment is defined from the bed shear stress and the pivoting angle of the grains and:

$$\text{DFM} = \tau_0/n \times D/2 \cos \Phi \tag{3.13}$$

where n is the number of particles in a unit area, D is particle size, Φ the pivoting angle (equation 3.7), and τ_0 is bed shear stress (e.g. equation 1.7). At the point of incipient motion, this force is balanced against the submerged weight moment of the particles, which is defined as:

$$\text{SWM} = g(\rho_s - \rho)(\pi/6)D^3 \times D/2 \sin \Phi \tag{3.14}$$

(where $\pi/6 \times D^3$ is the volume of a sphere). Initial motion occurs when equating the moments of forces, as defined in equations 3.13 and 3.14:

$$\tau_0/n \times D/2 \cos \Phi = g(\rho_s - \rho)(\pi/6)D^3 \times D/2 \sin \Phi \tag{3.15}$$

and the critical shear stress (τ_c) thus becomes:

$$\tau_c = ng \, (\rho_s - \rho) \, \pi/6 \, D^3 \tan \Phi \tag{3.16}$$

or:

$$\tau_c = \eta g \, (\rho_s - \rho) \, \pi/6 \, D \tan \Phi \tag{3.17}$$

where η is a measure of packing density and is equal to nD^2 (e.g. Knighton, 1998). In practice (and given the difficulties involved in measuring packing densities and pivoting angles), equation 3.17 is usually approximated by:

$$\tau_c = k \, (\rho_s - \rho) \, g \, D \tag{3.18}$$

where k is a coefficient that depends on average packing densities and pivoting angles. Numerous values for k have been suggested in the literature (see, for instance, Carson and Griffiths, 1987), with $k = 0.056$ and $k = 0.045$ being frequently mentioned. Even under ideal conditions of roughly uniform size and shape, the value of k that should be used to predict critical shear stresses is subject to interpretation (Carson and Griffiths, 1987; Buffington and Montgomery, 1997). For $k = 0.045$ (and considering that water density and sediment density can be considered as constant), it follows from equation 3.18 that:

$$\tau_c = 0.73 \, D \tag{3.19}$$

for τ_c expressed in N m^{-2} (or Pa) and D expressed in millimetres.

EXAMPLE

If, for instance, a channel is designed with a slope of 0.002 and with uniform spherical bed material with a diameter of 12 mm, one may expect that the channel will remain stable (no sediment movement) for a range of flow stages of up to 0.45 m in depth.

$$\tau_c = 0.73 \, D \, (mm) = 8.76 \, N \, m^{-2}$$
$$\tau_c = 8.76 \, N \, m^{-2} = \rho \, g \, d \, S$$

The maximum depth that the designed channel will be able to sustain before becoming unstable is therefore:

$$d = 8.76/(\rho \, g \, S) = 0.45 \, m$$

A dimensionless approach can also be used for the determination of critical shear stress. The dimensionless shear stress is usually represented by theta (θ), and it is simply defined from the ratio of critical dimensional shear stress to submerged weight:

$$\theta_c = \tau_c/(\rho_s - \rho)gD \tag{3.20}$$

where θ_c is also known as the Shields parameter (Buffington, 1999). Shields' studies in the 1930s were the first widely known investigations to use a dimensionless expression of bed shear stress to assess incipient sediment movement in coarse-grained channels. Dimensionless shear stresses (or Shields parameters) are also used frequently in sediment transport studies to refer to any measured value of bed shear stress (i.e. with or without reference to the critical stage).

It is worth noting at this stage that lift forces acting on sediment particles resting on a stream bed are usually neglected in initial motion studies. A vertical pressure gradient is nonetheless exerted on sediment grains, with a net pressure gradient being exerted upwards (the fluid pressure is greater where the fluid velocity is lower, i.e. the underside of the particles). Most studies of incipient motion will assume that lift forces can be neglected and that the drag force and the submerged weight will determine the initial motion of a sediment grain of a given size.

When applied to natural conditions, a number of problems and additional factors need to be taken into account. Under natural conditions, a range of particle sizes is usually observed on the stream bed. This natural sorting of bed material has led to numerous studies on thresholds of initial motion

Table 3.4 Observed empirical values of a and b in $\theta_c = a\,(D_i/D_{50})^{-b}$ (after Komar, 1987a, 1996)

Source	D_{50} (mm)	D_i (range in mm)	a, b values
Day (1980) – laboratory measurements	0.42 0.44 1.75 1.55	0.15–2.86 0.15–2.03 0.15–11.1 0.15–4.06	$a = 0.047; b = -0.53$ $a = 0.045; b = -0.66$ $a = 0.026; b = -0.29$ $a = 0.029; b = -0.66$
Andrews (1983) – East Fork, Snake and Clearwater Rivers, (USA)			$a = 0.083; b = -0.87$
Carling (1983) – Great Eggleshope Beck (UK)	20	10–200	$a = 0.039; b = -0.82$
Hammond et al. (1984) – English Channel	7.5	5–40	$a = 0.045; b = -0.58$
Ashworth and Ferguson (1989) – Lyngsdalselva, Norway; Dubhaig and Feshie Rivers, UK	23–98		$a = 0.089; b = -0.74$
Ashworth et al. (1992a); Sunwapta River, Canada	20–30		$a = 0.049; b = -0.69$
Petit (1994) – laboratory measurements	12.8 19.6 24.2 39.2		$a = 0.049; b = -0.66$ $a = 0.049; b = -0.68$ $a = 0.047; b = -0.73$ $a = 0.045; b = -0.81$

for heterogeneous bed sediments (e.g. Table 3.4). Dimensionless critical shear stresses for heterogeneous sediments can be summarized by:

$$\theta_{ci} = a \, (D_i/D_{50})^{-b} \tag{3.21}$$

where θ_{ci} is the dimensionless critical shear stress needed to move a particle of size D_i, D_{50} is the median bed particle size, and a and b are empirically derived coefficients (Komar, 1987a, b).

It has been widely observed in numerous empirical studies that the exponent b varies between 0 and −1 (Komar, 1987a, b; 1996; Table 3.4), with an average value of about −0.6 (Komar, 1996). This in turn implies *selective entrainment* of natural heterogeneous bed material. An exponent of 0 in equation 3.21 would indicate a constant dimensionless shear stress (as for uniform particle sizes), while a value of $b = -1$ would imply *equal mobility*, or particles of all sizes being mobilized at an identical bed shear stress (e.g. Andrews, 1983). Most observations in natural streams (with exponents b varying between 0 and −1) suggest some degree of selective entrainment (Figure 3.3; Wilcock, 1988; Robert, 1990). With an observed empirical exponent b taking any value between 0 and −1, this last expression (equation 3.21) implies that as the particle size, D_i, within a given mixture increases, the *dimensionless* shear stress required to move that particle decreases. This is the condition commonly observed in coarse-grained channels. Moreover, most estimated values of a (in equation 3.21) from various empirical studies are in the region of 0.045 (Table 3.4). It is worth noting that this corresponds with the expected value of θ_c for uniform particle size. From equation 3.21, it can be seen that it also corresponds with the expected value of θ_c when D_i/D_{50} is equal to 1, i.e. the expected critical dimensionless shear stress for the median size of the bed material (Buffington and Montgomery, 1997).

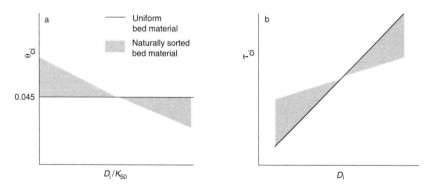

Figure 3.3 Summary diagrams of empirical results regarding critical shear stress as a function of grain size in naturally sorted coarse-grained channels (the dimensionless form of the relation is illustrated on the left-hand side of the diagram). Each diagram illustrates the differences between critical shear stress for uniform bed material and the range of empirical results observed in natural, coarse-grained alluvial channels. After Robert (1993), figure 2; reproduced by permission of Arnold Publishers, London, UK.

Church *et al.* (1991) also analysed the question of equal mobility from a different perspective. Using traps distributed along a bar in a cobble/gravel channel, they sampled a range of particle sizes (<10 mm) over periods of time ranging from several hours to several days. They showed that, at various times, the size distribution of the trapped material varied significantly, and that strict equal mobility was not observed. They concluded that equal mobility of fine material was at best a statistical phenomenon, which holds for a limited range of grain sizes over a seasonal period.

There are three main reasons that have been invoked to explain the decrease in dimensionless shear stress with an increase in particle size:

(a) relative protrusion or grain exposure effects (e.g. Fenton and Abbott, 1977; Andrews, 1983; Kirchner *et al.*, 1990);

(b) imbrication or clustering of particles (Brayshaw *et al.*, 1983; Carson and Griffiths, 1987; Reid *et al.*, 1992); and

(c) pivoting or friction angle effects in poorly sorted coarse-bed streams (Wiberg and Smith, 1987; Komar and Li, 1988; Wilcock and Southard, 1988; Komar and Carling, 1991; Wilcock, 1993; Komar, 1996).

Grains of smaller size are entrained at larger dimensionless shear stresses because, on complex and irregular surfaces, their exposure to the flow is much reduced when compared with larger grains. Some may even be completely shielded by upstream grains, being effectively lost to the flow unless and until larger grains are set in motion (Kirchner *et al.*, 1990). The arrangement of individual particles on the stream bed, especially in heterogeneous gravel-bed rivers, is important, as this arrangement exerts a significant control on thresholds of initial motion. While rolling or sliding on the stream bed, particles become imbricated, and these structures do affect the ease with which individual clasts will be removed (Brayshaw *et al.*, 1983; Reid *et al.*, 1992; Reid and Frostick, 1994). Particles in open-plane bed positions (i.e. without imbrication) will be dislodged at bed shear stresses or stream power values less than those observed for tightly imbricated structures (with other factors being the same). Finally, the role of friction angle or pivoting angle on the 'rollability' has been explained in detail before in this chapter. As particle size increases, its pivoting angle tends to decrease. A decrease in pivoting angle in turn tends to be associated with a smaller dimensionless shear stress. The three factors combined therefore lead to the observations summarized in equation 3.21, where the critical shear stress in natural heterogeneous bed material is best approximated by using separate grain size fractions in the ratio D_i/D_{50}.

The methods used to assess incipient motion also may affect directly the estimates of θ_{ci} (Wilcock, 1988). Three broad categories of methods have been used to determine (empirically) incipient motion:

(a) visual observations (e.g. Yalin and Karahan, 1979);

(b) extrapolation of bedload transport rates to either zero or a very low reference value (e.g. Wilcock and Southard, 1988; Wilcock *et al.*, 1996); and

(c)   empirical relations between measured average bed shear stress and the largest mobile grain size (from which one can determine a critical shear stress for a given grain size; e.g. Andrews, 1983; Carling, 1983).

Visually based estimates are usually somewhat lower than those determined from extrapolation of bedload transport, for instance, and each method should be used with caution (Wilcock, 1988). Estimates of θ_{ci} based on the largest particle in transport clearly describe the coarsest bedload sizes, while estimates based on extrapolation of bedload transport rates describe the motion of the full bedload distribution (see Buffington and Montgomery, 1997, for a comprehensive review).

The bed roughness conditions at the local scale may also play a significant role in controlling differences in estimates of critical dimensionless shear stress (Wiberg and Smith, 1987). Petit (1994), Richards (1988) and Robert (1990) suggested, for instance, that for a given ratio of D_i to D_{50}, the critical dimensionless shear stress varies with the bed roughness conditions. More specifically, the value of θ_c has been shown to be sensitive to variations of y_0/D_{50} (with θ_c increasing with the roughness length for a given D_i and D_{50}). Alternatively, it has been suggested (Richards, 1988; Robert, 1990; Petit, 1994) that θ_c is a function of a 'bed roughness index' defined as D_i/y_0. When $D_i/y_0 < 30$ ($D_i/y_0 = 30$ being the expected value for a uniform bed), the roughness length is inflated relative to grain size because of the effects of wakes generally observed around large particles and related eddy shedding processes. Under those conditions, and especially if θ_c is estimated from mean flow conditions at the reach scale, the measured shear stress may well be the sum of the different stress components (Wiberg and Smith, 1991). Since only grain stress is responsible for bedload transport, variations in dimensionless critical shear stress may be the result, at least in part, of the additional energy losses associated with bedform structures of different scales.

Finally, the last point to consider in relation to the threshold of initial motion is the role of turbulence. Virtually all the previously mentioned studies were based on time-average estimates of bed shear stress (from various methods and at different spatial scales). Drake et al. (1988) showed from detailed observations that entrainments of grains are localized and occur over relatively short periods of time. More specifically, the bed shear stress varies tremendously over short periods of time as a function of turbulence, with sweep fluid motions being particularly important in controlling the occurrence and the initiation of bedload motion on a stream bed. As schematically illustrated in Figure 3.4, instantaneous shear stresses can be considered as a random variable characterized by a probability distribution. Similarly, the 'susceptibility' of grain movement for particles resting on a stream bed can also be described as a random variable (characterized by a specific probability distribution of the susceptibility of the grains to movement), this distribution being a factor of various variables, including obviously size, but also protrusion, exposure, friction angle variability,

Figure 3.4 Schematic illustration of the existence of a probability distribution of instantaneous bed shear stresses and a probability distribution of the susceptibility of individual grains to movement. The threshold of initial motion is achieved when the two probability distributions overlap, with the degree of overlap controlling the amount of sediment movement. After Grass (1970, 1983) and Komar (1996), figure 4.5. Reproduced by permission of John Wiley & Sons Ltd, Chichester, UK.

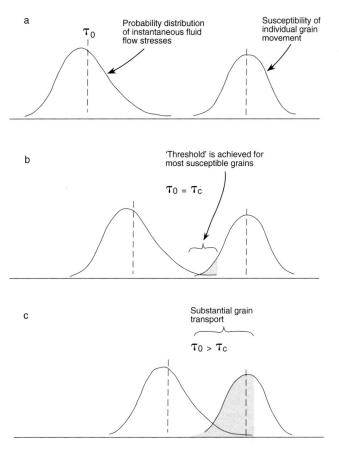

imbrication, etc. As flow velocity increases, the probability distribution of instantaneous bed shear stress may gradually overlap that of susceptibility to grain movement (Komar, 1996). A threshold is achieved when there is significant overlap between the distributions, with the degree of overlap controlling the quantity of sediment movement. With the development of new technologies and visualization techniques, this approach would be worth pursuing further in laboratory experiments, and could potentially be embedded into refinements of sediment transport models.

3.4 MODES OF TRANSPORT AND SUSPENDED SEDIMENT

3.4.1 Transport stages

Once the threshold of initial motion has been reached, particles are displaced downstream, and the mode of transport varies with sediment size and flow intensity. Modes of movement are usually summarized in three

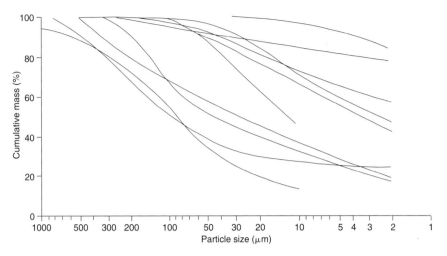

Figure 3.5 Examples of characteristic grain size distributions of suspended sediment for various world rivers. After Walling and Webb (1992), figure 3.2a. Reproduced with the permission of the publishers, Blackwell Science Ltd, Oxford, UK.

categories: in contact with the bed surface, i.e. particles rolling or sliding on or along the bed, in saltation (intermittent contacts with bed surface), or in suspension within the flow. Coarse particles such as gravels (or grains coarser than gravels) generally move as bedload, fine and medium sands usually move predominantly in suspension, and coarse sands either as bed-load or suspended load, depending on the flow conditions (Middleton and Southard, 1984, p. 196). For most river systems, particles within the medium size range (i.e. between 0.1 and 1 mm) appear to correspond with the largest fraction generally transported in suspension (Gomez, 1991; Walling and Webb, 1992; Figure 3.5). Particles smaller than 0.1–0.2 mm are rarely included as part of the bedload, since this is part of the material that goes directly into suspension when disturbed (Gomez and Church, 1989; Gomez, 1991). Saltation may be viewed as an intermediate step between rolling and suspension (as illustrated in Figure 3.6), but the usual definition of bedload includes rolling, sliding and saltation (Gomez and Church, 1989; Gomez, 1991).

Figure 3.6 is often used to illustrate the role of various modes of transport and how they vary with flow intensity. It was initially derived by Abbott and Francis (1977) in shallow flows and for uniform particles of 8.3 mm in diameter. Similar diagrams could be derived for particles of various sizes. Immediately after the initial motion of a grain, coarse particles may predominantly be transported in contact with the bed, with particles either in continuous contact with the surface via rolling or sliding, or just rolling from one resting 'pocket' position to another (e.g. smaller grains being intermittently trapped between larger grains and moving only short distances downstream). With an increase in flow stage, grains begin to be lifted up

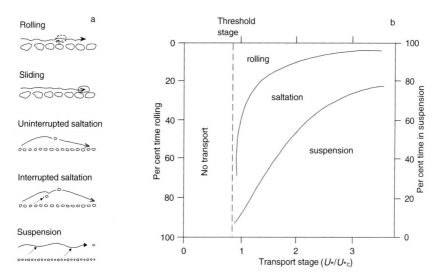

Figure 3.6 Transport modes of solitary grains as a function of stage ($U*/U*_c$); water depth 48 mm, and grain size 8.3 mm. After Abbott and Francis (1977) and Knighton (1998). Diagram of transport stages reproduced with the permission of the publishers, The Royal Society, London, UK.

above the bed and make some jumps. This may be considered as the onset of saltation, where the drag and lift forces are sufficient for particles to jump into the flow at an angle of about 50°. They then follow a characteristic saltation trajectory that is concave downwards. Under saltation, grains may rise to a height that is up to few grain diameters, for instance. When bouncing back on to the surface, the transfer of momentum may be sufficient to further dislodge grains resting on the surface. As flow intensity (transport stage) is increased further, the grain trajectories become longer and more irregular. Particles are carried higher into the flow and over longer distances, and this roughly corresponds with the transition towards the suspension transport mode.

More explicitly, two criteria can be used to distinguish between modes of movement and to establish suspension stages. These are the ratio of shear velocity ($U*$) to settling velocity (V_0) and the ratio of RMS$_v$ to V_0 (i.e. the ratio of the root-mean-square of the vertical velocity fluctuations to the settling velocity of the particles). Using the former criterion, a conservative estimate suggests that suspension occurs when $U*/V_0$ is greater than 1. When the ratio of $U*$ to V_0 is roughly equal to unity, grains are travelling at speeds that are almost equal to that of the fluid, in which case suspension is likely to be the dominant transport mechanism (Figure 3.7). (It should be noted however that a ratio of unity is a rough guide only, and values ranging form 0.2 to 2.0 have been mentioned in the literature; e.g. Chanson, 1999, p. 191). Based on the assumption that suspension occurs when the particles can be maintained in the flow by the upward component of turbu-

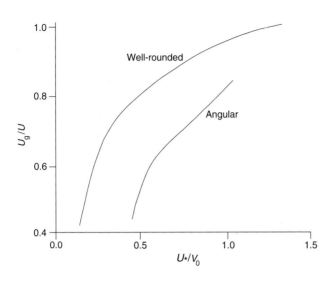

Figure 3.7 Mean forward velocity ratio (U_g/U) for two different grain shapes as a function of $U*/V_0$. Grain sizes within the range 4.8–9.6 mm (U_g: mean velocity of individual grains; U: average downstream flow velocity; $U*$: shear velocity and V_0: settling velocity). After Francis (1973), figure 2. Reproduced with the permission of the publisher, The Royal Society, London, UK.

lent velocity fluctuations, a similar approach can be used where the ratio of RMS_v to V_0 is considered. In this case, it can be expected that grains will tend to be transported in suspension when the standard deviation of the vertical velocity fluctuations is of the same order of magnitude as the settling velocity of the particles considered (or greater, obviously). The use of the ratio of RMS_v to V_0 or $U*/V_0$ may be considered as being equivalent, under the assumption that the maximum values of RMS_v near the bed are approximately equal to the shear velocity, and that suspension occurs when RMS_v and $U*$ are larger than the fall velocity of the grains (Middleton and Southard, 1984; Dyer, 1986).

3.4.2 Sampling of bed material transport

In practice and in nature, the distinction between the various modes of movement may not be so apparent. Particles moving along the bed surface (bedload) are usually sampled from either a Helley-Smith sampler (Plate 3.2) and/or some form of bedload trap embedded into the stream bed (e.g. Reid and Frostick, 1986, 1987; Church et al., 1991). Traps of various designs can be used to estimate the amount of near-bed sediment movement (Harris and Richards, 1995), with some allowing continuous weight recording (e.g. Reid and Frostick, 1986). Transport rates, as locally sampled on the stream bed, can then be expressed in units of mass per unit time per unit channel width. Helley-Smith bedload samplers (Emmett, 1980) have a characteristic 7.6-cm entrance width and 7.6-cm height (as in Plate 3.2) with 0.25-mm mesh sample bags. The sampling 'efficiency' of these devices varies somewhat with the range of particle sizes considered. Emmett (1980) concluded that the sampler had a sediment-trapping efficiency of near 100 per cent for particles ranging in size from 0.5 to 16.0 mm, but this decreases somewhat

Plate 3.2
Helley–Smith
bedload sampler.

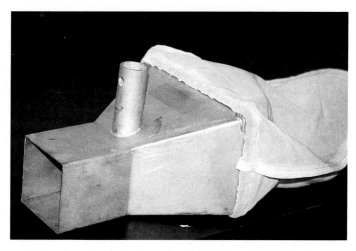

(to about 70 per cent) for particle sizes ranging from 16 to 32 mm (this cali-bration was achieved by comparing measurements from the Helley-Smith samplers to volumes and sizes of sediment collected in bedload traps). Given the height of the sampling orifice, some of the material transported in suspension may also be intercepted by the hand-held Helley-Smith sampler. To avoid this problem and to prevent scouring caused by a relatively large sampling device positioned above a sand-bed surface, smaller versions of Helley-Smith bedload samplers have been developed and used successfully (Dietrich and Smith, 1984).

Suspended sediment load, on the other hand, can be estimated from a range of devices. Samplers usually extract a mixture of water and sediment from streams (Goudie, 1994). Most samplers consist of a heavy streamlined container, within which there is a removable sample bottle. Water and sedi-ment mixtures can be sampled either at fixed points within cross-sections and integrated over a given time period (point-integrating samplers; e.g. McLean *et al.*, 1999) or used to obtain depth-integrated samples at various places across a stream channel. In this case, the sampling device is lowered from the water surface to the bed and then raised up again to the water sur-face. The suspended load is therefore sampled at various positions above the bed surface, and the sampler integrates the sample of load at various positions above the bed, in proportion to the local velocity.

Alternatively, local values of suspended sediment concentrations can be sampled at high frequencies using an optical suspended sediment sampling device (e.g. Lapointe, 1992, 1996; Hardisty, 1993; Clifford *et al.*, 1995). The output of these optical sensors must be first calibrated against measured sediment concentrations in field samples in order to account for a range of particle sizes and mineralogies in suspension at a specific field site or in a particular environment (Lapointe, 1992). The sensors provide high-frequency outputs that may be more suitable for turbulent flow investiga-tions and to establish links between flow turbulence and sediment transport processes.

3.4.3 Vertical profiles of suspended sediment concentration

Suspended sediment concentrations vary systematically with position above the bed surface (with concentration usually decreasing with distance from the bed). Suspended sediment concentration is therefore larger in the immediate vicinity of the bed, and vertical turbulent diffusion leads to an upward migration to regions of lower concentration (Chanson, 1999). This is called an advective or gradient diffusion process. Under equilibrium conditions (i.e. in steady uniform flow with equilibrium between rising and falling sediment; Richards, 1982), the time-averaged concentration profile can be summarized by:

$$-V_0 c_s = \epsilon_s \, dc_s/dy \qquad (3.22)$$

where V_0 is the particle settling velocity, c_s is the local sediment concentration at a distance y above the bed, and ϵ_s is the sediment diffusivity coefficient or sediment mixing coefficient. In addition to gradient diffusion (equation 3.22), suspended sediment transport also occurs by convection. This may be observed when the length scale of the turbulent mixing process is large, and convective transport may be described as the movement of sediment in suspension due to large-scale vortices (Chanson, 1999, p. 211).

The sediment diffusion coefficient ϵ_s in equation 3.22 is analogous to the eddy coefficient in equations 2.20 and 2.21 (i.e. analogous to the coefficient of momentum transfer or turbulent mixing coefficient). In practice, the sediment diffusion coefficient is not exactly the same as the eddy coefficient, for a number of reasons, including the fact that diffusion of grains differs from that of fluid particles, and the presence of sediment particles may interfere with the transfer of momentum (Chanson, 1999).

The sediment diffusivity coefficient in open-channel flows may be estimated from:

$$\epsilon_s \approx \kappa \, U_* \, (d - y) \, y/d \qquad (3.23)$$

where κ is the von Karman's constant, U_* is shear velocity, y is height above the bed and d is flow depth. Equation 3.23 can be used to provide an approximation of the sediment diffusivity coefficient, at least for the lower portion of the boundary layer (Chanson, 1999).

Finally, and in practice, mean suspended sediment concentration is used in transport rate estimates. Field measurements of suspended sediment concentration at a vertical or at a cross-section are presented as suspended sediment transport rate (Q_s) where:

$$Q_s = <c_s> U \, d \qquad (3.24)$$

where $<c_s>$ is the depth-averaged sediment concentration, U is the mean flow velocity and d is flow depth.

Interestingly, there have been very few studies on turbulent suspension processes in alluvial channels. Lapointe (1992, 1996) investigated alluvial suspension processes (sediment mixing) in relation to momentum mixing.

High-frequency devices were used to measure both flow turbulence and suspended sediment concentrations. The results in sand-bedded rivers illustrate the highly intermittent character of momentum and sediment fluxes where 20–90 per cent of the suspension work occurs during 'events' occupying only 1–5 per cent of the record duration. His results also suggest that turbulent (eddy) length scales equal to a few multiples of channel depth appear to be dominant in controlling alluvial suspension processes. The degree of intermittence in the suspension process was observed to be greater in deeper flows, but the origin or the cause of the large-scale eddies remain elusive. Additional similar work would be needed to determine the origin or the cause of these long-period fluctuations in natural rivers. This will be further discussed in Chapter 4.

3.4.4 Spatial and temporal variations (suspended sediment)

Suspended sediment concentrations and load are highly variable both spatially and over time. Many of the processes involved in this spatial and temporal variability occur at the drainage basin scale, and will only be briefly reviewed here. Additional information can be found in Knighton (1998), for instance, or in review chapters such as Walling and Webb (1992). When dealing with the spatial variation of suspended sediment transport, it is important to clearly distinguish between suspended load or yield (total yield being usually expressed in mass per unit area per unit time) and suspended sediment concentration (mass per unit volume). It is not unusual to observe contrasting values of yields, but similar concentrations (since load is derived from the product of flow discharge and suspended sediment concentration) and these questions also have to be addressed in relation to a specific spatial scale of investigation or a range of scales.

The sediment yields of small rivers can vary considerably. For instance, for basins of about 100 km^2, yields may vary by as much as three orders of magnitude, because of variations in climate, land use, relief, rock type, etc. (Walling and Webb, 1992). Larger basins tend to have smaller specific sediment yields. Headwater regions in drainage basins tend to provide a larger quantity of sediment per unit area. This is due to steeper valley slopes and increased surface erosion and sediment mobilization on hillslopes within smaller drainage basins. At smaller spatial scales (e.g. small headwater catchments), soil characteristics, surface vegetation and spatial variation in hillslope gradients exert a predominant control on the suspended solids (both yields and concentrations) during storm flows. At very large spatial scales, clearly, climate and associated environmental factors become the dominant factors (e.g. an increasing concentration in response to increasing aridity; Walling and Webb, 1992).

Traditional concepts of drainage basin sediment delivery suggest that specific sediment yield is inversely related to drainage basin area. Local geological conditions, however, may also play a very significant role. In the Canadian landscape, for instance, large quantities of glacial deposits are still

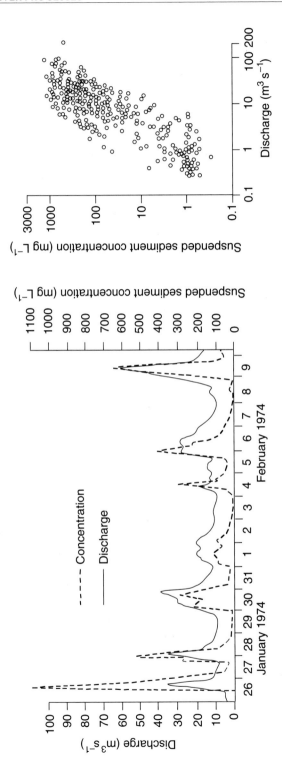

Figure 3.8 A characteristic record of the variation of the suspended sediment concentration during successive runoff events, and an example of a scattergram of the relationship between suspended sediment concentration and discharge. After Walling and Webb (1992), figure 3.4c, d. Reproduced with the permission of the publishers, Blackwell Science Ltd, Oxford, UK.

in storage in the main stream valleys in some areas, and dominate at the surface over extensive areas in other parts of the country. Under those conditions, immediate valley side sediment sources and erosion of the stream banks may dominate over upland erosion (Ashmore, 1993; Ashmore *et al.*, 2000), and removal of these surficial deposits may lead to a downstream increase in specific (unit) sediment yield.

Suspended sediment concentration at a given point in a stream channel is also highly variable over time. Water discharge is clearly a dominant factor, with a large proportion of the solids transported in suspension clearly mobilized by storm runoff (Figure 3.8). In addition to discharge, the time elapsed since the last storm event is important, as it affects the supply of sediment. There are numerous other variables that will affect the temporal variation in suspended sediment concentration (SSC), and this leads to considerable scatter in diagrams of measured SSC vs. flow discharge (Figure 3.8). Nonetheless, the following type of relation is frequently observed where:

$$SSC = a\, Q^b \tag{3.25}$$

where the exponent b usually varies between 1 and 2. Plots of SSC and Q therefore appear roughly linear on log–log diagrams. An exponent greater than one also implies that concentration usually increases faster than discharge. Since load is the product of SSC and flow discharge, the total suspended sediment load also clearly increases with flow discharge.

Short-term fluctuations in SSC with water discharge can also be very significant (and contribute to the scatter in diagrams in SSC vs. Q). As illustrated, for instance, in Figure 3.8, peaks in discharge and in SSC coincide overall. However, similar discharges may lead to fairly different values of SSC. Numerous reasons can be invoked to account for such differences. Among them is the time elapsed since the last storm event, the magnitude of the previous sediment-transporting events, and their frequency in the recent past (all of these factors affecting to some extent the sediment supply). Most rivers operate at less than their maximum sediment transport capacity, and therefore it is the supply of sediment to the stream and its spatial and temporal variability that controls, for the most part, observed changes in SSC over time.

Frequently observed differences in suspended sediment concentrations between rising and falling stages also contribute to the scatter observed in plots of SSC vs. water discharge. Systematic patterns of change in SSC with increasing and decreasing discharges during a storm event are referred to as hysteretic relationships. Different patterns of variation can be observed and the response can be a complex result of numerous factors (Williams, 1989). An example of such a hysteretic effect is schematically illustrated in Figure 3.9, where the response in terms of SSC is characterized by a time lag, i.e. the peak in SSC being observed some time after the peak in discharge. This in turn implies that, for the same flow discharge, the suspended sediment concentration can vary significantly during the course of single storm event (i.e. whether it is associated with the rising or falling discharges for a given

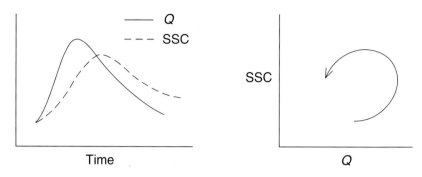

Figure 3.9 Illustration of one example of a characteristic response of suspended sediment concentration to changing discharge.

precipitation event; Figure 3.9). Different types of responses can be observed (Walling and Webb, 1992). The pattern presented in Figure 3.9 (counter-clockwise variation in SSC) represents only one example that could correspond with a large basin where SSC may peak a considerable time after the peak in discharge (when upstream sediment sources continue to supply a significant portion of the load, even after the passage of the peak in the flood wave). A clockwise variation in suspended sediment concentration (i.e. a peak in sediment prior to the peak in discharge) could in turn correspond with a characteristic pattern in small drainage basins where most of the sediment reaches the stream while discharge is still rising. In these cases, sediment concentration is higher during the early part of the storm, and is followed by a depletion of material during the falling stages. In addition to the size of the drainage basin, the specific response at a given station will be a function of the runoff mechanisms dominating in a given drainage basin, how their significance varies over time during a single storm event, as well as the susceptibility to erosion of the stream bed and banks in response to the increasing flow discharge.

The size of the particles transported in suspension may also vary with stream discharge. However, no clear or systematic pattern of variation in particle size can be established. In some cases, suspended sediment may become finer as discharge increases, because of an increased supply of fine material from hillslopes. In other cases (or at the same time), coarser material may become mobilized and transported in suspension because of the increased critical bed shear stresses and increased turbulence with increasing discharge. Bed and bank material characteristics, the magnitude of hillslope erosion, vegetation characteristics on hillslopes and dominant runoff mechanisms in a given drainage basin will all determine the range of particle sizes transported in suspension and its variation with discharge during sediment transport events. Finally, long-term sediment records will frequently show some clear fluctuations in response to, for instance, land clearance and/or modifications in terms of land use. The impact of land-use change on sediment yields can be very significant.

3.5 BEDLOAD TRANSPORT

3.5.1 Controls

Bedload transport rates are notoriously difficult to predict. The particles that composed the bedload move at speeds that are less than the transporting flow, and bedload processes are confined to a thin layer (a few grain diameters thick) in the immediate vicinity of the stream bed (Gomez, 1991). A large number of semi-empirical equations have been suggested in the past, and a summary of these can be found, among others, in Carson and Griffiths (1987) and Gomez and Church (1989). Part of the difficulty involved in the prediction of bedload transport rates is related to the complexity and irregularity of natural coarse-grained surfaces. This in turn leads to specific problems, outlined earlier, in defining when bedload transport is initiated for a wide range of particle sizes, the effects of bedforms on shear stress partitioning and on bedload movement itself (e.g. downstream migration of sand bedforms), the high spatial variability of local traction forces exerted on the bed surface due to spatial segregation in grain sizes, changes in local flow gradients, bed undulation, and various features associated with channel configurations, such as bars, meander bends, etc. There are also considerable practical difficulties associated with the assessment of distance of movement of individual grains and the spatial and temporal scales at which these complex problems need to be addressed. Most of the points listed above will be addressed separately, either in the context of bedload transport prediction or in relation to bedform development and evolution.

3.5.2 Transport rates and prediction equations

As mentioned before, bedload transport rates are usually expressed in units of mass (dry mass) per unit width per unit time. A range of empirical results has been presented in the literature for sand, bimodal sediments (sand–gravel mixtures), and coarse-grained channels. Empirical studies were based on either field measurements of bedload transport rates (e.g. Leopold and Emmett, 1976; Bagnold, 1980; Reid and Frostick, 1986, 1987) or flume investigations (e.g. Wilcock and Southard, 1989). In this section, some of the most widely used bedload equations will be introduced, and some of the problems listed above will be discussed.

The rate of bedload transport is almost entirely a function of the transporting capacity of the flow. Two variables are commonly used to estimate or predict bedload transport rates: the bed shear stress (τ_0) and the stream power (ω) per unit bed area (defined as the product of bed shear stress and average velocity; see equation 1.13). Values of stream power per unit bed area as defined by equation 1.13 have units of W m^{-2}. The reasons for the use of the bed shear stress are obvious, since this represents the flow force (per unit area) acting on the stream bed. The use of stream power in bed-load transport equations is due to the work of R. A. Bagnold (e.g. Bagnold, 1977, 1980, 1986). Stream power represents the potential rate of doing work or rate of energy expenditure (changes in energy result in work being done; work and energy having the same units – see Chapter 1). Bagnold rational-ized that a component of energy is expended in moving sediment, and therefore bedload transport rates should be directly related to the total stream power.

Most bedload transport equations also explicitly take into account the threshold of initial motion. That is, most equations assume that the rate of bedload movement is a function of the 'excess' shear stress (or excess stream power), i.e. the difference between the measured or estimated bed shear stress and the shear stress at incipient motion (the rationale being that only the flow force beyond that needed to initiate movement is an effective force in moving sediment). Therefore, two common expressions are used in bed-load transport equations, where the transport rate (I_b) is a function of excess shear stress or excess stream power, i.e.:

$$I_b = f (\tau_0 - \tau_c) \tag{3.26}$$

$$I_b = f (\omega - \omega_c) \tag{3.27}$$

where the subscript 'c' refers to the critical stage and f indicates a functional relationship.

When bedload transport rates are plotted against excess bed shear stress or excess stream power, what is usually observed is not a linear increase, but is best represented by a power function, where:

$$I_b \propto (\tau_0 - \tau_c)^b \tag{3.28}$$

and:

$$I_b \propto (\omega - \omega_c)^b \tag{3.29}$$

where 'b' is often of the order of 3/2. Given the considerations specified ear-lier in this chapter on the complexities associated with the identification of thresholds of initial motion in naturally sorted river bed material, the use of the equations above emphasizing excess shear stress and excess stream power can be problematic, and this certainly provides limitations to the use-fulness and reliability of prediction equations in natural environments.

With regard to the use of bed shear stress (above the incipient motion point), perhaps the most widely used bedload transport equation has been that of Meyer-Peter and Mueller (1948). Numerous versions of the Meyer-Peter and Mueller equation have been referred to over the years (see, for instance, Richards, 1982; Carson and Griffiths, 1987; Gomez and Church, 1989; and Reid and Frostick, 1994). When expressed in dimensionless terms, the Meyer-Peter and Mueller equation can be written as:

$$g_b/[((\rho_s - \rho)/\rho) \, g D^3]^{1/2} = 8 \, (\theta' - \theta_c)^{3/2} \tag{3.30}$$

where, as before, ρ is water density, ρ_s is sediment density, g is acceleration due to gravity, D is the size of the bed material (usually the median bed material size), g_b is the transport rate (volumetric transport rate per unit width, expressed in $m^2\ s^{-1}$), θ' is the dimensionless grain stress and θ_c is the critical dimensionless shear stress (McLean *et al.*, 1994, 1996). In the original work of Meyer-Peter and Mueller, the critical dimensionless shear stress θ_c was set equal to 0.047, and the grain stress, τ_0', used in the estimation of θ', was determined from:

$$\tau_0' = K^{3/2}\ \rho\ g\ d\ S \qquad (3.31)$$

where K is defined as the ratio of n_g/n, with n_g being the Manning coefficient due to grain roughness alone (equation 2.40), while n is the total roughness determined from flow data (equation 2.39). The value of K is therefore smaller than 1, and that allows the estimation of τ_0'. Surely, alternative means of estimating the grain stress component from the total mean boundary shear stress can be considered (e.g. equation 2.42, with an appropriate value of k_s at the grain scale) and the grain stress to be used in equation 3.30 can also be derived from law of wall estimates of bed shear stress or Reynolds stress projections (McLean *et al.*, 1994, 1996).

The use of the grain stress estimate τ_0' (or θ'), although often neglected, is important. Failure to include it can potentially lead to very significant overestimations of bedload transport rate (Carson, 1987; Carson and Griffiths, 1987). In the presence of bedforms (and as explained before), a significant proportion of the total stress is due to form drag on the bedform. This component of the total stress is ineffective in moving sediment. The effects of bedforms are therefore to reduce bedload transport rates (when compared with a flow with the same mean velocity but without bed undulations or bedforms; McLean *et al.*, 1994).

Using stream power measurements, Bagnold (1977) in turn showed that for sand-bed channels:

$$I_b \propto (\omega - \omega_c)^{3/2}\ (d/D)^{-2/3} \qquad (3.32)$$

which means that, in addition to the excess stream power, the bedload transport rate is an inverse function of the relative roughness or ratio of flow depth (d) to grain size (D). That is, for a given stream power ω, the power at the bed, ω_b, directly available for bedload transport, is an inverse function of the depth to grain size ratio. In dimensionless terms, the expression above can be converted to:

$$I_b/(\omega - \omega_c) = 1.6\ [(\omega- \omega_c)/\omega_c]^{0.5}(d/D)^{-0.67} \qquad (3.33)$$

(Carson and Griffiths, 1987). In subsequent articles (Bagnold, 1980, 1986), the stream power expression for bedload transport rate was further revised and generalized to a wider range of particle sizes (with separate exponents attributed to D and d):

$$I_b \propto (\omega - \omega_c)^{3/2}\ (d/d_r)^{-2/3}(D/D_r)^{-1/2} \qquad (3.34)$$

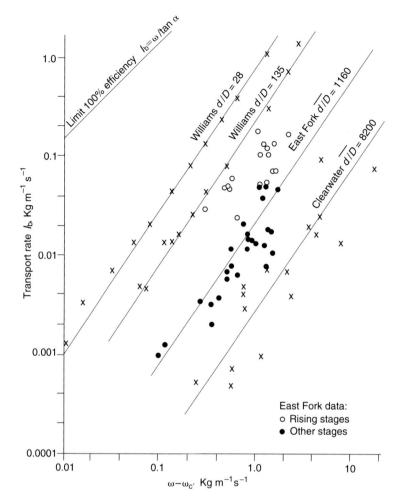

Figure 3.10 Comparative plots of measured bedload transport rates (I_b) as a function of excess stream power. After Williams (1970) and Bagnold (1977), figure 5a. Reproduced with the permission of the publishers, the American Geophysical Union, Washington, D.C.

where d_r and D_r are arbitrary reference values of flow depth and grain size, respectively (introduced by Bagnold to 'collapse' data from various sources and demonstrate the generality of the trends between rates of energy expenditure and bedload transport rates).

Various empirical data used in stream power bedload transport equations are presented in Figure 3.10. It should be noted that, in Figure 3.10, the units of both stream power and transport rate are kg m^{-1} s^{-1}. The dimensional character of stream power per unit area is $M\,T^{-3}$. When this quantity is divided by acceleration due to gravity, its dimensional character becomes $M\,T^{-3}/(L\,T^{-2})$, that is, equal to $M\,L^{-1}\,T^{-1}$ (hence the units of kg m^{-1} s^{-1} used in

Figure 3.10). The ratio of ω/g (where ω is stream power per unit bed area, and g is acceleration due to gravity) is usually referred to as specific or unit stream power. Since specific stream power and bedload transport possess the same units, the ratio of I_b to unit stream power has been used in the past to define a measure of 'efficiency'. This efficiency ratio represents the proportion of the stream power used in moving sediments (as opposed to energy expended in overcoming resistance for instance). More specifically, the efficiency ratio e is defined as:

$$e = 0.62\ I_b/(\omega/g) \qquad\qquad (3.35)$$

Observed values of e are usually very small (e.g. <5 per cent, and even in some cases <1 per cent for some gravel-bed rivers), which suggests that only a very small fraction of the work done by rivers is associated with the transport of sediment as bedload (e.g. Reid and Frostick, 1986, 1994).

Alternatively, bedload transport rates (I_b) can be made dimensionless. This is particularly useful for comparisons of various grain size fractions. In a manner similar to that used in equation 3.30, the dimensionless transport rate (I_{b*}) thus becomes:

$$I_{b*} = (I_b/\rho_s)/[gD^3\ (\rho_s-\rho)/\rho]^{0.5} \qquad\qquad (3.36)$$

(where D is usually taken as the geometric mean of the size fraction involved, and where I_b is expressed in kg per metre per second; e.g. Ashworth and Ferguson, 1989; Ferguson et al., 1989).

3.5.3 Movement of individual particles

An alternative and complementary approach to the bedload transport prediction equations summarized above (and others listed, for instance, in Gomez and Church, 1989) is to look at bedload transport rates from the movement of individual particles, where the movement of bedload is considered as a random phenomenon. Grain movements in these approaches are therefore considered as a series of steps of random length, separated by periods of rests of random duration as well (Hassan et al., 1991). Studies emphasizing statistical analysis of grain displacements using painted or magnetically tagged particles refer to the original theoretical work of Einstein in the 1930s, and further similar flume and field investigations conducted a few decades ago. Using tracer techniques, Schmidt and Ergenzinger (1992) showed a tendency for size-selective transport of coarse bedload in a high gradient stream. The scatter, however, is considerable, and is mainly due to different particle shapes and positions in the river bed. The step length and the duration of the rest periods both appear to be stochastic in nature, and both processes appear to be approximated by probability distributions.

Very similar conclusions are also reported by Hassan et al. (1991) and Hassan and Church (1992). Using data from a range of fluvial environments, they also showed that the distance of movement for large particles declines rapidly with increasing size, that bars interrupt particle progress, and that a weak correlation exists between mean distance of movement and excess stream power (Hassan and Church, 1992; Hassan *et al.*, 1992). Similarly, Wilcock (1997) showed that the variation (with grain size) of total displacement length depends on the degree to which individual grain size fractions (D_i) on the bed surface are mobilized, with the displacement length being independent of grain size for smaller fully mobile sizes, but decreasing rapidly with D_i for larger size fractions. Although the movement of unconstrained clasts appears to be dependent on grain size, additional analysis of constrained and buried particles indicates clearly that the effect of the bed surface structure is to reduce the differential movement (Church and Hassan, 1992). Burial depth and probability of re-exposure to the flow are significant factors to consider when analysing relations between distance of movement, particle size, flow intensity, and rest periods. Using flow visualization, Drake *et al.* (1988) were also able to show the role played by turbulence (especially sweep motions) in controlling the location and intensity of bedload movement and the fact that, for instance, distance of travel appears to be independent of particle size. Further visualizations of grain displacements and turbulent flow structures are required.

3.5.4 Spatial and temporal variations

Bedload transport rates are also very variable, both spatially and over time. There are essentially three scales of temporal variations: long-term variations in the rate at which the sediment is supplied to the channel; short-term variations due to the temporary changes in sediment supply conditions and the passage of bedforms; and, as discussed before, instantaneous variations in transport rates due to the inherently stochastic or probabilistic nature of the processes governing the initial motion and grain displacements of coarse sediments (Gomez *et al.*, 1989; Hoey, 1992). Fluctuations in bedload transport rates at various time scales may occur independently of variations in water discharge or flow intensity (e.g. Reid and Frostick, 1986, 1994). The extent to which all these scales of variation in transport rates can be identified from continuous sediment transport records depends essentially on the duration of sampling and the spatial extent of the sampling locations. Some of the observed 'pulses' in transport rates (e.g. Reid and Frostick, 1986) have not been clearly explained, and may not be related to the passage of bedform features. However, bedform migration does exert a great control on bedload transport rates and related temporal fluctuations (e.g. Iseya and Ikeda, 1987; Gomez *et al.*, 1989). For the simple case of two-dimensional bedforms that migrate downstream entirely by bedload transport (to be discussed for instance in Chapter 4, on bedforms), bedload transport rates can be estimated from:

$$I_b = \rho_s (1 - p) B \, h \, U_b \qquad (3.37)$$

where ρ_s is sediment density, p is porosity, h is bedform height, U_b is the mean bedform migration rate and B is a bedform shape factor (which can be approximated by 0.6 in most studies; van den Berg, 1987; Kostaschuk *et al.*, 1989). This type of equation based on bedform morphology and migration rate is difficult to apply with a reasonable degree of precision, mostly because of the three-dimensional and somewhat irregular morphology of most bedforms and the difficulties involved in measuring accurate and reliable migration rates.

The role of bed structure (i.e. the degree of 'consolidation') and the degree of imbrication of bed particles in gravel-bed rivers can also be very significant in controlling transport rates (Laronne and Carson, 1976; Reid and Frostick, 1994). The time between successive floods appears to be important in controlling the inception of bedload transport, presumably because of an increase in the degree of consolidation of the bed with an increase of the time period between major bed disturbances. Along the same lines, the role played by microtopographic features in controlling bed roughness (and stress partitioning) and the release of a large number of smaller grains associated with the movement of obstacles and the breaking of imbricated structures may be responsible for a significant portion of the observed spatial and temporal variability (e.g. Hassan and Reid, 1990; Clifford *et al.*, 1992a).

The presence of an *armour* layer in gravel-bed rivers also needs to be considered when dealing with temporal variations in transport rates (Gomez, 1983). Most gravel-beds are characterized by two active layers, with the coarse surface layer usually being referred to as the armour layer. The term *pavement* layer has also been used extensively to describe the upper surface layer of coarser sediment. A thin armour layer therefore forms at the surface. Underneath the surface coarse layer is the sub-armour layer, which may be of variable thickness. Typical values of the armour/sub-armour ratio in terms of mean grain size are of the order of 1.5 to 2 (Carson and Griffiths, 1987; Reid and Frostick, 1994).

Based on field data for rivers in North America, Parker and Klingeman (1982) and Parker *et al.* (1982) concluded that pavement is a mobile bed phenomenon and that the size distribution of the bedload bears more resemblance to the sub-armour than the armour layer. Parker and Klingeman (1982, p. 1422) emphasized a vertical winnowing process as being the primary cause of pavement. In this process, each time a large grain from the surface is dislodged, it leaves a 'hole' into which smaller grains can fall, working their way below the armour layer and therefore reducing their probability of re-erosion. Selective downstream winnowing of small particles from the surface framework is also frequently emphasized as a primary formative mechanism (Knighton, 1998). This is fundamentally different from a vertical winnowing process (in that vertical winnowing requires the movement of large grains). Changes in sediment supply have also been shown to play a significant role in the development of spatially variable bed armouring (Dietrich *et al.*, 1989). More specifically, it has been shown that surface coarsening occurs in gravel-bedded rivers when the local bedload supply from upstream is less than the ability of the flow to transport it (Iseya and Ikeda, 1987; Dietrich *et al.*, 1989). Bedload supply (and therefore the spatial extent of surface coarsening) can be affected by numerous factors in most rivers. Changes in sediment supply have also been shown to play a dominant role in the development of migrating accumulations of sediment with coarse grains at the leading edge (Iseya and Ikeda, 1987; Dietrich *et al.*, 1989; Powell, 1998; see section 4.5 on bedload sheets). The presence of a coarse surface layer in natural gravel-bed rivers clearly has implications for sampling of bed material, use of grain size in bedload transport formulae, and temporal variations in bedload transport rates.

The armour layer limits the supply of sediment and, at least during the initial stages of bedload motion, the transport rates may be lower than predicted by transport formulae. Moreover, the exponent of 3/2 commonly used in bedload transport equations (involving bed shear stress or stream power, as in equations 3.28 and 3.29) in general refers to large values of flow intensity and highly mobile bed conditions. In field gravel-bed streams, the ratio of bed shear stress to the critical value exceeds a factor of two or three only in exceptional cases (Parker and Klingeman, 1982). During the initial stages of sediment transport in gravel-bed streams, the increase in bedload transport rate with increasing flow intensity can be much larger than indicated by an exponent of 1.5. This results in very sensitive bedload transport relations with exponents commonly within the range 3–5 (Church, M., personal communication), and this is due to the fact that, under low (partial) mobility, displacements of individual grains take place over an increasingly larger proportion of the bed surface as the ratio of bed shear stress to the threshold value increases beyond unity. When the bed is fully mobilized, further intensification can only occur by increasing the depth of the mobile layer (as is frequently the case in sand-bed rivers) and it is usually under those conditions that the 3/2 power limit for bedload transport relations applies. Classic formulae, mostly developed from flume experiments in sands, express this high mobility limit.

Also contributing to the problems associated with the use of bedload transport equations is the frequent implicit assumption in the formulae that bedload motion will stop below the threshold of initial motion. Although it is well recognized that flow intensity at bedload cessation is different from that at incipient motion, this is rarely taken into account in the prediction of bedload transport rates. Reid and Frostick (1986), for instance, showed from their continuous measurements of bedload transport along Turkey Brook in the United Kingdom that cessation of bedload transport occurs at values of mean bed shear stress or stream power much lower than that observed at incipient motion. The threshold for the cessation is less than that for entrainment (or initial motion), because a smaller force is needed to keep a particle in transport than it is to entrain it. Numerous reasons can be invoked to account for such differences, such as the momentum of the moving grains, the absence of a need to overcome frictional resistance, and the absence of imbricated structures which act to retard incipient motion but become insignificant once the bed is fully mobilized.

Spatially, bedload transport rates are highly variable both within individual cross-sections and in the downstream direction (Gomez, 1991). In laboratory channels, cross-sectional variations can sometimes be neglected but, in natural conditions, the variability in transport rates across the stream can be pronounced, and can vary significantly with discharge (Gomez, 1991). At the reach scale, variability in the downstream direction can be due to various factors, including riffle and pool sequences (e.g. Clifford and Richards, 1992) and spatial distribution of local shear stresses in meander bends (e.g. Dietrich and Smith, 1983; 1984). These questions are better addressed directly when dealing with bedforms and channel patterns (see subsequent chapters).

3.5.5 Downstream grain size variation

It is well known that the average particle size at any point along a channel in a given drainage basin is a function of distance downstream or drainage basin area. In the absence of tributaries, grain size systematically decreases downstream. More specifically, the size of the bed material at any given point is determined by the initial conditions of supply and the subsequent action of *sorting* and *abrasion* processes during downstream transport. The term abrasion here refers to the wearing of moving particles (and those over which they move) by a range of processes, such as chipping, grinding, and breakage, which all lead to a reduction in size of individual particles (Rice and Church, 1998). Sorting, in turn, refers to selective transport (size selection during entrainment, transport, and deposition) or differential transport of particles as a function of their size. Ferguson *et al.* (1996a) mention that the distance within which the median size of the bed material is reduced by 50 per cent varies from 10 to 100 km (and is reduced to only 1 to 3 km in large braided proglacial rivers; Dawson, 1988). Moreover, when the median particle diameter is reduced to about 20 mm, a rapid transition to a sand bed is frequently observed within relatively short distances (which can be of the order of 0.2 km in small rivers and up to 10 km in larger river systems).

The processes of abrasion and sorting may lead to an exponential decline in grain size with distance downstream where:

$$D = D_0 e^{-aL} \tag{3.38}$$

(where D is particle size, D_0 is initial grain size, L is distance downstream and a is a coefficient representing both sorting and abrasion). However, Brierley and Hickin (1985) showed that, for a gravel-bed river in southwestern British Columbia (Canada), the rapid decline in particle size immediately downstream of a major sediment source is better modelled by power functions (which has implications with respect to the rate of change in particle size with distance downstream). The relative importance of sorting and abrasion in the grain size diminution with distance downstream is still a matter of debate, but recent studies seem to point towards a very influential role played by differential transport (i.e. sorting). Brierley and Hickin (1985), for instance, showed that different rock types with very distinctive susceptibility to abrasion or attrition showed identical downstream rates of size reduction. Ferguson *et al.* (1996a) also present strong evidence for rapid fining through selective transport for a gravel-bed river in Scotland with no lateral water and sediment input and no human disturbance. Detailed sampling of bed material at various locations along a 2.5-km reach showed a very rapid fining of the bed material. Bedload trap measurements and the monitoring of the downstream movement of tracer pebbles also clearly show the dominant role played by sorting during transport. Their results also complement the laboratory study of Paola *et al.* (1992), in which it is shown that, during aggradation, downstream fining can develop through sorting processes alone.

Additional significant factors that affect downstream fining in natural channels are the presence of larger organic debris in channels (Rice and Church, 1996b) and the role played by tributaries in disturbing downstream trends of fining of bed material (Rice, 1998; Rice and Church, 1998). Rice and Church (1996b) showed the dominant role played by large organic debris (LOD) in low-order streams located on the west coast of Canada. In particular, they showed that LOD and the 'contamination' of fluvial sediments from various inputs lead to an erratic pattern of surface grain size distributions or surface texture over short distances. The role played by LOD in terms of providing non-alluvial storage mechanisms appears to be dominant in controlling the stochastic variation in surface grain texture. Tributaries (or, in more general terms, lateral sediment sources), are also very significant, because they provide input of material to the stream that has characteristics independent of that operating downstream along a given channel (Rice, 1998; Rice and Church, 1998). The effects of a large number of tributary inputs on downstream surface sediment texture can lead to discontinuities in exponential declines (Knighton, 1998) and, in some cases, to complex patterns of spatial variation and negligible fining over long distances (Rice and Church, 1998).

4

BEDFORMS

4.1 BED – FLOW – SEDIMENT TRANSPORT INTERACTIONS

Alluvial channels are almost always characterized by bed undulations that result from sediment transport. These bed undulations can be of different sizes and shapes, and are collectively described as *bedforms*. Our ability to predict their occurrence, their morphology, and their effects on the turbulent flow fields and sediment transport processes has increased significantly during the last two decades or so (e.g. McLean *et al.*, 1994). Bedforms result from sediment transport and often constitute the bulk of sediment transport itself. Near-bed flow fields control local rates of sediment transport. These flow fields in the near-bed region are essentially controlled by the shape of the bottom topography, and changes in bed elevation along and across streams are modified by sediment fluxes. Sediment transport may also affect flow fields through form drag effects and increased flow resistance or changes in flow turbulence because of related increase in suspended sediment concentrations (e.g. Bridge and Best, 1988). These processes are complex and interrelated (Best, 1993, 1996; Clifford *et al.*, 1993b; Nelson *et al.*, 1993; McLean *et al.*, 1994).

Bedforms can be broadly divided into three major categories as a function of particle size: sand bedforms, gravel bedforms, and features observed in sand–gravel mixtures. This is the categorization that has been adopted herein, and each group will be discussed separately in a subsection. The distinction between these categories is widely accepted since the geometric properties vary significantly from one group to another. The complex interactions linking bedforms (development and maintenance), flow turbulence and sediment transport processes have been at the centre of research activities during the last few decades (e.g. Best, 1993) and this approach will be emphasized in the following sections.

4.2 SAND-BED RIVERS

4.2.1 Geometry of sand bedforms

In sand-bed channels, particles are relatively easy to transport and the flow force is often sufficient to transport most of the bed material. Under those conditions, the bed shear stress obviously exceeds the critical shear stress for incipient motion, and particles are transported either as bedload or suspended load (depending on flow intensity and grain size, as explained before). Processes of erosion and deposition are responsible for the formation of bed undulations and, as a result of sediment transport, the bed surface is rarely flat and the bed configuration usually shows some very distinctive geometric properties.

Bed undulations in sand-bed channels are easily characterized by their shape, size and spacing. Most bedforms formed in sand-bed rivers present the characteristic geometry illustrated in Figure 4.1. Sand bedforms generally possess a gentle upstream slope and a steeper downstream surface with a slope approximately equal to the tangent of the *angle of repose* (the angle of repose being essentially the equilibrium friction angle as defined before in Chapter 2, and usually of the order of 32°). Most bedforms also are characterized by a fairly sharp crest, from which we can distinguish between the stoss surface or the upstream gentle sloping surface and the lee surface (the term 'slip face' is sometimes also used), which corresponds with the downstream part of the bedform unit (i.e. downstream from the crest to the middle of the trough or the lowest surface elevation along a bedform unit). Most bedforms are characterized by a steepness (the ratio of height to spacing) that is very distinctive and which varies with the specific type of bedform considered. Not all bedforms are sharp-crested, however (Davies, 1982). Some large-scale bedforms in sand-bed channels may indeed be characterized by a relatively flat crest (Davies, 1982; Kostaschuk and Villard, 1996; Best and Kostaschuk, 2002). This observation, in turn, has implications for flow turbulence and sediment transport, as will be discussed later. These

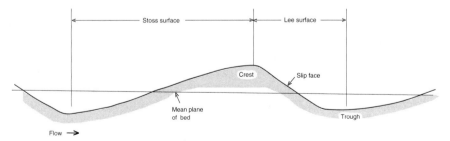

Figure 4.1 Characteristic asymmetrical shape of sand bedforms and related definitions and regions. After Middleton and Southard (1984), figure 7.8. Reproduced with the permission of the SEPM (Society for Sedimentary Petrology), Oklahoma, USA.

Figure 4.2 Sequence of changing sand bedforms with increasing flow intensity.

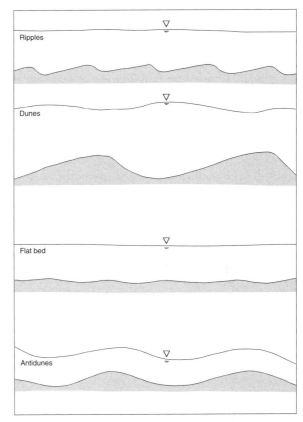

sand bedform features are not stationary once the threshold of initial motion is exceeded. That is, they usually migrate in the downstream direction (at a velocity much lower than the average flow velocity) while maintaining their shape. In general terms, bedform migration takes place via bedload transport processes, with erosion occurring on the stoss surface and deposition being observed downstream from the crest, along the lee face.

If experiments are conducted in a laboratory channel on bedform development in sand-bed streams, a succession of such bedforms will be observed as the flow discharge or flow intensity is increased (Figure 4.2). Starting from a relatively flat surface made of fairly uniform sand (in the medium sand range; e.g. 0.3 mm), the bed will quickly develop into a series of relatively small-scale features described as ripples (e.g. Allen, 1968, 1982; Costello and Southard, 1980; Baas, 1994, 1999; Raudkivi, 1997). As flow intensity further increases, larger dune features will develop. As opposed to ripples, the presence of dunes on the bed creates undulations on the water surface, with the bed undulations and water surface undulations usually being out of phase (Figure 4.2). Dunes can be either sharp-crested or flat-crested (flat-crested dunes being illustrated here in Figure 4.2). Dunes with a sharp crest present a degree of asymmetry similar to that of ripples, and are simply larger in size. Flat-crested dunes on the other hand are more symmetrical in shape (and have been referred to as low-angle dunes; e.g. Best and Kostaschuk, 2002). Ripples superimposed on dunes are also frequently observed and this may correspond with a specific stage across the transition from ripples to dunes (Davies, 1982; Robert and Richards, 1988). As bed shear stress or flow intensity is further increased, dunes are gradually transformed into an upper-stage plane bed (Bridge and Best, 1988). Finally, under very high flow intensity conditions, bed features known as antidunes can form. The transition to antidunes is controlled by the Froude number of the flow (Fr), and antidunes are usually observed when Fr exceeds 0.84 (Southard and Boguchwal, 1990). Antidunes are symmetrical (rounded) bed elevations and periodic waves. As opposed to dunes, antidunes move in the upstream direction, and water-surface undulations are in phase with the bed-surface elevations. Although easily generated in laboratory channels, antidunes are rarely observed in the field, as their formation necessitates a very large average flow velocity relative to flow depth (and conditions that are uncommon in most natural sand-bed rivers) and, if formed, their morphology may be destroyed during the falling stage of a major storm event.

Ripples are generally small features with height (h) of the order of 1 to 3 cm and wavelength l (i.e. spacing between successive crests) usually smaller than 40 cm (Allen, 1982; Baas, 1994, 1999). Dunes have much larger dimensions; their height may vary tremendously from a few centimetres to a few metres in large river systems (e.g. Kostaschuk and Church, 1993; Julien and Klassen, 1995; Kostaschuk and Ilersich, 1995; Carling et al., 2000a; Prent and Hickin, 2001) and their spacing can vary from 0.5 m to more than one hundred metres (e.g. Carling, 1999). Ripples tend to have a higher steepness (h/l) than dunes. The characteristic ratio of height to spacing for equilibrium ripples in fine sands is of the order of 0.12 (Baas, 1999). Dunes, on the other hand, have characteristic ratios of height to spacing varying between 0.03 and 0.06 (e.g. Kostaschuk and Villard, 1996), with a maximum value of 0.08 when in equilibrium with steady, uniform flow (Ashley, 1990; Carling, 1999). Ripple dimensions usually scale with grain size (Baas, 1994, 1999), i.e. their height and spacing tend to increase with an increase in bed material size, while it is generally considered that dunes scale with flow depth (i.e. dune size increases with an increase in the flow depth). The morphology of equilibrium ripples is therefore largely independent of flow velocity (except for the maximum ripple size, which tends to increase with flow velocity; Baas, 1999). From initiation to equilibrium morphology, ripple development goes through a number of stages, each characterized by a distinctive morphology. From a flat bed, ripples initially develop into straight, two-dimensional bedforms, followed by sinuous and non-equilibrium three-dimensional or linguoid ripples, to equilibrium linguoid morphology. The time needed to achieve equilibrium morphology varies inversely with flow velocity, and it may vary between several minutes and hundreds of hours (Baas, 1994, 1999).

Bedform geometric properties can be directly measured from bed surfaces, or from longitudinal transects obtained from such surfaces. Series analyses in both the time and frequency domain have been used in the past to characterize the main geometric properties of such surfaces (e.g. Jain and Kennedy, 1974). Despite some variability in size and shape (even under equilibrium conditions), sand ripples and dunes possess a striking degree of regularity or periodicity. Both the stochastic component of the bedform morphology (i.e. the inherent variability in size and shape for a given flow velocity, depth and bed material size) and the periodicity or the ability to characterize the bedform type by a dominant amplitude and wavelength, can be modelled adequately by the variogram and related geostatistical methods (Robert, 1988; Robert and Richards, 1988). The variogram method was developed for the statistical analysis of spatially dependent variables. Oliver and Webster (1986) advocated its use for the analysis of spatially dependent geomorphic variables, and Robert and Richards (1988) applied the method to the investigations of form–process relations and the formation of sand bedforms of various morphologies. If we consider a transect of bed elevation measurements along a rippled bed for instance, the variogram of that series will be a diagram of the average squared difference in bed elevation at a given lag (or distance) between successive observations. More specifically, the empirical semi-variance at lag h ($\gamma(h)$) is determined from:

$$2\gamma(h) = <(z_{i+h} - z_i)^2> \tag{4.1}$$

where z_i is the bed elevation (or more generally the 'random' variable of interest), h is the distance separating two points, and the angle brackets represent a spatial average at a given lag, h. Over short distances, the average squared difference between successive bed elevation measurements tends to be small, and the values of $\gamma(h)$ tend to increase with distance (as long as there is some spatial autocorrelation between successive measurements at a given lag). Characteristic semi-variograms (plots of semi-variance versus distance) for sand bedforms are illustrated in Figure 4.3. Similar examples of semi-variograms for aeolian ripples are also provided by Anderson (1990). The regularity of the bedforms is immediately obvious from the oscillations of the semi-variance. These semi-variograms can be adequately modelled by a combination of two functions: an exponential increase of the semi-variance with distance between successive observations (which represent the stochastic component of the bedforms and the degree of irregularity of the bedform sequence) and a periodic function from which an objective estimate of bedform amplitude and wavelength can be obtained (Robert and Richards, 1988). The parameters derived from this type of analysis have clear physical meaning. This approach has proved to be useful in process-based studies with, for instance, relationships being established between the degree of variability of bedform arrangement (non-equilibrium bedforms) on the one hand, and flow depth and flow velocity on the other hand (Robert and Richards, 1988).

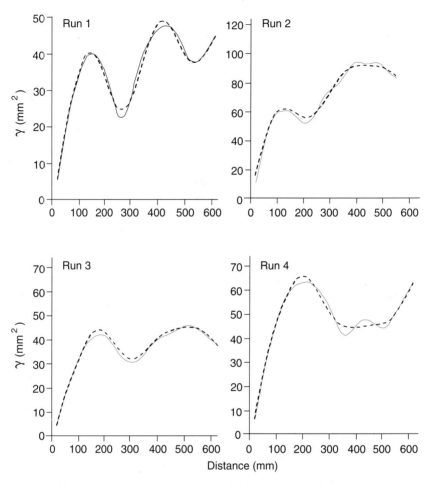

Figure 4.3 Sample semi-variograms for sand bedforms (solid line: observed semi-variance; dashed line: predicted by a combination of periodic and exponential components). After Robert (1988), and Robert and Richards (1988).

4.2.2 Bedform existence fields

The type of bedform and its main characteristics therefore depend to a large extent on the flow intensity. Furthermore, grain size plays a significant role in the development of bedforms, and some sand bedform features will only be observed within a specific range of grain sizes. Because of the processes responsible for their formation, ripples are not usually observed in coarse sands (i.e. in sands greater than 0.7 mm in diameter). Dunes, on the other hand, are usually associated with medium and coarse sands, although dunes in gravelly bed material have been reported recently under high flow conditions (Dinehart, 1992; Carling, 1999).

A number of diagrams have been established in the literature, where bed-

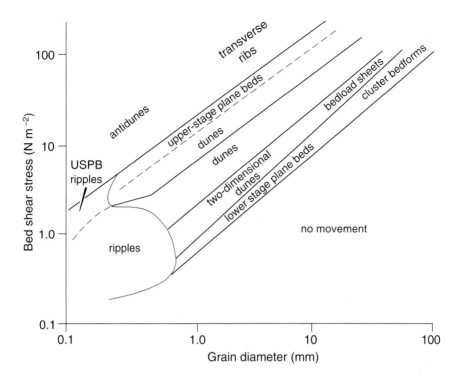

Figure 4.4 Bedform existence fields across a range of grain sizes. After Best (1996), figure 3.3. Reproduced with the permission of the publishers, John Wiley & Sons Ltd, Chichester, UK.

form fields can be determined from flow intensity and grain size indices. These diagrams are called bedform phase diagrams, and they illustrate bedform existence fields. These bedform phase diagrams plot grain size on the horizontal axis and some measure of flow intensity on the vertical axis (usually bed shear stress). An example of this type of diagram is presented in Figure 4.4. It represents a recent attempt to determine bedform existence fields for a wide range of particle sizes and shear stresses, and all the bedforms listed will be discussed in this chapter. It should be noted that the lines separating the fields are not exact transition lines; the transitions from one field to another should be interpreted as a zone within which there can be overlap of empirical observations and some level of uncertainty. These bedform phase diagrams are nonetheless useful, for instance, to predict the occurrence of bedform fields for specific flow conditions or, conversely, to infer flow conditions from characteristics of sediment deposits. Other similar bedform phase diagrams involve dimensionless bed shear stress (Allen, 1983), flow velocity (Baas, 1999), stream power and various combinations of grain size, flow depth, and flow velocity (Davies, 1982; Middleton and Southard, 1984).

4.2.3 Separated flows

Along bed undulations, the flow is developing with distance downstream, and its main characteristics are a function of the position considered along a bedform unit (Wiberg and Nelson, 1992; Nelson *et al.*, 1993; McLean *et al.*, 1994). The flow above a sand bedform unit can be characterized by a number of fairly distinct flow zones. In particular, a flow separation zone is usually observed immediately downstream from the bedform crest (Figure 4.5). Flow separation obviously occurs because of the rapid change of the boundary orientation, and the phenomenon is widespread along sharp-crested bedforms. Flow separation is crucial in the sense that it controls a number of related flow turbulence and sediment transport processes. The flow reattaches to the boundary at some distance downstream from the crest (reattachment point or zone; Figure 4.5). The length of the separation zone (*l*) is a function of the height of the bedform, and values of *l/h* of the order of four to five are frequently observed (McLean *et al.*, 1994; Best and Kostaschuk, 2002).

When the flow separates near the crest of a ripple or a dune, a region of very high shear at the top of the separation zone is produced. This region of high shear represents the transition between the inner part or the separation 'bubble' in which there is no net downstream flow and the mainstream flow immediately above it (turbulence being generated at the interface of two zones where the fluid moves at different velocities). As described in Chapter 2, this zone of rapid velocity change is called a shear layer, in which there is normally intense mixing. Within the flow separation zone, flow recirculation is frequently observed, i.e. fluid moving slowly in the upstream direction. This fluid motion in the opposite direction to the separation zone happens because of turbulent mixing within the shear layer and because of an up-channel diversion of a part of the shear layer at reattachment (Middleton and Southard, 1984). The shear layer created at the interface of the separation zone and the main flow immediately above it advects and diffuses downstream, and this creates a wake structure within the flow field (Nelson *et al.*, 1993; McLean *et al.*, 1994). Along the shear layer or the interface between the separation zone and the external flow, turbulence intensity (equations 2.52 to 2.55) and Reynolds stresses (equation 2.56) are maximized. In the vicinity of the reattachment point, the instantaneous bed shear

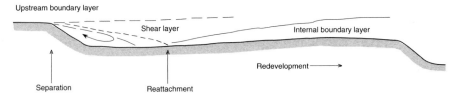

Figure 4.5 Identification of various flow zones downstream of a bedform crest. After Middleton and Southard (1984), figure 7.9. Reproduced with the permission of the SEPM (Society for Sedimentary Geology), Oklahoma, USA.

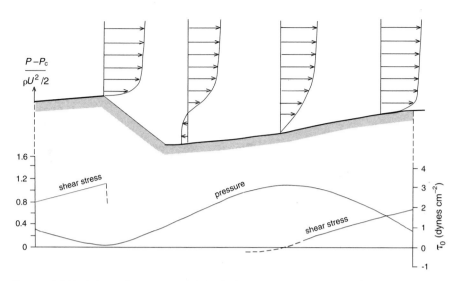

Figure 4.6 Variation of pressure and bed shear stress along a bedform unit. Arrows schematically represent direction and magnitude of local average velocity at various positions above the bed surface (P: pressure; P_c: pressure at crest; U: average velocity; ρ: water density). After Middleton and Southard (1984), figure 7.10. Reproduced with the permission of the SEPM (Society for Sedimentary Geology), Oklahoma, USA.

stresses can be highly variable and exceptionally high values can be observed in response to the 'arrival' of eddies (Allen, 1994).

Downstream from the reattachment zone, there is the development of what is called the *internal boundary layer*. Because the flow is able to re-establish its contact with the bed surface, its properties will gradually adjust to the boundary conditions. In this zone, the flow accelerates because of topographic forcing, from the point of reattachment to the bedform crest. Along this internal boundary layer, the local velocity gradient and bed shear stress vary systematically as the flow accelerates along the upstream surface (Figure 4.6). On the upstream or stoss side of the bedform, pressure decreases as the fluid moves towards the bedform crest. When pressure decreases, the spatial rate of change (or gradient) is said to be negative or favourable, so that there is a net force in the direction of motion causing acceleration. Downstream from the crest, when pressure increases, the pressure gradient is said to be positive (or adverse). Under those conditions, there is a net force opposing the motion, and adverse pressure gradients are associated with flow deceleration. Also presented in Figure 4.6 is a schematic illustration of the variations in local velocity gradients as the flow accelerates along the stoss side. Flow reversal within the recirculation zone is clearly illustrated, as well as the increase in velocity gradients from the point of reattachment to the bedform crest.

The development of this internal boundary layer is also strongly influenced by the presence of the highly turbulent wake layer immediately above. The turbulence from the surrounding wake layer may occasionally impinge upon the internal boundary layer, thereby affecting the turbulent flow characteristics in the near-bed region and potentially the sediment transport dynamics (Nelson *et al.*, 1993; McLean *et al.*, 1994, 1996). Separated flows, such as those commonly occurring above ripples and dunes, therefore exhibit characteristics that are completely different from those of uniform turbulent boundary layers (McLean *et al.*, 1996). The interactions between the turbulent wakes created by flow separation and the underlying boundary layer create turbulent flow characteristics that vary with position downstream, and these characteristics in turn significantly control sediment response and therefore bedform dynamics.

Not all sand bedforms exhibit clear and permanent flow separation. In large river systems in particular, bedforms often appear to be more symmetrical, with stoss and lee-side angles being of similar length and characterized by rather gentle sloping angles (e.g. <10°; Kostaschuk and Villard, 1996; Carling *et al.*, 2000a, b; Best and Kostaschuk, 2002). In these large river systems, most sand can be transported in suspension (e.g. Kostaschuk and Ilersich, 1995). In the Fraser River Estuary for instance (British Columbia, Canada), Kostaschuk and Villard (1996) observed that, although a well-defined zone of flow deceleration occurs in the trough, the characteristic zone of flow separation appears to be absent from measurements of velocity profiles in the lee of large symmetrical dunes. Similar observations were also reported by Carling *et al.* (2000a, b) from electromagnetic current meter measurements in the lee of large dunes along the River Rhine in Germany. Although detailed and accurate measurements of near-bed velocities are difficult to obtain in the near-bed region along large dunes in natural river systems, the aforementioned field studies showed no evidence of such permanent flow separation along large symmetrical and low-angle dunes.

The physical processes leading to this distinction between asymmetrical and symmetrical dunes and the presence/absence of flow separation are not yet fully understood. Some authors, however, suggested that the dominant sediment transport mechanism observed in a specific environment could play an important role. Smith and McLean (1977) and Kostaschuk and Villard (1996) mentioned that, while asymmetrical dunes are dominated by bedload transport processes, symmetrical and low-angle dunes may be dominated by the transport of sediment in suspension (corroborated by measurements reported by Kostaschuk and Ilersich, 1995). It has been proposed by these researchers that, while the downstream face of asymmetrical dunes is maintained by avalanching of bedload down the lee surface, symmetrical dunes with low-angle lee-sides result from deposition of sediment in suspension along the lee surface and in the trough between dunes (Best and Kostaschuk, 2002).

Field observations on the apparent lack of flow separation along large dunes in natural rivers, and the inherent difficulties in making field measurements of velocities have led to an experimental study of low-angle dunes (where the Fraser River observations of the bed morphology were used as a prototype; Best and Kostaschuk, 2002). Their laboratory measurements confirm that permanent flow separation does not occur over low-angle, symmetrical dunes. Intermittent flow reversal is observed (which may be present for up to 4 per cent of the time only) instead over a relatively small region. Shear layers are nonetheless generated from intermittent separated flows and/or from flow deceleration in the lee of the low-angle bedforms. However, shear layers generated above low-angle dunes appear to have a much smaller velocity differential than those generated in the lee of sharp-crested dunes (Best and Kostaschuk, 2002).

4.2.4 Turbulent flow fields above sand bedforms

During the last decade or so, a lot of effort has been directed towards the identification of flow fields (both mean flow fields and turbulent flow characteristics) above sand bedforms, both in the laboratory above fixed sand bedform features (e.g. Nelson and Smith, 1989; Nelson et al., 1993, 1995; McLean et al., 1994; Bennett and Best, 1995, 1996; Robert and Uhlman, 2001; Best and Kostaschuk, 2002) and in the field above much larger dune bedforms (e.g. Kostaschuk and Villard, 1996; Carling et al., 2000a, b; Kostaschuk, 2000). The advance of technological means, which allow measurements of flow properties at very small spatial and temporal scales, permitted considerable advances in the study of bedform dynamics. The use of

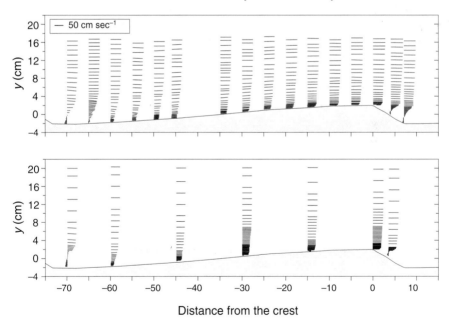

Figure 4.7 Example of flow vector patterns over asymmetrical, two-dimensional bedforms. The scale is shown in the upper left-hand corner. After Nelson et al. (1993), figure 1. Reproduced by permission of the American Geophysical Union, Washington, D.C.

fixed-bed features clearly facilitates measurements, and provides opportunities for detailed investigations of turbulent and mean flow fields in the near-bed region. The use of fixed-bed features in laboratory experiments is, at least in part, justified by the fact that the time-scale of the bedform evolution is much longer than that of the flow and sediment responses. As a result of the different time scales involved, numerous aspects of flow fields can be investigated using fixed bedform features (McLean *et al.*, 1994, p. 12 731). Even though this type of approach using fixed sand-bed features neglects the potential effects of sediment motion on the flow (Carbonneau and Bergeron, 2000), it has allowed a clear understanding of the effects of topographic forcing and flow separation on the boundary layer structure and turbulent flow fields above sand bedforms.

Figure 4.7 (after Nelson *et al.*, 1993) is first introduced here to illustrate the level of detail generally obtained in most of the aforementioned laboratory studies, and the predominant role played by topographic forcing and flow separation. Both the flow separation zone and the topographically induced flow acceleration along the stoss-side are clearly identified from the velocity vectors. Perhaps more revealing are the diagrams of turbulent flow statistics presented in Figures 4.8 to 4.10. These diagrams were obtained from interpolation from a very dense grid of point measurements made above *dune* bedforms. The examples used herein refer to only a few cases among the numerous turbulent flow properties that can be analysed. The most basic measurement usually reported is the turbulence intensity for the horizontal and vertical flow components, as calculated from equations 2.52 and 2.53, respectively. Other flow fields frequently mapped are Reynolds stress measurements (equation 2.56) and the skewness of the frequency distributions of instantaneous velocity measurements (both horizontal and vertical components; e.g. Bennett and Best, 1994, 1995,

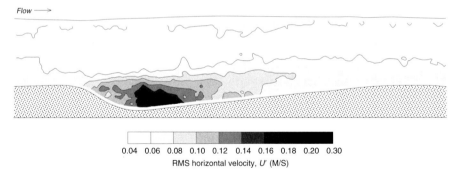

Figure 4.8 Spatial distribution of the turbulence intensity for the downstream flow component (root-mean-square of downstream velocity fluctuations) above a dune bedform in a fixed-bed laboratory channel (dune height: 40 mm; dune length: 630 mm; flow depth at crest: 0.10 m; average flow velocity at crest: 0.57 m s^{-1}). After Bennett and Best (1994), figure 2. Reproduced with the permission of the World Scientific Publishing Co. Ltd, Singapore.

1996). The results of quadrant analysis are also frequently illustrated in the form of vertical flow fields (e.g. Figure 4.10), and this will be discussed in more detail below.

The measurements presented in Figures 4.8 and 4.9 were obtained above asymmetrical and two-dimensional dunes with a height of 0.04 m and a spacing of 0.63 m (Bennett and Best, 1994). The measurements were conducted with a mean flow velocity of 0.57 m s^{-1} and a flow depth above dune crests of 0.1 m. These are identical to the flow conditions that were used to create dunes under mobile bed conditions (from which the concrete bedforms were recreated). The measurements of turbulent velocity fluctuations, obtained by Bennett and Best (1994) and reproduced here, were obtained using a two-component laser Doppler anemometer at a sampling frequency varying between 20 and 100 Hz. The data on the standard deviations of velocity fluctuations for the horizontal and vertical velocity components illustrate several fundamental aspects of turbulence structure over dunes. Other examples of equally detailed work exist in the literature, as exemplified by the work of Nelson *et al.* (1993) and Bennett and Best (1995, 1996). The examples presented herein were chosen because of the clarity and the simplicity of the flow fields illustrated. The data clearly show how flow separation and reattachment affect the overall distribution of RMS$_u$ (root-mean-square of horizontal velocity fluctuations; equation 2.52) above and along the bedform unit. That is, turbulence intensity for the horizontal flow component (RMS$_u$) is clearly maximized in the vicinity of the reattachment zone, i.e. within the flow separation zone itself, at reattachment and, to some extent, downstream from it (Figure 4.8).

In turn, the contour map of the root-mean-square of the vertical velocity component (RMS$_v$) for the most part illustrates the predominant role played

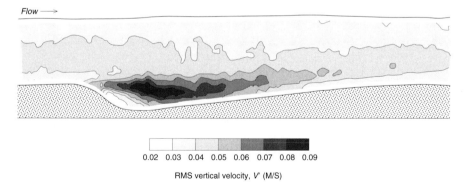

Flow ⟶

0.02 0.03 0.04 0.05 0.06 0.07 0.08 0.09

RMS vertical velocity, *V* (M/S)

Figure 4.9 Spatial distribution of the turbulence intensity for the vertical flow component (root-mean-square of vertical flow component) above a dune bedform in a fixed-bed laboratory channel (dune height: 40 mm; dune length: 630 mm; flow depth at crest: 0.10 m; average flow velocity at crest: 0.57 m s^{-1}). After Bennett and Best (1994), figure 3. Reproduced with permission of the World Scientific Publishing Co. Ltd, Singapore.

by the flow separation and the 'free' shear layer (Figure 4.9). These generate highly turbulent zones where turbulence intensity and vertical fluid motions are maximized. The RMS values of the vertical velocity component reveal maximum values within, above and just downstream of the flow separation zone. Also very noticeable is the downstream persistence of zones of high intensity along the free shear layer or wake zone generated by flow separation and its extension into the outer flow region (Bennett and Best, 1994, 1995). These high values of RMS_v may play a significant role in controlling the transport of sediment in suspension along and above bedform units (Nezu and Nakagawa, 1993).

The diagram on the frequency of quadrant II events (Figure 4.10) perhaps best illustrates the generation of a turbulent wake region and related turbulent flow phenomena due to flow separation. As explained in Chapter 2, quadrant II events correspond to observations with positive vertical velocity fluctuations and negative horizontal instantaneous deviations from the mean (events which may be instrumental in controlling suspended sediment mixing). Illustrated in Figure 4.10 are the frequencies of relatively high-magnitude quadrant II or ejection events (defined by the authors as being above a value of $H = 4$; see equation 2.57). The highest values are clearly located just above the flow separation cell, and the relatively high values of frequency of quadrant II events persist over long distances downstream along the bedform unit, diffusing downstream and upwards into the main flow and being a major component of the turbulent wake region. Reynolds stress measurements and quadrant IV events (not illustrated here) were also investigated in detail by Bennett and Best (1995). Frequent high-magnitude quadrant IV events are observed along the shear layer bounding the separation zone, near the reattachment point and in the vicinity of the dune crest. These zones also appear to significantly control the magnitude of the Reynolds stresses and their spatial variability. The high near-bed

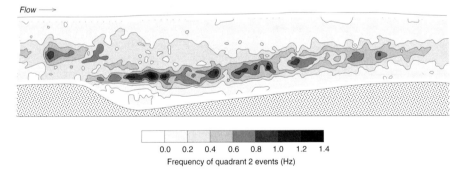

Flow ⟶

0.0   0.2   0.4   0.6   0.8   1.0   1.2   1.4
Frequency of quadrant 2 events (Hz)

Figure 4.10 The spatial distribution of the frequency of quadrant II events above a dune bedform in a fixed-bed laboratory channel (dune height: 40 mm; dune length: 630 mm; flow depth at crest: 0.10 m; average flow velocity at crest: 0.57 m s^{-1}). After Bennett and Best, 1994, figure 4. Reproduced by permission of the World Scientific Publishing Co. Ltd, Singapore.

velocities near the bedform crest, and the high levels of turbulence intensities resulting from flow separation and shear layer development may well enhance the capacity of the flow to transport material in suspension (McLean *et al.*, 1994). These interactions between flow turbulence and sediment transport processes, however, still remain to be fully elucidated.

Above a rippled bed, similar patterns of spatial variability in turbulent flow fields have been observed. Bennett and Best (1996) reported observations on turbulent flow fields above fixed ripples, using the same experimental design as in Bennett and Best (1995) for flow above dunes. The concrete ripples used in their experiments were characterized by an average height of 13 mm and an average spacing of 100 mm. The smaller dimension of the sand ripples is associated with the fact that their effects on the flow are restricted to a shallower portion of the boundary layer, in the near-bed region (y/d <0/3; Bennett and Best, 1996). As for sand dunes, turbulence intensity measurements (RMS$_u$ and RMS$_v$) and time-averaged Reynolds stress measurements are maximized within the flow separation zone, along its shear layer and near reattachment. As for dunes, high-magnitude quadrant II (ejection) events occur along the free shear layer downstream from reattachment (these arising from vortex shedding) and low-magnitude quadrant IV events (sweeps) occur near reattachment (Bennett and Best, 1996). Generally speaking, turbulence intensity and Reynolds stresses are maximized downstream from reattachment in the wake region (i.e. mid-bed region encompassing the free shear layer).

When comparing results from laboratory studies above fixed dunes and fixed ripples, Bennett and Best (1996) were able to pinpoint some significant differences in the turbulent flow fields between the two bedform types. Among the major differences are the vertical extent of the separation cell shear layer (restricted to near-bed region above ripples, but extending towards about 0.6d above dunes), the magnitude and vertical extent of quadrant II events (low magnitude and limited spatial extent above

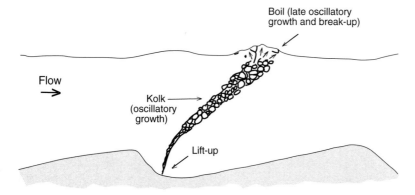

Figure 4.11 Schematic illustration of a kolk and boil feature above a dune sand bed. After R.G. Jackson (1976) and Best (1996), figure 3.19c. Reproduced by permission of John Wiley & Sons Ltd, Chichester, UK.

ripples), and the frequency and magnitude of quadrant IV events near reattachment (and the magnitude of the Reynolds stresses in this area). All the major observed differences appear to be related to the difference in size between the two bedform types.

Another major difference between ripples and dunes is the presence of macroturbulent boils observed above dunes. Dunes, for instance, experience periodic ejections of macroturbulent kolks through their troughs that rise to the water surface (Rood and Hickin, 1989). At the surface, they manifest themselves as boils (R.G. Jackson, 1976; Leeder, 1983; Figure 4.11). These kolks and boils were clearly observed by Kostaschuk and Church (1993) above a dune field on Fraser River Estuary. These features were observed from acoustic profiles measured along the large dunes (Figure 4.12) where the 'clouds' on the acoustic records probably reflect increased suspended sediment concentration due to the entrainment of sediment by the macro-turbulent kolks (Kostaschuk and Church, 1993). The frequency of the observed kolks reported by Kostaschuk and Church (1993) suggest that some are associated with persistent 'wave instability' in the lee of large symmetrical dunes, while kolks with longer periods of occurrence may originate from intermittent ejections within the internal boundary layer.

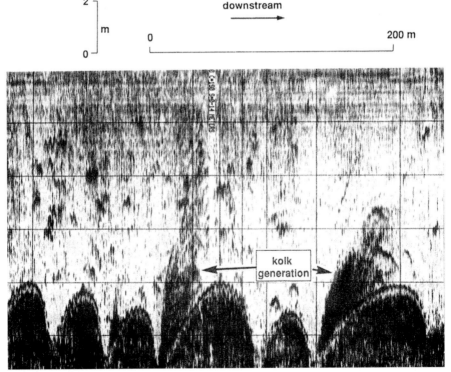

Figure 4.12 Acoustic record along a survey line above a dune bed along the Fraser River, B.C., Canada. Kostaschuk and Church (1993), figure 2. Reproduced by permission of Elsevier Science Publishers, Oxford, UK.

4.2.5 Initiation of bed defects and transitions between stages

The bursting process and the presence of low-speed streaks, adjacent sweeps and hairpin vortices were described at length in Chapter 2. These concepts are utilized here to describe and explain bedform initiation along a smooth and flat sand-bed surface. The initiation of ripples from a flat bed surface represents the first step in a series of changes in bedform types in sand-bed rivers as flow intensity increases. The initiation and growth of ripples in fine and medium sands has been the subject of numerous publications since the early 1970s. Turbulent boundary layer research has allowed some significant progress in the understanding of ripple initiation.

Recent visualization experiments and observations reported by Best (1992, 1996) suggest that ripples are formed from the coalescence of sweeps on an initially flat bed surface. The presence of streaks and adjacent zones of high-speed fluid (sweeps) generates hairpin vortices (Figure 2.8). In turn, the generation of patches of streaks and sweeps may result in sediment entrainment along multiple longitudinal corridors, and this process may be responsible for the initiation and formation of sand ripples. As explained before and reiterated here in the context of ripple initiation, a streak bursting cycle has been observed in turbulent boundary layers, whereby low-speed streaks are uplifted and eventually burst into the outer boundary layer (Allen, 1985). This bursting process in turn induces subsequent movement of fluid towards the boundary (Figure 2.9) and these are referred to as high-velocity sweep inrushes (Best, 1992). Research on bursting within the boundary layer also showed that the inner region of such a boundary layer is characterized by a series of hairpin vortices, whose 'legs' are actually formed by the low-speed streaks with opposite rotation signs (Smith *et al.*, 1991; Smith, 1996) and with secondary vortices generated around the primary hairpin. Such hairpin vortices can occur in groups, which in turn may lead to the generation of grouped sweeps between the legs of hairpins (Best, 1992).

The coalescence of sweeps produces corridors where initial sediment movement is concentrated and the formation of sediment ridges parallel to the downstream flow. Observations suggest that the ridges coalesce at their end and bed defects are created across the stream (transverse to the flow and a few centimetres wide). These transverse ridges grow and reach a size sufficient to generate flow separation. Once this critical height is reached, flow separation phenomena subsequently control the downstream generation, propagation and growth of a rippled surface. Although there are still numerous factors that may remain to be fully elucidated, the visualization work of Best (1992) has led to further evidence that bursting processes are primarily responsible for ripple formation.

Once formed, further increase in overall flow intensity leads to the transition from ripples to dunes (in fine and medium sands). Based on separate observations on two groups of fixed bedforms, Bennett and Best (1996) suggested a three-stage model of transition as flow velocity, bed shear stress and sediment transport increase. As flow intensity increases, ripples increase in size (mean height and spacing) and migration rate. At a critical stage during the transition, a 'rogue' ripple may be formed, i.e. a bedform unit of much greater height than the surrounding ripples (perhaps due to amalgamation of ripples of various sizes and migration rates). The formation of a larger ripple in turn would lead to a number of significant changes in the turbulent flow structures and turbulent flow fields. Similar conclusions were reached by Robert and Uhlman (2001), who investigated flow fields above fixed features corresponding with three different stages across the transition (Figure 4.13). In particular, they clearly illustrated a gradual increase in turbulent flow intensity and Reynolds stresses across the transition from ripple to dunes at various fixed positions above the bed surface and changes in the vertical extent of the flow separation and turbulent wake layer flow phenomena (the vertical extent increasing as the transition progresses). Observations reported in Robert and Uhlman (2001) also suggest that the non-equilibrium morphology of ripples changes across the transition (i.e. as velocity increases), from a two-dimensional configuration to a linguoid, irregular and three-dimensional shape. The linguoid morphology not only appears to be the ultimate morphology of ripples under equilibrium conditions (regardless of flow velocity; Baas, 1994, 1999) but also a component of the transitional process as bedforms are gradually transformed into dunes as bed shear stress increases.

The influence of greater sediment transport rates on the bed morphology, turbulence intensities, and separated flow dynamics also appear to be critical in the subsequent transition to upper-stage plane beds (Bennett and Best, 1996). Bridge and Best (1988) showed that horizontal and vertical turbulent velocity fluctuations decrease progressively in the dune troughs

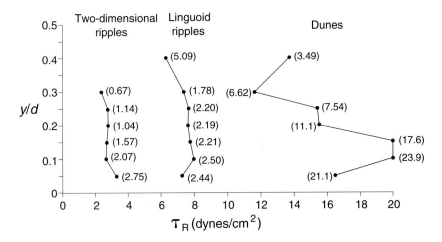

Figure 4.13 Spatially averaged profiles of Reynolds stresses (with standard deviations in brackets) across the ripple-dune transition (y is height above bed surface and d is local flow depth). After Robert and Uhlman (2001).

across the transition to upper-stage plane beds, while bedload transport rates and suspended sediment concentrations increase from dunes to upper-stage plane beds (Bridge and Best, 1988). In particular, the observed increase in transport rates just downstream of reattachment appears to be due to the damping of upward-directed turbulence by the increased sediment concentrations. Although more work is clearly needed on sediment transport processes across these transitions, the aforementioned investigations combining laboratory studies on fixed bedforms, flow visualization, field studies on large natural river systems and classic turbulent boundary layer research have led to significant advances in our knowledge of bedform dynamics in sand-bed rivers.

4.3 SMALL-SCALE BEDFORMS IN COARSE-GRAINED CHANNELS

Small-scale characteristics of gravel-bed topography have been studied to some extent in the recent past, because of the increasing recognition of their control on flow resistance and bedload transport. The role of imbricated structures of pebbles, for instance, has already been emphasized when dealing with the incipient motion of bed material and its potential effect on bedload transport rates (e.g. Brayshaw, 1983; Clifford et al., 1992b). The geometric properties of small-scale gravel bedforms also have significant influence on flow resistance, vortex shedding and energy dissipation (Lawless and Robert, 2001a, b).

Although a more rigorous classification of small-scale gravel bedforms can be undertaken (Bluck, 1987), it appears convenient to divide small-scale gravel bedform features into three categories: (a) transverse ribs; (b) step-pool systems; and (c) pebble clusters.

4.3.1 Transverse ribs

Transverse ribs (Koster, 1978) are widespread microtopographic features in gravel-bedded streams (Robert, 1990). The morphological properties of these features can be summarized as a series of regularly spaced pebble, cobble, or boulder ridges oriented transverse to the flow (McDonald and Banerjee, 1971). These bedforms can be distinctive in the higher-gradient and shallower portions of the channels. 'Rib' spacing is proportional to the size of the largest particles in the ridge crest (Figure 4.14). It should be noted that Bluck (1987) makes a distinction between transverse ribs and transverse clast dams. Among the notable differences, clast dams do not have fine sediment filling the spaces between the fronts, and transverse ribs appear to persist in stream channels with a wider range of slopes. The two categories of small-scale bedforms do, however, display similar properties in terms of dimension or size and spacing (Bluck, 1987).

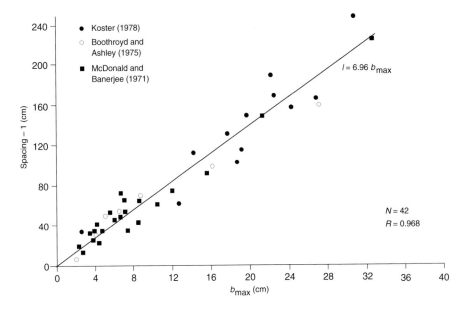

Figure 4.14 Empirical observations on the spacing of transverse ribs and the size of the largest particles (b_{max}) involved in their formation. After Robert (1990), figure 10. Reproduced by permission of Arnold Publishers, London, UK.

4.3.2 Step-pool systems

The second important group of small-scale bedforms can be described as *step-pool* systems (Figure 4.15b; Bathurst *et al.*, 1982; Whittaker and Jaeggi, 1982; Chin, 1989; Montgomery and Buffington, 1997; Wohl *et al.*, 1997; Wooldridge and Hickin, 2002). Step-pools are commonly observed in mountain streams (Chin, 1999a, b; Wohl, 2000), with slopes sometimes exceeding 2 per cent and bed material size within the range of cobbles and boulders. The stream channel along these features is said to be stair-like, with the water flowing through steps formed by the arrangement of boulders and cobbles across the stream channel. Step-pool headwater channels need to be distinguished from cascade systems (Figure 4.15a, b). Although both are common along steep mountainous streams, cascade reaches lack the clear sequence of pools characterized by gentle water surface gradients. Step-pool bedforms are characterized by a steepness or ratio of height to spacing of the order of 0.10 (Chin, 1999a). Recent studies suggest that step heights are controlled by the size of the particles comprising the step, while the spacing between successive crests is controlled by the formative discharge at high flow (Chin, 1999b). Both particle size and discharge vary with channel slope downstream, and empirical relationships have been established between step-pool size and spacing and channel slope (where, for instance, wavelength decreases as slope increases; Chin, 1999b).

It is worth noting that the morphology of step-pool systems (given their

Figure   4.15
Illustration of the bed morphological characteristics of (a) 'cascade' beds, and (b) step-pool systems (section view above and plan view below). Darker zones indicate areas of higher turbulence intensity. After Montgomery and Buffington (1997), figures 2a, b and 3a, b. Reproduced with the permission of the publisher, the Geological Society of America, Boulder, Colorado, USA.

SECTION VIEWS

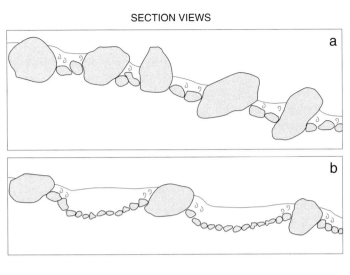

PLAN VIEWS

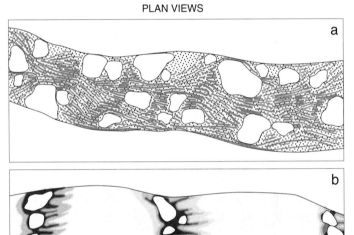

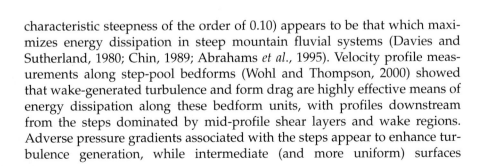

characteristic steepness of the order of 0.10) appears to be that which maximizes energy dissipation in steep mountain fluvial systems (Davies and Sutherland, 1980; Chin, 1989; Abrahams *et al.*, 1995). Velocity profile measurements along step-pool bedforms (Wohl and Thompson, 2000) showed that wake-generated turbulence and form drag are highly effective means of energy dissipation along these bedform units, with profiles downstream from the steps dominated by mid-profile shear layers and wake regions. Adverse pressure gradients associated with the steps appear to enhance turbulence generation, while intermediate (and more uniform) surfaces between the crests of the step-pool units are dominated by bed-generated turbulence (Wohl and Thompson, 2000). Form-process feedback mechanisms (Clifford, 1993b) may be at work along steep mountain stream channels, leading to a maximization of flow resistance due to the development and evolution of step-pool bedforms (Davies and Sutherland, 1980). Some work has also been done on the origin of these features, although firm conclusions are still lacking. An analogy is frequently made between step-pool systems and antidunes in sand-bed rivers (Whittaker and Jaeggi, 1982; Chin, 1999a), whereby bed waves in heterogeneous materials would form under active sediment transport conditions involving the coarse fraction of the bed material, and under critical or supercritical flow conditions (e.g. Froude number Fr >1.0). This hypothesis, however, appears to be inconsistent with the flume results of Abrahams *et al.* (1995). A recent study also suggests that there is no convincing evidence that special conditions govern their formation (Zimmerman and Church, 2001). The steps appear to be stable structures resulting from the interlocking of large stones (the random occurrence of large clasts controlling the locations and the development of imbricated structures; Zimmerman and Church, 2001).

4.3.3 Cluster bedforms

The last group of small-scale bedforms is described as *pebble clusters* (e.g. Brayshaw *et al.*, 1983; Brayshaw, 1984; Billi, 1988). These bedforms consist essentially of a single obstacle protruding above the neighbouring grains, a stoss-side accumulation of large pebbles and a wake deposit of finer particles (Figure 4.16). 'Pebble clusters' represents the general term used to describe bed protuberances caused by obstacles and the effects of these on neighbouring clasts. Cluster bedforms are common in naturally sorted coarse alluvial channels, and represent probably the predominant type of microtopography in gravel-bed rivers (Brayshaw, 1985). Two broad categories of cluster bedform are defined by Brayshaw (1983): loose clusters and imbricated clusters, the latter being characterized by an imbricated structure of pebbles on the stoss-side (upstream side) of the obstacle. The sorting pattern introduced along bedform units during their formation is the dominant characteristic of these features. Obstacle clasts represent extremely coarse size fractions, generally greater than the D_{95} (the size for which 95 per cent is finer). The particles of stoss-side accumulations constitute coarse clasts, and their deposits are significantly coarser than representative channel samples (Brayshaw, 1983). On the other hand, wake-side (or lee-side) deposits comprise fine-calibre material (usually finer than the D_{50} of the overall bed surface sediment). Smaller grains comprise wake accumulations, because their exposure to the flow is considerably reduced and they are trapped in the obstacle's downstream separation zone. The thickness of these bedforms is generally limited to a single grain (or a few grains, especially on the downstream side). Rolling and sliding of particles during bedload transport explain their formation. They form when particles in the

Figure 4.16 Idealized diagram of a cluster bedform. After Brayshaw, 1984, figure 2. Reproduced with the permission of the Canadian Society of Petroleum Geologists, Calgary, Canada.

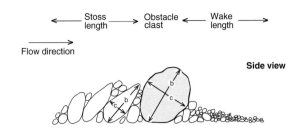

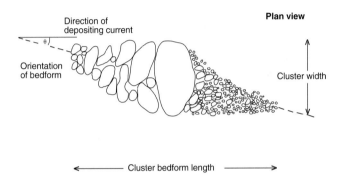

course of transport are stopped by larger grains protruding from the bed, which creates an accumulation of bed material on the stoss-side of the obstacles. Field measurements suggest that their mean spacing is of the order of $10D_{50}$ (Brayshaw, 1984; Naden and Brayshaw, 1987). As explained before, cluster bedforms play a dominant role in controlling the mobility and availability of individual particles. In the presence of cluster bedforms, the differences in flow intensity at the incipient motion are attributed to the enhanced stability of the particles on the upstream side of the obstacle, and to the reduction of lift and drag forces on the lee-side of the bedform's crest (Brayshaw *et al.*, 1983; Best, 1996).

More recent work by Lawless and Robert (2001a) has emphasized the effects of cluster bedforms upon the structure of the vertical velocity profiles and related shear stress estimates. From flume experiments, comparisons were established between velocity fields above fairly uniform coarse surfaces and surfaces where superimposed scales of roughness were present and where cluster bedforms dominated the near-bed flow field. A dense grid of near-bed velocity measurements showed the overall effects of topographic forcing at various locations along bedform units. They also showed that spatially-averaged velocity profiles are segmented, the upper portion of the segmented profiles reflecting form drag effects due to the presence of small-scale bedforms on the surface. The flow level at which segmentation takes place is controlled by the size of the cluster bedforms and the velocity gradient in the upper regions of the measured profiles, reflecting form drag over the bedform (the velocity gradient in the wake region of the spatially averaged profiles being significantly higher than in the absence of such cluster features). These results, in essence, confirm preliminary measurements about the role of microtopography in controlling flow resistance (e.g. Nowell and Church, 1979; Hassan and Reid, 1990).

Turbulent flow structures above beds dominated by cluster bedforms were also investigated in detail in the field by Buffin-Bélanger and Roy (1998), and in a laboratory channel by Lawless and Robert (2001b). Using an array of electromagnetic current meters, Buffin-Bélanger and Roy (1998) made detailed turbulent flow measurements along a transect encompassing a large cluster bedform along the Eaton River (Québec, Canada). Their results show the very significant flow acceleration immediately upstream of (and above) the obstacle, flow separation and recirculation in the lee of the large clasts, intense shedding above the shear layer generated from the separation, and vortex shedding around large particles (Paola *et al.*, 1986; Clifford *et al.*, 1992b; Kirkbride, 1993; Lawless and Robert, 2001b). They also showed the dominant role played by upwelling motions emerging from the reattachment. Sweeping motions, when impacting the bed near the reattachment zone, generate fluid upwelling characterized by regions of strong positive vertical velocities extending up to the water surface in depth-limited flows (Buffin-Bélanger and Roy, 1998). As opposed to turbulent flow fields observed above fixed dunes and described previously, these regions are highly dynamic and have fluctuating boundaries.

The complexity and the three-dimensional nature of flow fields and turbulence structures above cluster bedforms was further studied by Lawless and Robert (2001b). Using an ADV and therefore fine resolution and very near-bed velocity measurements, Lawless and Robert (2001b) presented evidence of the importance of lateral flow in the development of turbulence flow structures above and around pebble clusters. Figure 4.17 shows 'sectors' of the flow (i.e. variations across the stream of vertical profiles of turbulence intensity values). The results of Figure 4.17 emphasize the three-dimensional nature of the flow field around obstacles, as well as the role played by the lateral flow component. The vertical and lateral patterns of variations of RMS_u and RMS_w (the lateral flow component) show that narrow regions of high lateral and downstream turbulence intensity are present on both sides of the clusters and that a three-dimensional flow separation zone forms in their lee. These narrow regions of high turbulence intensity extending along the side of the cluster appear to dissipate downstream where the flow vectors converge inwards in the lee of the clusters (Lawless and Robert, 2001b). These observations may also suggest the presence of horseshoe-type vortices similar to those forming around isolated obstacles above smooth surfaces (e.g. Paola *et al.*, 1986), or 'standing vortices' as reported by Acarlar and Smith (1987).

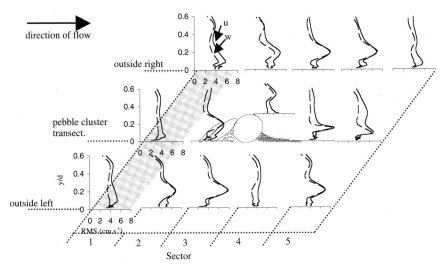

Figure 4.17 Vertical profiles of RMS$_u$ (horizontal flow component) and RMS$_w$ (lateral flow component) around an idealized cluster bedform as measured in a laboratory channel (solid line: downstream flow component; dashed line: lateral flow component). After Lawless and Robert, 2001b, figure 8.

4.4 RIFFLE-POOL SEQUENCES

4.4.1 Morphology

Riffles and pools are ubiquitous bed features in coarse-grained channels (Plate 4.1). Sequences of riffles and pools are characteristic reach-scale bedforms along low- and moderate-gradient rivers (e.g. channels with average gradients smaller than 1 per cent; Clifford, 1993a). They have been observed along straight and sinuous channels (Richards, 1976, 1982; Knighton, 1998), and their morphology is characterized by large-scale bed undulations that have dimensions scaling with the channel size. A prominent feature of riffle and pools is the sediment sorting pattern associated with the changes in bed elevations. Riffles correspond with high points in the bed topography (Figure 4.18), usually associated with faster flows (and shallower depths because of the higher bed topography), steeper water surface slope, and coarser bed material. Pools, on the other hand, represent the low points in the topography, characterized by gentle water surface slopes and finer bed material (Clifford and Richards, 1992).

It is well known that the spacing between successive high points (riffles) and low points (pools) scales with channel width. The traditional view of riffle-pool dimensions is that the spacing between successive riffle crests or pool midpoints varies between five and seven channel widths. Spacings of the order of five to seven channel widths have been widely reported in the

Plate 4.1 Example of a low-sinuosity riffle-pool stream (riffles and pools can be distinguished from the water-surface 'texture' variations).

literature (e.g. Keller and Melhorn, 1978; Richards, 1982; Milne, 1982; Clifford, 1993a; Robert, 1997). It has also been observed that changes in bed topography along riffle-pool sequences frequently display a clear degree of periodicity that can be adequately represented by 'pseudo-periodic' spatial-series models (Richards, 1982; Clifford *et al.*, 1992b; Clifford, 1993a, b), with a dominant wavelength usually within the range of five to seven channel widths.

A comprehensive analysis of the morphology of riffle-pool sequences in the River Severn (UK) points, however, towards a different scaling relationship, where smaller ratios of riffle crest spacing to channel width are reported (Carling and Orr, 2000). The morphology of almost 300 riffles and pools, which form a 32 km reach of the River Severn, were analysed and an

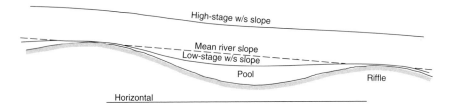

Figure 4.18 Schematic profile of a riffle-pool unit, showing the variation in water surface (w/s) slope with location and river stage (vertical scale greatly exaggerated). After Bagnold (1977), figure 3. Reproduced with the permission of the American Geophysical Union, Washington, D.C.

average riffle-pool unit length of $3w$ (where w is average channel width) was reported. These observations appear to be difficult to reconcile with previous reported measurements on the spacing between successive riffle crests. Measurements reported by Carling and Orr (2000) were recorded along fairly large river segments (with widths varying between 30 and 45 metres) and bed undulations were recorded automatically with an echo sounder (while previous observations were often derived from smaller rivers and along much smaller segments). The large variance in the measurements of riffle-pool spacing, the different methodologies used by various authors, and the range of channel sizes and channel gradients perhaps preclude some firm conclusions about a precise and widely applicable scaling relation between channel width and riffle-pool spacing (except for a general unmistakable tendency for riffle-pool dimensions to increase with channel size).

The height of riffles and pools (and steepness) has not been studied extensively, but preliminary reports suggest that the height varies with bedform spacing (e.g. Hey and Thorne, 1986; Robert, 1990; Carling and Orr, 2000). Earlier field observations suggest that the ratio of height of ripple-pool sequences to spacing is of the order of 0.01 (Prestegaard, 1983; Hey and Thorne, 1986; Robert, 1990, 1997), while Carling and Orr reported ratios of bedform height to spacing as high as 0.03. Carling and Orr (2000) also showed that, for the River Severn, riffle height rarely exceeds 2 metres (with most being less than 1 m) and the average pool depth was of the order of 1 m.

Published one-dimensional long profiles of pools and riffles suggest that bed undulations are generally symmetrical in shape (e.g. Richards, 1982; Robert, 1997). Carling and Orr (2000) actually showed that both riffles and pools showed no preferred asymmetry, which means that the lee and stoss slopes of riffles (for instance) were not, on average, significantly different (although this appears to be partly a function of the stream gradient). Interestingly, Carling and Orr (2000) also observed that, in addition to being a positive function of riffle length, reach-average riffle height is a constant proportion of bankfull depth (the ratio of reach-average riffle height to bankfull depth being equal to 0.16). Reach-average data from Carling and Orr (2000) also suggest that riffle-pool morphology is a function of stream gradient. On average, both riffle and pools appear to be longer, have a smaller steepness and are more asymmetrical as the channel gradient decreases. Similar dependence of bedform morphology on channel gradients have also been reported along high-gradient channels (channel gradients greater than 0.01; e.g. Wohl et al. (1993) and Thompson and Hoffman (2001)), although bedforms in small headwater catchments with relatively steep gradients should perhaps be separated from riffle-pool units on low- and moderate-gradient channel segments.

4.4.2 Bed sediment sorting along riffles and pools

It is widely recognized that pools and riffles present different surficial bed sediment characteristics. It is usually observed that the bed material in pools is finer (and often unambiguously finer) than that in riffles (e.g. Lisle, 1979; Milne, 1982; Clifford and Richards, 1992; Sear, 1996; Robert, 1997). In mixed-bedded or mixed-load channels, pools may be dominated by sandy material and riffles by gravelly material. In other cases, both pools and riffles can be characterized by a median bed material size in excess of 2 mm (i.e. within the gravel size range), with a clear tendency for the high points to be associated with the coarser bed material (Clifford, 1993a). Natural gravel-bed channels also often contain sand particles filling in the voids created by the framework of coarser gravel (Lisle, 1989; Lisle and Hilton, 1999). Patches of such fine material can also be observed along pool-tail sections of gravel-bed channels if the supply of fine material considerably exceeds the capacity of the coarse framework to store material (Lisle and Hilton, 1999).

Regardless of the specific grain size distributions associated with a given stream, the unambiguous sediment sorting pattern in pools and riffles has attracted the attention of numerous researchers during the last three decades. Considerable progress has been made towards understanding the formation and maintenance of riffle-pool sequences via field investigations of flow turbulence and/or sediment transport processes (e.g. Clifford and Richards, 1992; Clifford, 1993a,b; Sear, 1996) and models of flow–sediment interactions have been suggested to account for the observed differences in bed sedimentology at the scale of riffles and pools.

Probably the most widely known hypothesis to account for bed sedimentology patterns in pools and riffles is the velocity-reversal hypothesis. Under this hypothesis (initially suggested by Keller, 1971), the rate of change in velocity in pools is greater than that in riffles and, for flow conditions at or near bankfull, the velocity in pools exceeds that in riffles. In turn, higher velocities in pools under peak flow conditions imply the movement of the coarse fraction through the pools with deposition along riffles where velocities are somewhat lower. Below the cross-over point (i.e. the discharge condition at which the reversal phenomenon may occur), the inverse pattern is observed, with the fine fraction of the bedload still in movement along the riffles but deposited in pools (where the average velocity is lower). Keller's arguments concerning velocity trends have also been applied to other flow intensity parameters such as shear velocity or bed shear stress (e.g. Carling, 1991; Clifford and Richards, 1992).

Field studies have shown somewhat conflicting evidence of velocity or shear stress reversal (e.g. Petit, 1987; Carling, 1991; Clifford and Richards, 1992; Sear, 1996; Robert, 1997). In particular, it was observed that measurements of flow intensity frequently show some form of convergence between riffle and pool sections as discharge increases, but not necessarily a reversal of bed shear stress or flow velocity (near-bed vertical average or section average velocity). Carling (1991) and Robert (1997), in particular, showed unambiguous convergence of vertical average and spatially-averaged near-bed velocities, respectively (both derived from velocity profile measurements). However, very significant spatial variations of local bed shear

stresses and local average velocity within pools and within riffles may preclude firm conclusions unless comparable, consistent and reliable methods
of assessing flow intensity are utilized (Clifford and Richards, 1992). The
general lack of firm conclusions about reversals and the overall lack of consistent observations and measurements of flow intensity above riffles and
pools (and its variation with flow stage) may be related to the complexity of
the bed morphology, surface texture, sedimentary structures, and associated
bed–flow interactions along riffle-pool sequences (Clifford and Richards,
1992; Clifford, 1993a, 1996).

4.4.3 Flow and sediment transport along riffle-pool units

Recent evidence from field and laboratory measurements of flow turbulence
and/or sediment movement suggests that sediment transport through riffle-pool sequences does not necessarily require a reversal in velocity or bed
shear stress to explain longitudinal variations in surficial bed material size
associated with large-scale bed undulations (Iseya and Ikeda, 1987; Clifford,
1993a, b; Sear, 1996).

It has been clearly shown that, in addition to grain size, there are other
aspects of the bed sedimentology of riffle-pool sequences that may play a
very important role in the development and maintenance of the bed features (Clifford, 1993a; Sear, 1996). Riffle surfaces, for instance, appear to
experience more turbulent flows (for relatively low-magnitude, frequent
flow conditions) that lead to a more structured surface through *in situ* particle vibration and sporadic particle motion. Pools, on the other hand, do
not experience the same level of near-bed turbulence activity, and sediment
transport may be limited, for instance, to the movement of sand over an
otherwise static bed (Sear, 1996, p. 259). The bed surface therefore becomes
tightly packed and interlocked along the riffle sections, with the same type
of bed structure being poorly developed in pools. These differences in
microtopographic structuring in turn enhance bed stability along riffle
units, causing higher dimensionless entrainment thresholds. The higher
dimensionless entrainment thresholds for riffle sediments would therefore
contribute to the maintenance of these units as topographic high points
along the river bed, while scouring is experienced along pool segments
under flow conditions that are lower than that necessary to entrain riffle bed
material. Sedimentological evidence therefore suggests that surface particle
arrangement may best discriminate between pools and riffles, with larger
bed surface material and enhanced bed structure on riffle segments of the
bedform being responsible for the higher thresholds of initial motion and
greater stability of the high point in the bed topography (Table 4.1).

Sear (1996) also showed that as discharge increases, bedload transport
rates in pools increase more rapidly than in riffles (with values of bedload
transport rates rapidly exceeding those of riffles). From tracer experiments,
this study also concluded that coarser particles experience longer transport
distances and rates of travel (i.e. distance of travel in relation to the duration

Table 4.1 Sediment transport and characteristics of pools and riffles (after Sear, 1996)

Bedform	Riffle	Mid-pool	Pool-tail
Bed state	Congested	Smoothing	Smoothing
Sedimentary structure of surface	Tightly packed	Loosely packed	Loosely packed
Surface D_{50}	Coarser	Decreasing	Finer
Relative exposure of D_{50} riffle particle	Low	Increasing	High
Entrainment threshold	High	Decreasing	Low
Distrainment opportunity	High	Decreasing	Low
Particle movement	Short L_p Low U_p	High L_p High U_p	Moderate L_p Moderate U_p
Bedload balance	Aggrading	Degrading	Degrading

L_p: distance of travel of particles (m); U_p: rate of travel of particles (e.g. m h^{-1})

of flow above a critical entrainment threshold) in pools during peak flow conditions (Table 4.1). These observations are compatible with the maintenance of riffle-pool sequences during sediment-mobilizing floods. When combined with flume observations from Iseya and Ikeda (1987), Sear's observations on bed structure and bedload transport led to the conclusion that riffles are characterized by net aggradation during near-bankfull (bed mobility) flow conditions. Pools, on the other hand, exhibit finer and loosely packed bed material, lower dimensionless thresholds of initial motion, a lower frequency of high critical entrapment sites, higher particle velocities, and therefore degradation along most of their course. Although there are still some points that remain to be fully substantiated through further field and laboratory studies, these aforementioned recent studies provide the framework upon which a complete model of bed – flow – sediment interactions could be developed along riffle-pool units (Table 4.1).

4.4.4 Formation of riffle-pool sequences

Relatively little attention has been paid to the formation of riffles and pools. Yalin (1977, 1992) suggested (theoretically) that the turbulence generated at the boundary in a straight channel would produce large-scale eddies, eddies which are associated with alternate acceleration and deceleration of the flow. The spatial differences in near-bed velocities created by the autocorrelated nature of macro-scale flow structures would themselves lead to differences in surface sediment erosion and deposition, with bed undulations (at the scale of the large eddies) being the result of the downstream sequence of alternating zones of scour and fill (see Clifford (1993a) for a detailed account of Yalin's theory in the context of riffle-pool sequences).

Relatively little is known about macroturbulence in gravel-bed rivers and its significance in relation to riffle-pool sequences. Carling and Orr (2000), for instance, suggested that riffle dimensions scale with bankfull depth and that riffle spacings might scale with macroturbulent flow structures, with a dominant period or time interval between 'events' of the order of 50 to 100 seconds. Buffin-Bélanger et al. (2000) also clearly illustrated the presence of 'wedges' of high- and low-speed fluid in a gravel-bed river with a dominant period of the order of 8 seconds. Multiplying this dominant period by the average flow velocity during their measurements (0.36 m s^{-1}) gives a spatial dimension for the large-scale flow structures of the order of 2.8 m (about seven to eight times larger than the mean flow depth). Measurements of large-scale flow structures above coarse-grained surfaces remain somewhat elusive, and much work remains to be done on simultaneous high-frequency measurements at various locations along reaches dominated by large-scale bed undulations.

Clifford (1993a) offers a modified account of Yalin's model. From spectral analysis of quasi-continuous high-frequency velocity records, Clifford (1993a) observed dominant eddy length scales of the order of 1–3 m, which seem to relate to multiples of grain sizes and small-scale bedforms in gravel-bed rivers (Clifford et al., 1992a, b). A three-stage model for the formation and maintenance of riffle-pool sequences is proposed by Clifford (1993a), with randomly located obstacles playing a dominant role in the proposed initial stages of the model. The three stages in the proposed processes essentially involve the following elements:

(a) local scour of a pool in the vicinity of an obstacle (scour upstream and downstream of the obstacle);
(b) removal of obstacle and creation of two growing depositional areas surrounding the scour zone (initially created by an obstacle);
(c) and propagation downstream of further erosion and deposition areas (because of the downstream 'riffle' itself acting as a flow obstruction).

4.4.5 Controls

Thompson (2001) suggested that riffle-pool spacing is not a function of reach-scale morphological adjustments of channel form to macroturbulence. Thompson (2001) suggests instead that pool formation in coarse-bedded (and bedrock) channels is attributed to boulder (or bedrock) constrictions. Along the same lines, Thompson et al. (1999) and Thompson and Hoffman (2001) proposed a model for pool maintenance and sediment sorting patterns along riffle-pool units, in which constrictions play a dominant role, controlling local acceleration. Their findings suggest that the characteristics of constrictions (e.g. boulders) provide an important control of the scouring and longitudinal dispersion of sediments. More specifically, a 'recirculating-eddy' model is proposed to explain pool scour and sediment sorting associated with high and low topography. Constrictions in very coarse-bed or bedrock streams and associated recirculating eddies create flow convergence and high velocities at the upstream end of pools. This creates scour in the 'pool' area, and moves sediment towards the pool-tail section (or pool-exit slope, Thompson *et al.*, 1999). Flow divergence in the pool-exit zone and the upper part of the subsequent riffle leads to deposition, and velocity reversal is observed due to the formation of a recirculating eddy. The ideas suggested by Thompson *et al.* (1999) certainly share similarities with the three-stage model proposed by Clifford (1993a) for the formation and maintenance of riffle-pool sequences.

Another dominant control on pool-riffle morphology, especially along high-gradient forested drainage basins, is the presence of large woody debris (Montgomery *et al.*, 1995; Rice and Church, 1996b; Buffington and Montgomery, 1999). As mentioned before, the influence of large woody debris (LWD) on channel morphology and sediment transport depends on its size relative to channel size, its orientation relative to the flow, and its distance from the channel bed (Robinson and Beschta, 1990; Montgomery *et al.*, 1995; Rice and Church, 1996b). The presence of LWD locally induces flow convergence and bed scour and LWD can reduce pool spacing to values less than normally expected for 'free-formed' riffle-pool channels.

Montgomery *et al.* (1995), in a study of pool spacing in forest channels, showed that LWD loading (i.e. the numbers of pieces per unit surface) systematically affects pool spacing in forest channels, with average pool spacing being significantly less than that usually observed for channels without obstructions. Along high-gradient streams such as those studied by Montgomery *et al.* (1995), it is important to distinguish clearly between pools as part of a step-pool system, pools as a component of what is described by Montgomery *et al.* (1995) as 'forced pool-riffle' sequences (forced or induced by local obstructions or constrictions), and 'free-formed' riffle-pool sequences. The vast majority of Montgomery's observations refer to the former two categories.

Riffles and pools are observed in various environmental conditions. The characteristics of the sediment sorting pattern along riffle-pool sequences may vary significantly as a function of local environmental and sediment supply conditions. The morphology of the riffle-pool sequences also appears to be variable, and numerous interrelated factors may be at play in controlling the geometry of local riffle and pool units. As will be further emphasized in Chapter 6, the physical diversity introduced by the presence of riffles and pools is also important in terms of aquatic habitat (Thompson and Hoffman, 2001). Sediment transport processes at the scale of riffles and pools are significant from an ecological and a geomorphological perspective. Further work is needed along the lines suggested by Clifford (1993a, b) and Sear (1996), in particular. Systematic field studies of riffle-pool units need to be undertaken, with the goal of achieving a more complete characterization of the turbulent flow fields above such units, which would, in turn, provide adequate data to verify hypotheses and preliminary observations on the role of macroturbulent flow structures in shaping bed morphology. Scaled models of symmetrical bed features could also be investigated in the laboratory, as was done extensively for symmetrical bedform features (e.g. Wiberg and Nelson, 1992; Best and Kostaschuk, 2002), but with superimposed sediment sorting patterns characteristic of riffle-pool sequences. Both field and laboratory studies could also further refine the sediment transport model elaborated by Sear (1996) (Table 4.1), emphasizing the potentially dominant role played by bed structure differences between riffles and pools and its influence on sediment transport and the maintenance of riffle-pool units.

4.5 BEDLOAD SHEETS AND LOW-RELIEF BED WAVES

Bedload sheets appear to be a common but often unrecognized bedform in sand–gravel mixtures (Whiting et al., 1988). These bedforms presumably develop in poorly sorted sediment as a result of interactions between the coarse and fine fractions of the bed material during bedload transport (Iseya and Ikeda, 1987; Whiting et al., 1988; Dietrich et al., 1989). As originally described, bedload sheets are thin migrating accumulations of sediment, with a leading edge of only one or two coarse grains in height and with length to height ratios much in excess of that of dunes, for instance (from 25 to as much as 300; Whiting et al., 1988). An unambiguous sorting pattern is observed along bedload sheets, with accumulation of the coarse fraction near the leading edge ('congested' area described by Iseya and Ikeda, 1987), and intervening 'smooth' regions of finer material. The largest grains in the sand–gravel mixtures therefore tend to concentrate near the leading edge of the bedform and control its thickness. The fronts of the sheets appear to persist as the accumulations of sediment migrate downstream and as grains eroded from upstream are redeposited near the leading edge (as determined from field observations by Whiting et al., 1988). Bedload sheets have also been seen to overtake and merge at times with other downstream sheets and to form on the stoss-sides of dunes, downstream from the point of reattachment. Bedload sheets are highly dynamic features controlling sediment fluxes in heterogeneous sediments.

The presence or absence of bedload sheets also appears to be related to the surface coarsening and changes in sediment supply. Dietrich et al. (1989) determined from flume experiments that the spatial segregation of grain sizes into distinct zones, and the relative importance of bedload sheets, are controlled by changes in sediment supply rates. As sediment supply rates are reduced, bedload sheets become less frequent and distinct, coarse inactive zones expand and the increasing imbalance between the local bedload supply and the ability of the flow to transport it leads to the formation of a progressively coarser bed surface and a gradual change in bedforms from bedload sheets to narrow longitudinal fine-textured active bed areas (Dietrich *et al.*, 1989). Reductions in sediment supply therefore result in surface coarsening, i.e. a gradual expansion of coarse, inactive zones in which little or no sediment transport takes place (Dietrich *et al.*, 1989).

Bennett and Bridge (1995), in a series of flume experiments on bedforms in heterogeneous sediments, observed that the troughs of the bedload sheets appear to be characterized by coarser sediment, with the crests being somewhat finer (the pattern being removed or reversed when the bed material becomes fully mobile). As discussed before, these features also introduce significant 'pulsations' in bedload transport rates, with bedload sheets, for instance, generating pulses in transport rates that may vary by up to one order of magnitude over relatively short periods of time (Iseya and Ikeda, 1987).

Horton (2001), in a comprehensive laboratory study of bedforms in sand–gravel mixtures, also showed the very significant role played by bedload sheets (i.e. its morphology, surface texture and sorting pattern) in controlling turbulent flow fields above and along bedform units, which in turn interact with the bed to control sediment transport rates along bedform units and their variation over time. Horton (2001) also argues that low-relief bed waves represent a distinct bedform feature in sand–gravel mixtures. Although low-relief bed waves (LRBW) have been identified before (e.g. Bennett and Bridge, 1995), their morphological properties and relationships with turbulent flow characteristics and sediment transport processes have been neglected.

Horton (2001) showed that low-relief bed waves scale with the largest grains in transport, and that the height of LRBW is also to some extent dependent on flow depth (increasing with flow depth while bedload sheets only scale with the largest particles in transport). The low-relief bed waves observed by Horton (2001) were characterized by wavelengths varying between 2.3 and 4.8 metres (while bedload sheets had wavelengths not exceeding approximately 1 m). In most cases reported by Horton (2001), the thin bedforms (both bedload sheets and LRBW) migrated over a relatively coarse static armour layer (which corresponds with the trough region of the bedforms). In turn, the finest sediment transported was observed along the stoss-sides, with a gradual coarsening towards the bedform crest.

Bedform migration accounts for the fluctuations in bedload transport rates. For bedload sheets, the bedform crests and the bedload have similar grain size distributions and both tend to coarsen with increasing bed shear stress (Horton, 2001). For LRBW, the size distribution of the bedform crest, bedload, and the bulk mixture are similar. Bedload sheets and LRBW are responsible for significant topographically induced flow acceleration and deceleration. The vertical extent and the magnitude of quadrant II events generated by the presence of the bedforms are greater that that for ripples. Turbulent flow fields above bedload sheets and LRBW are dominated by shear layers generated from bedform crests and large clasts, as well as topographic forcing and overall surface roughness discontinuities (Horton,

2001). As for the low-angle dunes studied by Best and Kostaschuk (2002), flow separation downstream of the bed wave crests, if present, appears to be weak and intermittent.

For bimodal sand–gravel mixtures, Horton (2001) proposed a model of bedform development where ripples are initially formed at relatively low bed shear stress. As shear stress increases, bedload sheets are observed in conjunction with ripples, and this is accompanied by an increase in the quantity and size of the transported sediment (hence higher bedload sheets). The coarse material of the bedform trough, however, hinders erosion (Horton, 2001). With further increase in bed shear stress, LRBW develop. During the transitions from bedload sheets to low-relief bed waves, sediment transport rates and turbulence intensity rapidly increase.

4.6 ROUGHNESS TRANSITIONS

Longitudinal transitions in roughness therefore exist in heterogeneous sediments, especially at the crest of bedload sheets and low-relief bed waves. Similar transitions in roughness due to a rapid change in bed surface sediment can also be observed along some riffle-pool sequences (especially when pools are dominated by sand-bed material). Moreover, when the bed surface is characterized by sand (longitudinal) ribbons (Ferguson *et al.*, 1989), local channel geometry may lead to the flow crossing obliquely from coarse to fine grained sediment and therefore across a transition in roughness.

There have been numerous reports on the effects of roughness transitions on both average velocity profile properties and turbulence characteristics in the atmospheric boundary layer literature (e.g. Bradley, 1968; Antonia and Luxton, 1971, 1972; N.A. Jackson, 1976; Mulhearn, 1978). The significance of roughness transitions in the context of sediment transport and bedforms in heterogeneous sediments (bedload sheets, low-relief bed waves and riffle-pool sequences) has not, however, been thoroughly investigated. At a transition in roughness, an internal boundary layer develops (Figure 4.19). The height of the internal boundary layer and its characteristics are a function of the changes in the surface roughness conditions (Dyer, 1986; Robert *et al.*, 1992, 1996). The effects on the velocity profiles and the turbulence structure obviously vary as a function of direction, i.e. whether the transition is from smooth to rough or vice versa. As clearly illustrated in Figure 4.19, a transition from a relatively smooth bed surface to considerably rougher conditions, for instance, will affect near-bed velocity gradients and induce curvature in velocity profiles (the profiles becoming more concave upwards with distance downstream from the transition). Immediately downstream from the 'smooth-to-rough' transition, the local bed shear stress increases very significantly.

Robert *et al.* (1992) showed how transitions in roughness could affect near-bed velocity measurements in coarse-grained channels. In particular, it

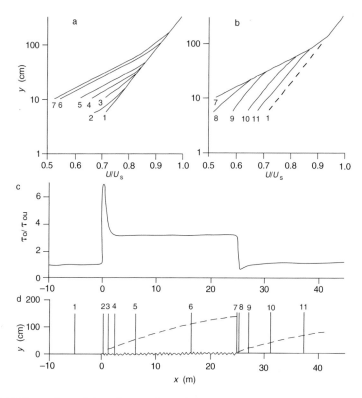

Figure 4.19 Illustration of the effects of roughness transitions on velocity profile characteristics and bed shear stress variations. (a) Velocity profile characteristics along a smooth-to-rough transition – the location of each profile and the corresponding number are illustrated at the bottom of the diagram. The velocity is normalized by that near the water surface; (b) velocity profile characteristics along a rough-to-smooth transition; (c) ratio of local bed shear stress to shear stress upstream of the roughness transition; (d) location of the vertical profiles with regard to the changes in bed roughness conditions and the vertical extent of the internal boundary layer. After Dyer (1986), figure 3.9. Reproduced with the permission of the publishers, John Wiley & Sons Ltd, Chichester, UK.

was observed that immediately at the transition, boundary shear stress and roughness length (as determined from near-bed velocity gradients) increase considerably. Downstream from the transition, velocity profiles become progressively concave upwards. Downstream and upstream sections show significant differences in terms of spatially-averaged velocity profiles (Figure 4.20), with the shear velocity and roughness length being greater past the transition because of the larger bed features and the superimposed scales of roughness. Robert *et al.* (1992) suggested that bed areas characterized by such transitions (smooth to rough) might be areas where bedload transport is initiated (given the maximization of local bed shear stress at and immediately downstream from the change in roughness).

Figure 4.20 A comparison of velocity profiles measured upstream and downstream from a 'smooth-to-rough' transition in roughness along a coarse-grained channel. After Robert *et al.* (1992), figure 9. Reproduced with the permission of the publishers, Blackwell Science Ltd, Oxford, UK.

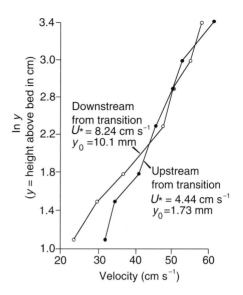

The rapid change in surface texture characteristics also affects flow turbulence (Robert *et al.*, 1993, 1996). Profiles of turbulence intensity measured along a channel characterized by a smooth-to-rough transition show a general increase in turbulence intensity below the transition (Robert *et al.*, 1992), and the maximum values appear to be at a height approximately equal to twice the median size of the bed material (and therefore somewhat higher above the bed surface under rougher downstream conditions). In a subsequent report on turbulence structure at a transition, Robert *et al.* (1996) showed from field measurements that the presence of protuberant clasts past the transition in roughness appears to dominate turbulence generation, with systematic effects of roughness changes on turbulence intensity, momentum exchange, and stress production (as discussed before when dealing with cluster bedforms and turbulent flow above obstacles).

4.7 FORM ROUGHNESS AND MACRO-SCALE BEDFORMS IN COARSE-GRAINED CHANNELS

The prediction of total flow resistance in alluvial channels has been a central research question in hydraulics and civil engineering for decades. In sand-bed rivers, numerous methods have been suggested to address the problem and to predict form drag over bedforms (some of which are mentioned in Chapter 2). Among the recent investigations is that of McLean *et al.* (1999), who show that a reasonable approximation of form drag above sand dunes can be obtained by using a form drag equation (see equation 2.47) with a drag coefficient (C_d) of 0.19 and a reference velocity which corresponds to that located one bedform height above the crest. Detailed field and laboratory investigations along riffle-pool units could lead to the development of a form drag equation, with a better understanding of what controls the morphology of riffles and pools, as well as appropriate determination of a drag coefficient and reference velocity.

Some attempts have been made to determine form roughness in gravel-bed channels (Parker and Peterson, 1980; Bathurst *et al.*, 1982; Prestegaard, 1983; Hey, 1988; Griffiths, 1989). Prestegaard (1983), for instance, divided the water surface slope into components associated with grain and bar roughnesses (equation 2.44) for 12 gravel-bed streams at bankfull stage. The relative importance of the grain resistance was determined from the Keulegan equation (equation 2.36 with $k_s = D_{84}$ at the grain roughness scale) and the form resistance estimated from the difference between total flow resistance and grain roughness. Prestegaard (1983) observed that bar roughness accounts for 50 to 75 per cent of total resistance in each case. It was also observed that the component of water surface slope associated with bar resistance increases with the steepness of the large-scale bed undulations (or 'bar magnitude', defined as the ratio of bedform amplitude to spacing).

Griffiths (1989), in turn, emphasized flow resistance under mobile bed conditions. He showed that form resistance can be a major component of hydraulic roughness in steady, quasi-uniform turbulent flow over mobile gravel beds. Under subcritical flow conditions (see Froude number and equation 2.18), the dimensionless form shear stress (θ'') was shown to be a function of the Shields parameter (equation 3.20) and relative roughness (d/D, where d is flow depth and D is particle size). More specifically, Griffiths (1989) showed that under subcritical flow conditions and for a given relative roughness, the form shear stress contribution increases with the Shields parameter (and thus with the transport rate). Moreover, for a given Shields stress, relative form roughness (ratio of form to grain stress, expressed in dimensionless terms) increases with relative roughness, owing to the growing contribution from bedforms as the ratio of d to D increases (Griffiths, 1989, p. 353).

Adequate prediction of total bed shear stress and total flow resistance in heterogeneous coarse-grained channels is important at different levels, and much progress remains to be made. In addition to allowing a more accurate estimate of grain stress to be used in bedload transport equations, accurate determination of flow resistance in this type of complex sedimentary environment would allow better estimates of changes in average flow velocity and depth as discharge increases at a give station and downstream along stream channels (hydraulic geometry relations; Knighton, 1998).

FLOW AND SEDIMENT DYNAMICS IN CURVED, BRAIDED, AND CONFLUENT CHANNELS

5.1 CHANNEL PATTERNS: CLASSIFICATION

As illustrated in Chapter 1 (Figure 1.3), channel configurations – when considered in plan view – are highly variable. The study of channel patterns and governing factors has been an important field of investigation. As for bedforms, sediment supply and transport capacity play dominant roles in controlling the type of planform geometry observed under specific environmental conditions (Ferguson, 1987).

Patterns are usually simply categorized as straight, meandering and braided (Leopold and Wolman, 1957). However, a more appropriate approach may consist in looking at channel patterns and planform geometry as a continuum, where a range of configurations can be observed as a function of stream power, degree of channel stability, sediment calibre and the size and shape of the cross-section. This conceptual approach encompasses numerous controlling factors, and illustrates the complex relationships existing between channel geometry, flow, and sediment transport variables. Stream channels develop a range of planform geometries as stream power increases. Moreover, variations in the degree of channel stability, sediment calibre (amount and size of bedload), channel gradient and cross-section shape (ratio of width to depth) will be associated with various degrees of meandering, size and volume of bars within channels, and therefore different types of braiding.

Bars are ubiquitous features in alluvial channels (Figure 5.1). They represent zones of temporary sediment storage along channels. The location, size, and texture (sediment size and heterogeneity) of bars may vary tremendously with the type of planform geometry observed. The size of the bedload, the capacity of the stream to transport it, and the relative stability of

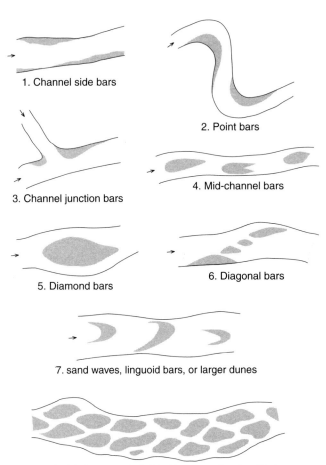

1. Channel side bars

2. Point bars

3. Channel junction bars

4. Mid-channel bars

5. Diamond bars

6. Diagonal bars

7. sand waves, linguoid bars, or larger dunes

8. Braided pattern: individual bars may be classified according to the preceding forms

Figure 5.1 Sediment storage in bar structures. After Kellerhals and Church (1989) and Church (1992), figure 6.10. Reproduced with the permission of the publishers, Blackwell Science Ltd, Oxford, UK.

the channel banks are key variables in the identification of channel patterns and controlling factors. The relation between planform geometry and sediment calibre depends on channel gradient and discharge. Both variables are involved in stream power per unit channel length (see equation 1.11) and the role of stream power is clearly illustrated in the conceptual approach suggested, for instance, by Ferguson (1987).

Although changes in planform geometry are best viewed as gradual and transitional, various empirical equations have been suggested to establish some potential threshold equations (for the onset of braiding, for instance) and to differentiate between environmental conditions leading to meandering or braiding (Carson, 1984a). Many of these equations involve channel gradient and discharge (e.g. mean annual discharge; see a summary of such equations in Bridge, 1993, p. 24). A well-known example of this type of empirical relation defining the transition from meandering to braiding (for a specific set of observations) is:

$$S_b = 0.013 \, Q_b^{-0.44} \tag{5.1}$$

where S_b is channel slope and Q_b is bankfull discharge (Leopold and Wolman, 1957). On a diagram of discharge versus slope, a line corresponding to equation 5.1 can be used to differentiate between fields corresponding to braided reaches and to meandering channels. From equation 5.1, for instance, it can be inferred that the threshold slope above which a channel would exhibit a braided pattern decreases as bankfull discharge increases. However, Leopold and Wolman's (1957) equation is too general and is not widely applicable. That is, further studies showed that the predicted threshold for braiding is often too low for gravel-bed rivers and too high for braiding in sand (Ferguson, 1987). Bank and bed material size also play a role in the occurrence of meandering or braiding, and equations such as 5.1 can be further refined to include channel sediment size as an additional controlling variable. Two specific examples can be used to demonstrate this approach (Ferguson, 1987). Using bed material size as an additional variable:

$$S_b = 0.0049 \, D_{50}^{0.52} \, Q^{-0.21} \tag{5.2}$$

(D_{50} is median bed material size in mm and Q is mean annual discharge in $m^3 \, s^{-1}$; Ferguson, 1987). Equation 5.2 therefore implies that, for a given mean annual discharge, the channel slope needed for the onset of braiding increases with an increase in bed material size. Alternatively, for channels with cohesive banks but sandy beds, an expression similar to equation 5.2 can be derived where the percentage of bank 'mud' (B) is used instead of bed material size and:

$$S = 0.0013 \, Q^{-0.24} \, B^{1.0} \tag{5.3}$$

(Ferguson, 1987).

EXAMPLE

Equations 5.2 can also be interpreted in terms of thresholds of stream power (for a given bed material size). That is, if one considers, for instance, a bankfull discharge of 40 $m^3 \, s^{-1}$, a corresponding channel width of 19 m (as approximated from characteristic hydraulic geometry relations) and a median bed material size (D_{50}) of 10 mm, the minimum channel slope associated with the onset of braiding (as determined by equation 5.2 and keeping in mind all the usual restrictions associated with the use of empirical equations beyond the context within which they were originally derived) is $S_b = 0.00748$. Since the stream power per unit bed area is defined as the product of $\rho \, g \, Q \, S/w$ (where w is channel width) and assuming, for instance, a bankfull width of 19 m, it follows that the onset of braiding for the conditions listed above and as predicted by equation 5.2 for a D_{50} of 10 mm would be 154 Wm^{-2}. Threshold stream power values of this order of magnitude for coarse-grained channels have been observed before (e.g. Ferguson, 1981).

5.2 MEANDERING CHANNELS

5.2.1 Meander geometry

Because of their influence on flow and sediment dynamics in curved channels, three geometric properties of river meanders need to be defined. The
first two are radius of curvature (r_c) and sinuosity (s). Radius of curvature
can be broadly defined as the radius of a circle drawn around a meander
bend. It therefore expresses the degree of 'tightness' of a specific bend, with
wide-open meander bends of a given size having a much larger value of r_c
than tight meander bends. In order to take into account the effect of channel
size on meander morphology, this is usually expressed as a dimensionless
ratio of r_c to w (where w is channel width). In addition to radius of curvature, meander wavelength clearly needs to be taken into consideration
when assessing meander geometry. The wavelength is simply defined as the
distance between successive meander bends, either measured as a straight-
line distance (axial wavelength $-\lambda$) or along the channel itself (arc wavelength $-\lambda_{arc}$). Sinuosity or degree of meandering, in turn, can be defined
from the ratio of λ_{arc} to λ (Richards, 1982; Goudie, 1994). It is well known
that meander spacing or wavelength tends to increase with channel size,
with average wavelength (λ) being of the order of 12 times the channel
width (Richards, 1982). Similarly, although the ratio of radius of curvature
to channel width for individual bends varies significantly along meandering
reaches, average values of r_c/w of the order of two to three are frequently
reported (e.g. Hickin and Nanson, 1984; Williams, 1986). It follows therefore
that the radius of curvature tends to increase with meander wavelength

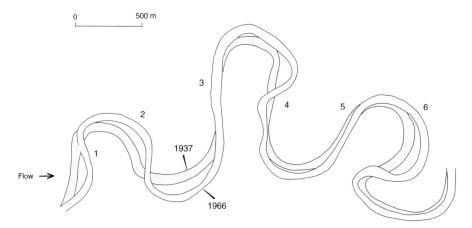

Figure 5.2 Example of the evolution of meander bends (White River, Indiana, USA
1937–66). Note delayed inflections at points 1, 2, 5, and 6. After Carson and Lapointe,
1983, figure 12. Reproduced with the permission of the University of Chicago Press,
Chicago, USA.

(with meander shape being related to meander size), with an average value of r_c/λ of the order of four to five being frequently observed. As r_c/w decreases, the increase in curvature and the presence of tight meander bends may be sufficient to induce flow separation along the inner bend (a rapid change in channel orientation favouring the development of a zone of flow separation; Ritter *et al.*, 1995). The ratio of r_c/w may also provide useful information with regard to bank erosion and meander migration rate.

Another striking characteristic of meander planform geometry appears to be a delayed inflection (Carson and Lapointe, 1983; Parker *et al.*, 1983; Davies and Tinker, 1984; Carson and Griffiths, 1987). That is, most meander loops are asymmetrical (Figure 5.2). The nature of this asymmetry is not random, but is rather well defined and consistent. This characteristic asymmetry consists of inflection points alternating on opposite sides of the valley axis (hence the term 'delayed inflection'). Because of the location of the inflection points on opposite sides of the main valley axis, most meander bends are therefore 'facing down valley' (a planform geometric property which may allow, for instance, flow direction in palaeostudies to be inferred directly from a meander trace). The delay in the inflection point (down-stream of the midpoint between successive bends; Figure 5.2) appears to be widespread, at least for suspended-load meandering channels (Carson and Griffiths, 1987). Delayed inflection has been attributed to delayed thalweg cross-over (itself related, for the most part, to the inertia of water flow downstream of bends; Carson and Lapointe, 1983). Delayed thalweg cross-over leads to spatial variations of bank erosion rates, which are then trans-lated into a delayed inflection in the channel trace.

5.2.2 Channel configuration

Flow and sediment transport dynamics along curved channels are con-trolled by changes in bed topography across the stream and downstream along channels. Changes in channel curvature and bed topography are

Figure 5.3 Characteristic channel shape and over-all surface flow direction in a meander bend.

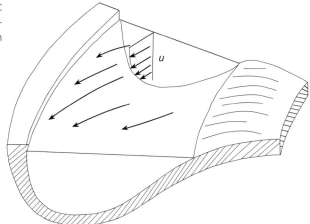

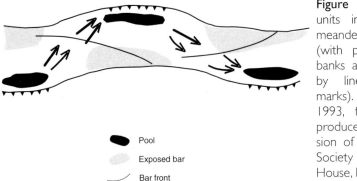

Pool

Exposed bar

Bar front

Figure 5.4 Pool-bar units in low-sinuosity meandering channels (with point bars; cut banks are represented by lines with tick marks). After Ferguson, 1993, figure 1b. Reproduced by permission of the Geological Society Publishing House, Bath, UK.

clearly interrelated, and the three-dimensional geometric properties of the channel need to be taken into account when assessing the effects of channel configuration on flow and sediment transport in meander bends (Hooke, 1975).

The cross-section shape at the meander bend apex is usually asymmetrical, with the deep portion of the channel being located along the outer bank (concave bank; Figure 5.3) and a broad, shallow (sometimes nearly flat) section extending from the inner bank towards the centre of the channel (Dietrich and Smith, 1984). The maximum depth itself also appears to vary inversely with the ratio of radius of curvature to channel width (Dietrich and Smith, 1983). When meandering reaches are considered in plan view (Figure 5.4), the scour hole (pool) wraps around the outside portion of each meander bend. Along the inner, shallow section of the channel is the area referred to as the bar. The elongated bars wrapping along the bends are termed 'point bars' (Plate 5.1). The presence of alternate bars with diagonal

Plate 5.1 Point bar formed in a meander bend of a coarse-grained channel.

fronts is therefore characteristic of meandering patterns, and pools and bars overlap more as sinuosity increases. As illustrated in Figure 5.4, a 'diagonal' riffle is running from one point bar to the downstream portion of the next point bar on the opposite side of the channel (Ferguson, 1993). The fundamental unit of channel morphology for both low sinuosity and meandering channels thus becomes the triplet bar–riffle–pool (Church, 1992). The topographic high points identified as riffles along longitudinal profiles in section 4.4 would correspond to the intermediate portions between successive pools. If one were to follow the main flow lines identified on Figure 5.4, for instance, the highest points along the longitudinal profile would be located immediately upstream of the bar front (about halfway between successive pool midpoints).

This characteristic channel asymmetry at cross-sections in meander bends in turn favours the development of a lateral sediment sorting pattern, where the coarse particles tend to concentrate near the bottom of the pool section, with a gradual fining towards the inner bank. Sediment particles resting on the sloping surface are subject to three forces (Figure 5.5): the drag force, which promotes downstream movement and is proportional to the square of the particle diameter, the gravitational force, which promotes downslope movement, across the channel (laterally towards the bottom of the scour pool), and a third force which is related to velocity currents across the channel (secondary circulation; see section 5.2.3 below). The gravitational force is proportional to the cube of the diameter (particle mass). For the same near-bed velocity, the largest particles therefore will tend to be deflected downslope more directly than finer ones due to their greater mass (e.g. Whiting, 1996; Powell, 1998). Moreover, finer particles tend to move inwards because of the influence of secondary circulation (as explained below). Transverse bed slopes therefore significantly affect particle trajectories and lead, at least in part, to an unambiguous lateral topographic sorting, with a tendency for the smaller grains to move inwards under the influence of secondary circulation and larger grains to move outwards, towards the topographic low points, under the influence of the gravitational force (Powell, 1998).

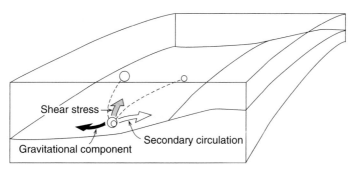

Figure 5.5 Forces acting on bedload particles in meander bends and related trajectories. After Whiting (1996), figure 6.11. Reproduced with the permission of the publishers, John Wiley & Sons Ltd, Chichester, UK.

This difference in forces acting on particles resting on the stream bed in meander bends contributes to the formation of surficial sediment sorting patterns frequently observed in meander bends, with the coarsest fractions concentrated near the bottom of the pool and a gradual fining upwards, across the stream towards the point bar area.

5.2.3 Secondary circulation in meander bends

Secondary circulation is generally observed in meander bends. Secondary currents (laterally, across the channel) in curved channels are caused by a combination of two forces acting in meander bends: centrifugal forces and pressure gradient forces. The centrifugal force acting on water flowing around a bend causes a build-up of water adjacent to the bank known as water super-elevation. This therefore results in a tilting of the water surface laterally across the channel. The magnitude of the change in water surface elevation (Z) across the stream due to the centrifugal force acting on the flow in a curved channel can be determined from:

$$Z = U^2 w/g\, r_c \tag{5.4}$$

where, as before, U is the average cross-sectional velocity, w is channel width, g is acceleration due to gravity and r_c is the radius of curvature of the meander bend (Richards, 1982).

From equation 5.4, it follows that the change in water surface elevation across the channel in a meander bend increases with the average down-stream velocity (Hooke, 1975) and becomes more significant as the tightness of the meander increases, i.e. as the ratio of r_c/w decreases (Hickin, 1978). Centrifugal forces acting on flows in meander bends therefore represent an outward-directed force (i.e. acting towards the outer bank). From the curved motion and the build-up of water along the outer bank arises a force equal and opposite to the mean centrifugal force, i.e. a force acting inwards (towards the inner bank). The balancing inward-acting force is a pressure gradient force. Centrifugal and pressure gradient forces are generally unbalanced locally (Allen, 1994; Powell, 1998). Near the water surface, where the velocity exceeds the cross-sectional mean, the centrifugal force exceeds the cross-stream pressure gradient and the flow is driven outwards. Conversely, near the bed, the flow velocity is smaller than the mean, the pressure-gradient force is dominant, and this tends to drive the flow inwards (towards the inner bank) over the bed surface. The result is spiral motion or a cell of secondary circulation being dominant over the thalweg (the deepest part of the channel) in relatively deep channels. The characteristic pattern of secondary circulation consists of a flow cell with a water surface orientation towards the outer bank, plunging along the outer bank and oriented towards the inner bank in the vicinity of the bed (Allen, 1994; Powell, 1998). In natural meandering reaches, combined effects due to channel curvature and pool-bar topography are observed, and these phenomena are summarized below.

5.2.4 Flow and sediment transport in curved channels

Among the most comprehensive field measurements of flow, bed topography, and sediment transport in meander bends reported to date are those of Dietrich *et al.* (1979) and Dietrich and Smith (1983, 1984). Other extensive field studies have been reported along sand-bed rivers (e.g. Bridge and Jarvis, 1982). The findings from the seminal papers on Muddy Creek (Dietrich and co-workers), where the bed topography was in equilibrium with the imposed flow conditions, will form the basis of the summary presented herein.

The reach studied along Muddy Creek (Wyoming, USA) by Dietrich *et al.* (1979) and Dietrich and Smith (1983, 1984) is illustrated in Figure 5.6. Along the reach where measurements were made, the stream is draining an area of 235 km^2 and has a gradient of 0.0014. Bankfull discharge was 1.6 m^3 s^{-1} and bankfull width, average depth and average velocity were 5.5 m, 0.6 m, and 0.35 m s^{-1}, respectively (with a maximum pool depth of 1.1 m). The ratio of radius of curvature to channel width for the central part of the bend illustrated in Figure 5.6 is about 1.5 (Dietrich and Smith, 1984; Dietrich, 1987). This in turn indicates a relatively sharp meander bend when compared to the average for most rivers (e.g. Williams, 1986; see section 5.2.1). Well-developed bedforms (mostly dunes) were present on the stream bed (characterized by median grain size of 0.7 mm). Most of the sediment is transported as bedload along this reach of Muddy Creek, with only about 10 per cent transported in suspension.

A major feature of the flow in a meander bend is a zone of high velocity that shifts from the inside to the outside of the channel with distance through the bend. Similarly, measurements of local boundary shear stresses at various locations across and along the channel in a meander bend have shown how the zone of maximum bed shear stress gradually shifts to the outside bank as the flow enters the central portion of the bend (see below for details). Other important features to be described in natural river meanders are the longitudinal and lateral variations in bed material size and the role of bedforms in curved sand-bed channels. Dune crests, for

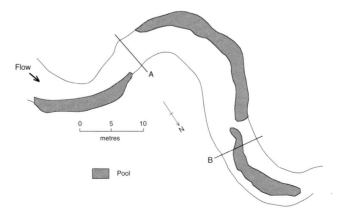

Figure 5.6 Plan-view illustration of the Muddy Creek study site. After Dietrich *et al.* (1979), Dietrich and Smith (1983, 1984) and Dietrich (1987). Part of the channel located between sections A and B will be further illustrated in Figures 5.8 and 5.9.

instance, are not usually oriented perpendicular to the flow, but present a systematic change in crest orientations while they migrate through meander bends. The angle of the bedform crest in relation to the direction of the main downstream flow (or 'bedform obliquity') has significant implications on both local direction and magnitude of sediment transport in curved channels (Dietrich *et al.*, 1979; Bridge and Jarvis, 1982; Dietrich and Smith, 1984; Dietrich, 1987; Bridge, 1993). Finally, secondary circulation and the influence of the point bar (or pool-bar topography) on flow through a meander bend are paramount, significantly affecting flow and sediment transport dynamics in curved channels. This will be the first item discussed below.

Downstream changes in bed topography, with the characteristic asymmetric shape of the cross-section at meander bend apices and the switch from bank to bank of the point bar and pool locations as a function of changes in channel curvature, strongly influence flow and sedimentary processes. In a channel with constant bed topography in the downstream direction, the pattern of secondary circulation is as described before, with an outward flow at the surface (water surface) and an inward flow near the channel bed (i.e. oriented towards the inner bank). This pattern of secondary circulation in the simple case of constant bed topography and smoothly varying channel curvature extends over the entire channel width. In natural river meanders, however, the downstream varying bed topography induces changes to this pattern of cross-stream velocity (Figure 5.7). The data from Dietrich and Smith (1983) clearly demonstrated a strong outward flow over the upstream part of the point bar, with the cross-stream velocity pattern of outward flow at the surface and the inward-oriented flow near the bed being restricted to the deepest sections of the channel (which, for Muddy Creek, represented only 20–30 per cent of the channel width; Dietrich and Smith, 1983; Dietrich, 1987). Shoaling of flow over the point bar causes a net outward discharge (i.e. oriented towards the outer bank) in the upstream part of the meander bend. This outward velocity near the bed over the top

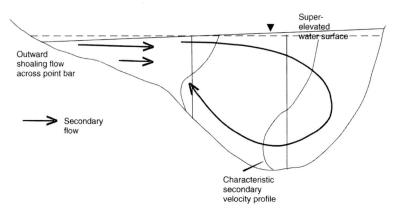

Figure 5.7 Pattern of secondary flow circulation in meander bends. After Powell (1998), figure 9a. Reproduced with the permission of Arnold Publishers, London, UK.

Figure 5.8 Shifting location of maximum boundary shear stress and sediment transport pathways as a function of position in a meander bend. After Powell (1998), figure 9b. Reproduced by permission of Arnold Publishers, London, UK.

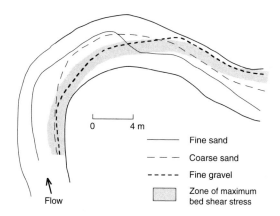

of the point bar (Figure 5.7) causes therefore a substantial transfer of momentum across the channel.

The cross-stream outward transfer of momentum also affects the pattern of outward shifting of high velocity and maximum boundary shear stress (Dietrich and Smith, 1983). As mentioned before, the zone of high velocity in a meander bend shifts from the inside to the outside with distance through the bend, and a similar pattern is observed for the zone of maximum boundary shear stress. From numerous measurements of bed shear stress from near-bed velocity measurements (within the first 10 cm above the bed surface; see law of the wall and equation 2.26), Dietrich *et al.* (1979) showed that the zone of maximum bed shear stress shifts from near the inside bank in the upstream part of the bend, and crosses to the outside bank as the flow enters the central portion of the bend (Figure 5.8). A very similar pattern of downstream and cross-stream pattern of shear stress fields was also reported by Dietrich and Smith (1984), even though the method that they used to estimate bed shear stress was different and yielded systematically lower bed shear stress values (a method which excluded form drag effects from mobile dune bedforms).

Boundary shear stress fields are related to channel curvature. In addition to the rotational motion (or secondary circulation) induced by channel curvature, the tilting of the water surface generated by the curvature also generates these large cross-stream variations in bed shear stress and corresponding variations in velocity. Hence, the effect of centrifugal forces on the flow through a meander is to produce a zone of maximum bed shear stress (and maximum average flow velocity) that shifts from near the inside upstream bank to near the outside downstream bank (Dietrich, 1987). This phenomenon is further enhanced by the pool-bar topography, which alters the near-bed flow velocity (as described before), increases the lateral or cross-stream variation in bed shear stress, and promotes fairly rapid shifting of the zone of maximum bed shear stress across the channel (Figure 5.8).

The zones of maximum bedload transport in curved sand-bed channels show a spatial pattern similar to that of maximum boundary shear stress.

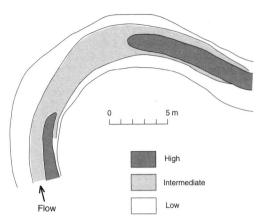

Figure 5.9 Spatial variation in bedload transport rates in a meander bend. After Dietrich and Smith (1984).

Figure 5.9 is a map of bedload transport fields emphasizing the zone of maximum transport for the Muddy Creek bend. It shows that, as for the maximum bed shear stress, the zone of maximum bedload transport gradually shifts outward through the bend. Dietrich and co-workers estimated bedload transport rates from bedform migration rates (Dietrich *et al.*, 1979), and from numerous sampling points using a smaller version of the standard Helley-Smith sampler (see Plate 3.2). It was noted by Dietrich and Smith (1984) that, although estimates of bedload transport from bedform measurements appear to underestimate transport rates, both methods provided similar assessment of bedload transport fields through the meander bend. A comparison of Figures 5.8 and 5.9 clearly indicates that, as for the maximum bed shear stress field, the zone of maximum sediment flux shifts across the channel from near the inside bank at the 'entrance' of the bend toward the pool area in the downstream section (although in the downstream part of the bend, the zone of maximum sediment transport tends to be closer to the middle part of the channel than the boundary shear stress maximum). A summary of the channel curvature and bed topography effects on boundary shear stress fields is presented in Figure 5.10.

Figure 5.8 also illustrates the fact that relatively fine and coarse sediments trade positions as they move through the bend. This pattern, where coarse and fine particles trade positions as they move through the meander bend, results at least in part from the relative magnitude of the inward-acting secondary flow and the outward-acting gravitational force. Hence, for the same near-bed velocity, large particles tend to move outwards under the influence of the gravitational force acting on the transverse slope (see Figure 5.5), and smaller particles tend to be carried inward towards the shallower portion of the channel, under the influence of secondary circulation. This cross-stream movement in opposite directions of relatively coarse and fine sediments results in the characteristic switch (from bank-to-bank) in cross-stream variation in bed material size. Upstream from the meander apex, the bed material size tends to be coarser inwards, whereas at the downstream end of the bend, the bed material tends to be finer inwards, i.e.

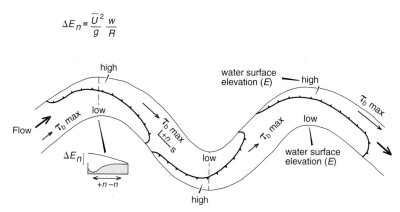

$$\Delta E_n \cong \frac{\overline{U}^2}{g} \frac{w}{R}$$

Figure 5.10 Effects of channel curvature and bed topography on the water surface elevation and the boundary shear stress field in a meandering reach. Break in bar slopes is indicated by lines with tick marks. After Dietrich (1987). Reproduced with permission of Blackwell Science Publishers, Oxford, UK.

from the deeper portion of the channel to the point bar (Dietrich and Smith, 1984).

Moreover, Dietrich and Smith (1984) observed that net inward cross-stream bedload transport occurs in meander bends of sand-bedded rivers and that dunes contribute significantly to the generation of inward sediment transport (Dietrich, 1987). That is, any oblique negative step (e.g. dune crest) to a mean flow direction will generate a current along the step (Dietrich, 1987). Considering that bedform migration rate is proportional to the bed shear stress, and considering the cross-stream variation in boundary shear stress across the channel (e.g. near the upstream end of the channel), a strong skewing of the bedform crest is also expected as the bedforms migrate through the meander bend. Observations reported along Muddy Creek and from other investigations (see Bridge, 1993) support the hypothesis that bedform orientation shifts systematically through a meander bend, and that this contributes significantly to cross-stream sediment transport. Hence sediment is carried by a trough-wise flow along oblique bedforms across the channel, and this contributes to a net transport of sediment from the inside bank to the outside bank (Dietrich and Smith, 1984). More specifically, in the upstream part of a bend, the downstream end of a bedform crest stretching across the channel obliquely would be in the area where the bed shear stress is maximized, i.e. near the inside (or convex) bank, and would shift across the channel towards the concave (outer) bank in the downstream part of the meander bend. Where the zone of maximum boundary shear stress crosses into the pool downstream of the meander bend apex, the dunes therefore rotate and a trough-wise current oriented towards the outward bank is observed, a current that is capable of transporting sediment towards the pool area (even if the average near-bed flow direction due to secondary circulation is towards the inner bank).

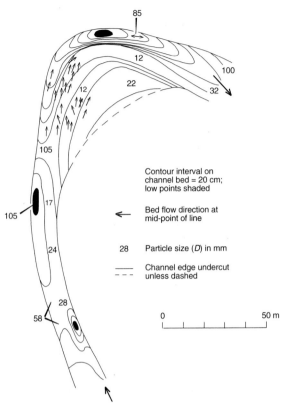

Figure 5.11 Bed topography, particle size, and bedflow directions at the bankfull stage in a meander bend along a high-energy meandering river (Waireka Stream, New Zealand). After Carson (1986), figure 2. Reproduced with the permission of the publishers, the Geological Society of America, Boulder, Colorado, USA.

Most of the studies on river meanders have been conducted on sand-bedded rivers. Carson (1986) and Carson and Griffiths (1987) argue that significant differences exist between gravel-bed and sand-bed rivers in terms of both meander geometry and flow/sediment transport processes. A first major difference in meander geometry can be described by a different type of meander asymmetry in bedload channels. Examples from New Zealand rivers are presented by Carson and Griffiths (1987), where a 'premature' inflection (premature cross-over of the thalweg, i.e. upstream of the mid-valley axis) is observed instead of a delayed inflection as described before for low energy sand-bed channels. Premature inflection then results in up-valley channel migration (Carson, 1986). This characteristic of high-energy meandering rivers is also often associated with 'over-widened' bends (Figure 5.11; Carson, 1986) and both phenomena can be frequently observed in this type of environment.

Carson (1986) and Carson and Griffiths (1987) also indicated that the near-bed flow over most of the point bar in high-energy meandering channels is oriented towards the outer bank. The near-bed flow directions plotted on Figure 5.11 also show a clear convergence towards the outer bank and the deepest part of the channel. The net effect of this convergence is the presence of a deep scour zone along the downstream part of the outer bank.

Another characteristic of high-energy meandering channels is that the low-flow channel sometimes does not occupy the trough along the outer bank (Carson and Griffiths, 1987). The flow instead cuts across the point bar. This tendency for the low-flow channel to cut across the point bar appears to be characteristic of gravel-bed rivers with high specific stream power (Carson and Griffiths, 1987).

This shoaling of the thalweg produced when the low-flow channel cuts across the point bar, and the presence of over-widened bends, are sometimes described as features characteristic of a stage intermediate between meandering and braiding. This type of channel configuration has been referred to as 'pseudo-meandering' or wandering channels (Carson and Griffiths, 1987).

Avulsions (i.e. the relatively sudden switching of course from one channel to another; Ferguson, 1993) are frequent along such 'transitional' channels (Desloges and Church, 1989). Intervening channel islands are sometimes densely vegetated. Desloges and Church (1989) also observed that wandering reaches appear to be wider, shallower, and steeper than intervening more stable reaches. The term 'wandering channels' is also frequently used to refer to some intermediate stage between braiding and meandering (e.g. Brierley, 1991). Anastomosis is also a term that is sometimes used to refer to some intermediate stage between meandering and braiding. The distinction made by some researchers between anastomosing, wandering, and braiding is not always clear, however (see Knighton and Nanson, 1993, for instance, for discussion and details on classification). In the following discussion of braided rivers, a broad definition of braiding is used, and no explicit distinction is made between braiding and anastomosing.

5.3 BRAIDED CHANNELS

5.3.1 Types of channel braiding and control variables

Different types of channel braiding can be observed (as schematically illustrated in Figure 1.3). Carson and Griffiths (1987, p. 122), for instance, identify three major categories. The first type consists of 'multiple-channel watercourses', separated by bare channel beds. In this type of pattern, the flow can be frequently diverted from one channel bed into other channels, as a function of local sediment deposition. This type of braiding is frequently observed, for instance, downstream of valley glaciers (Plate 5.2). The second major type of braiding consists of a more stable multiple-channel pattern, even under high flow conditions, but with the sub-channels being separated by well-defined vegetated islands (Plate 5.3). The third type can be defined as 'multi-thalweg' rather than multiple channel, with the 'braids' being separated by submerged bars under peak flow conditions (Plate 5.4).

Plate 5.2 Braided pattern downstream of a valley glacier (meltwater of Saskatchewan Glacier, Alberta).

Although this categorization of braiding patterns provides some useful distinctions, transitional types do occur, and a continuum of patterns may be observed as a function of stream power, width–depth ratio, channel stability, and sediment supply.

Plate 5.3 Braiding and vegetated islands, Athabasca River, Alberta.

Plate 5.4 'Multi-thalweg' braiding type – North Saskatchewan River, Alberta.

Braiding processes are highly dynamic, with rapid interactions between channel configuration, flow, and sediment transport. As specified before, braided rivers are associated with high-energy environments, high sediment loads, and unstable channel banks. Although most braided rivers appear to adopt a braided pattern at all stages (Bristow and Best, 1993), the planform characteristics of braided channels can change radically with discharge. The number of bars exposed may vary significantly with flow stage, and complex sequences of erosion and deposition may take place as the stage varies. Bar growth and channel erosion occur more or less simultaneously, and most exposed bars are the result of complex multiple erosional and depositional events (Southard *et al.*, 1984).

Braiding occurs across a wide range of spatial scales, from laboratory-scale models to the largest alluvial rivers with braid plains of up to 20 km (e.g. Brahmaputra River; Bristow and Best, 1993; Richardson *et al.* 1996). Natural braided rivers are usually fairly large in size and are normally characterized by a ratio of d/D greater than 10 during active sediment transport events (Southard *et al.*, 1984). Given the practical difficulties involved in conducting extensive fieldwork under highly dynamic conditions (e.g. Ferguson *et al.*, 1992), flume experiments on braiding processes and bar characteristics have been instrumental in providing insights into the interactions between form and process in braided rivers (Ashmore, 1982, 1991a, b; Ashmore and Parker, 1983; Hoey and Sutherland, 1991). In contrast to meandering channels, studies of braided rivers have, for the most part, been conducted on gravel-bed rivers (Carson and Griffiths, 1987). However, most braided rivers contain a fairly wide range of particle sizes (from bank and bed erosion). As opposed to sand dunes, ripples, and coarse-grained small-scale bedforms, large-scale bar forms and corresponding braided patterns appear to be similar in rivers characterized by different ranges of particle sizes (Bristow and Best, 1993).

Braiding is seen to require greater stream power and therefore a steeper slope for any given discharge (e.g. equations 5.1 and 5.2). Sedimentary variables can be used to supplement or even replace discharge and slope in the 'prediction' of channel pattern. There are essentially two ways in which sediment properties interact with flow properties to determine the type of channel pattern (and therefore the presence or absence of braiding): the influence of bank materials (and bank strength overall) on bank erosion, and the influence of sediment supply on bedload competence and capacity. Braiding involves more extensive bank erosion than meandering, widening of channels, and 'destruction' of meander bends rather than their enlargement (Ferguson, 1987, p. 141). Braiding can therefore be seen as resulting from the combined influence of flow strength and bank erodibility. Relative ease of eroding and transporting particles supplied by bank erosion processes is actually instrumental in establishing differences between patterns (see Figure 1.3). In simple terms, if erosion is easier than transport or if sediment supply from bank erosion is much more significant than the capacity of the flow to transport it, aggradation will take place, and shoaling will lead to a braided pattern. As clearly pointed out by Ferguson (1987), braiding may result from a lack of capacity to remove sediment provided from the erosion of sandy banks, or a lack of competence to remove the size of sediment supplied by the erosion of gravelly banks (capacity refers to the volume of material that can be removed for any given flow condition, while competence refers to the ability of a stream to transport individual particles of a given size, or the largest particle that can be removed for a given flow condition).

5.3.2 Fundamental morphological units

Gravel accumulations that form topographic highs in braided rivers are collectively and commonly referred to as bars. A distinction is usually made between bars and islands, with the former being unvegetated and often submerged under peak (bankfull) flow conditions, while islands are vegetated and emerge even under bankful conditions. As specified by Bridge (1993), such a distinction may artificially separate forms which have similar geometrical properties and which may share similar origins. Bars are the salient features of braided rivers. Numerous terms have been used over the years to refer to various types of bars, their size, morphology, and location. Such classifications are difficult to establish because of the complexity of bar forms, and the terminology used to refer to bar forms has been somewhat confusing. The number of bars can also vary significantly, over relatively short distances and short periods of time. A braiding index can be derived to assess the level (or degree) of braiding. Such a braiding intensity index can be determined, for instance, by the number of active channels (or anabranches) per channel cross-section (e.g. Ashmore, 1991a).

The first distinction that has to be made is between unit bars and complex bars (the latter sometimes being referred to as braid bars; Smith, 1974). Complex bar forms in braided environments result from a history of numerous episodes of erosion and deposition. In turn, relatively unmodified bar forms with a morphology determined mostly by depositional processes are often referred to as unit bars (e.g. Ashmore, 1982, 1991a; Bluck, 1987). Following Smith (1974), Miall (1977), and Church and Jones (1982), four major types of unit bars can be distinguished in braided rivers. A first major type is the longitudinal bar. These are diamond-shaped in plan view and elongated parallel to the flow direction. Steep downstream lee faces in longitudinal bars are not frequently observed, and most longitudinal bars taper off downstream (Miall, 1977, p.13). They grow by upward and downstream accumulations of finer material (Church and Jones, 1982).

Transverse bars constitute the second major category These are generally considered as being more common at bifurcations or downstream from confluences and in the presence of sudden channel expansions (Church and Jones, 1982). Transverse bars have a characteristic lobate shape, with relatively steep and sinuous downstream or lee faces. Transverse unit bars are usually not attached to the banks. Longitudinal and transverse bars are closely related to mid-channel bars (see Figure 5.1). Point bars make up the third major category. Point bars have been described before in section 5.2.2 on river meanders. Point bars are also elongated in the flow direction and are frequently observed along curved individual anabranches (e.g. Smith, 1974). Point bars possess relatively steep outer faces. Vertical and lateral accretion are important and longitudinal, transverse and point bars all tend to fine downstream.

Diagonal bars appear to be common in gravel-bed rivers, and represent the fourth major type of unit bars. Diagonal bars are attached features (attached to both banks), run across the channel obliquely, and may be characterized by a relatively steep downstream front. Many diagonal bars can probably be referred to as riffles (in the riffle-pool sequence described in detail in section 4.4). The term 'diagonal riffle' has been used (e.g. Church and Jones, 1982) to refer to stable macroforms, which may significantly contribute to flow resistance in coarse-grained channels (see section 4.7). In braided rivers, stable riffles do not develop, and individual bars migrate and may be of short duration.

Bars in braided environments are often of compound and complex origins, and the basic classification summarized above has clear limitations.

Two additional terms are commonly used to refer to complex bar forms. The first is 'medial bars' (or 'linguoid bars'; Miall, 1977; Church and Jones, 1982). Medial or linguoid bars are symmetrical and detached bar forms. The characteristic shape of medial bars is lobate, with downstream, sinuous, 'avalanche' slopes (Miall, 1977). Medial bars may result from the evolution of unit bars (e.g. longitudinal and transverse bars) into more complex forms (Church and Jones, 1982). The second term often used to refer to a type of complex bar form is 'lateral bar'. These also represent evolutionary complex features (and therefore more stable bar forms), asymmetrical in shape and attached to one bank.

An alternative to considering bars as fundamental units is to look at pool-bar units as forming a single entity. Pool-bar units are seen by many researchers as fundamental elements in gravel-bed rivers of all channel patterns, not just braiding (Ferguson, 1987, 1993). In braided rivers, pool-bar units occur alongside each other in two or more parallel rows (Figure 5.12). The pattern of pool-bar units illustrated in Figure 5.12 is similar to two back-to-back meandering traces. Pools are linked by thalwegs, and pool-bar units in turn lead to a downstream succession of converging and diverging flows. Individual anabranches (channels) therefore resemble gentle meander bends. Bank erosion along the outer banks of meandering sections (as defined in the previous subsection) can therefore be a significant source of sediment for bar construction (Ferguson, 1993).

By focusing on channels rather than bars, a third type of fundamental unit in braided environments can be ascribed to the widespread presence of numerous channel confluences and bifurcations (or diffluences). These most distinctive features of braided channels can be conveniently divided into Y- and X-shaped channel configurations. Confluences or junctions can be characterized by Y-shaped or reversed Y-shaped configurations, while X-shaped configurations refer to a junction followed by a bifurcation. These Y- and X-shaped configurations have been adopted as basic units for field

Figure 5.12 Example of pool-bar units in braided channels. Medial bars composed of a back-to-back double row of alternate bars. Bar fronts are indicated by curved lines. After Ferguson (1993), figure 1c. Reproduced with the permission of the Geological Society Publishing House, Bath, UK.

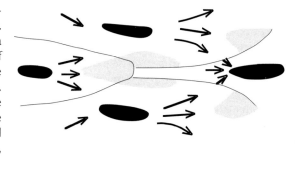

Pool

Exposed bar

Bar front

investigations and process measurements (e.g. Davoren and Mosley, 1986; Ashworth *et al.*, 1992a; Ferguson *et al.*, 1992).

In addition to being distinctive features of braided channels, confluences represent obvious nodal points within drainage networks. Bed morphology, flow and sediment transport dynamics at confluences have been studied extensively since the mid-1970s, and this topic will be addressed separately in section 5.4 below. Despite their importance in braided environments, diffluences or bifurcations have not been the subject of intense research effort. This is despite the fact that areas dominated by the downstream division of flow may be of fundamental importance for bar development (Ashmore, 1991a; Ashworth *et al.*, 1992a; Bristow and Best, 1993).

5.3.3 Mechanisms of braid development

The traditional model of braid development generally referred to in numerous textbooks has been the central bar mechanism initially suggested by Leopold and Wolman (1957). Recent work derived for the most part from laboratory investigations (exemplified by Ashmore, 1991a) showed that braiding mechanisms are complex. A summary of these various mechanisms is presented below.

Generally speaking, braiding can be initiated by erosional (dissection of topographic highs) or depositional processes. From laboratory models of

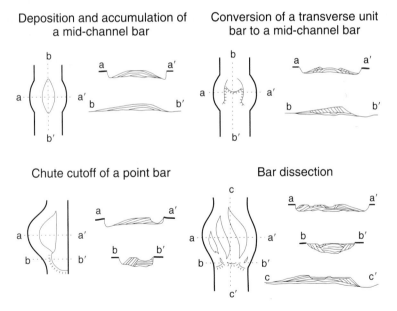

Figure 5.13 Braiding processes and depositional morphology. Based on laboratory observations (Ashmore, 1991a) and field observations (Brahmaputra River; Bristow and Best, 1993). After Bristow and Best, 1993. Reproduced with the permission of the publishers, the Geological Society Publishing House, Bath, UK.

gravel-bed rivers, Ashmore (1991a) identified four mechanisms of braid development: accumulation of a central bar (as in Leopold and Wolman, 1957), chute cutoff of point bars, transverse bar conversion and lobe (or bar) dissection. A schematic illustration of the morphological elements associated with these various mechanisms of braid development is presented in Figure 5.13 (as derived from the flume experiments of Ashmore, 1991a, and field observations referred to in Bristow and Best, 1993).

The first mechanism for braid development to be described is therefore the central bar mechanism originally described in detail by Leopold and Wolman (1957) from laboratory observations. This type of depositional braiding mechanism leads to the formation of longitudinal or medial bars near the middle of a channel. The traditional explanation involves deposition of coarse bedload where the stream is locally incompetent to transport sediment supplied from upstream (the larger particles being deposited near the centre of the stream where the local competence is not sufficient to move them; Figure 5.13). This in turn favours further deposition towards the surface and downstream, with larger particles trapping smaller ones in the building bar (Leopold and Wolman, 1957). Bar growth near the centre of a wide and shallow channel leads to a concentration of flow in the narrower flanking channels, which leads to more active erosion of bed and banks and thus to the formation of an 'island' (mid-channel bar). The feedback process is then repeated elsewhere along the channel, which leads eventually to the formation of a braided pattern. Ashmore (1991a) observed that the central bar mechanism may be rather uncommon, and restricted to flow conditions close to the threshold of initial motion (with dimensionless shear stresses of the order of 0.06). In shallow coarse-grained channels and under conditions slightly in excess of the threshold of initial motion, a small change of the local flow depth may therefore be sufficient to reduce the local bed shear stresses to a value below that needed to move the coarse fraction of the bedload, which would therefore favour local deposition and initiation of a central, longitudinal bar.

Ashmore (1991a) also observed that loss of competence (as described above) and vertical accretion of bedload sheets (described in section 4.5) are the dominant elements of the central braiding mode. During the bar building process, Ashmore (1991a, p. 332), observations suggest that the central bar gradually increased in size by lateral and headward accretion of bedload sheets that passed along the channel. This accretion process due to the passage of bedload sheets was also linked to a progressive downstream fining of the sediment along the bar, with the coarse fraction being deposited near the upstream bar margin, and the finer sediment being transported near the downstream margin of the emerging bar.

The second major type of depositional mechanism leading to the formation of bars is described by Ashmore (1991a) as transverse bar conversion. Transverse bars, often with downstream avalanche faces, were very common in Ashmore's experiments, and were better developed under high stream power conditions. The morphological features resulting from such a transverse bar conversion process are illustrated in Figure 5.13 (top right-hand corner) in plan view, across the channel and along the bar unit in the downstream direction. Bar formation in this case was initiated by the presence of transverse bars formed downstream of confluence scour zones (Smith, 1974; Ashmore, 1982; Ashmore and Parker, 1983; see section 5.4 for details on bed morphology and scouring at channel junctions). As for the central bar mechanism, bedload sheets migrating across the surface of the bar appear to contribute to the vertical accretion of the bar form. As bedload sheets 'stall' on the top or the front of the emerging 'lobe', flow is gradually deflected off the edges of the emerging bar, and the outcome is the formation of an approximately symmetrical braid bar (Ferguson, 1993). The transverse bar conversion mode was observed when flow conditions were substantially above that for the initiation of sediment movement.

The transverse bar conversion mechanism shares some similarities with the central bar initiation mode, i.e. vertical accretion of bedload sheets,

Figure 5.14 Schematic illustration of two major types of braiding development (by dissection): (a) Chute cutoff process (arrows show flow direction, dotted lines refer to diffuse bar margins, S indicates loci of bed scour, and shaded patterns indicate exposed bars. After Ashmore (1991a) and Ferguson (1993).

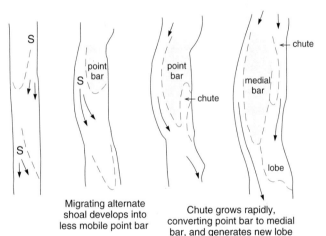

a Chute cutoff

Migrating alternate shoal develops into less mobile point bar

Chute grows rapidly, converting point bar to medial bar, and generates new lobe further downstream

(b) Multiple lobe dissection. Symbols as in (a), plus the solid lines surrounding the bars indicate avalanche faces. After Ferguson (1993), figure 4. Reproduced with the permission of the publishers, the Geological Society Publishing House, Bath, UK.

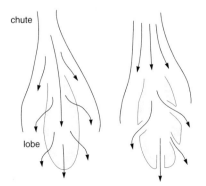

b Lobe dissection

initiation of braiding by 'stalling' of bedload in the centre of the channel, and subsequent flow division around the emerging bar. What distinguishes bar conversion braiding is the much higher sediment mobility (and there-fore flow intensity), more pronounced bar forms, and greater bed scour. In turn, the central bar mechanism is characterized by the absence of bed scour and relatively low bank erosion rates (Ashmore, 1991a).

The other two major braiding mechanisms identified by Ashmore (1991a) can be described as erosional mechanisms and are referred to as chute cutoff and multiple bar dissection (multiple lobe or tongue dissection, Rundle, 1985a,b). The development of 'chute' channels across point bars represents a widespread mode for the initiation of braiding (Figure 5.14). Chute channels represent relatively narrow channels developing upon existing bar surfaces where the flow is concentrated, scouring of the bar form takes place, and where therefore active bedload transport becomes predominant. Chutes occur whenever water spills over a steep gradient. The processes leading to the formation of a chute channel have been described as analogous to gully erosion with rapid headward extension (Rundle, 1985b, p. 27). Chute cutoff may occur on single point bars along established braided streams or across alternating point bars in (initially) relatively straight channels (as in Ashmore's experiments). Visualization of bedload transport sequences revealed that the onset of the cutoff process often coincides with the arrival of bedload pulses from upstream, often in the form of bedload sheets. Once fully established, the chute channel may become similar in size to that of the original main channel on the opposite side of the point bar (Figure 5.14). This chute cutoff process is similar to what has been described in section 5.2.4 on flow and sediment transport processes along high-energy meander-ing rivers (Carson, 1986). The chute cutoff process not only plays an impor-tant role in the initiation of braiding, but also contributes to the maintenance of the braided pattern (Ashmore, 1991a).

The fourth mode of braid development is also erosional, and it involves the multiple dissection of a lobate bar (Figure 5.14). Multiple bar dissection processes were initially presented by Rundle (1985a, b) as a dominant braid-ing mechanism along braided rivers in New Zealand rivers. Ashmore (1991a) reported that this process was uncommon in his laboratory observa-tions, but this may be due, at least in part, to the restricted channel width in flumes and the use of steady discharges in his experiments (while multiple lobe dissection may require dissection of the bar surface on the falling stage of a storm event; Ferguson, 1993). Observations suggest that the flow is ini-tially concentrated into isolated and discontinuous chutes. Bedload trans-port occurs along the chutes and sediment is often deposited at the downstream end of these channels (Rundle, 1985b). Hence sedimentary tongues are created downstream of the erosional chutes. Flow division occurs around these tongues, and chute channels gradually become a net-work of interconnected channels within which the flow is concentrated (Ashmore, 1991a).

Once braiding is established, any of the processes enumerated above may occur to further increase braiding intensity, and more than one of these mechanisms may be responsible for the maintenance of the braided pattern. The conditions of sediment mobility and channel instability in the stream will determine which of these braiding modes will be prevalent (Ashmore, 1991a, p. 339). Apart from the central bar mechanism, instability of flow and bedload transport appears to be prominent in braiding initiation and maintenance. These processes involve reworking of initial deposits by flows that are sufficiently competent to initiate and propagate braiding.

Finally, there are two additional situations associated with braiding processes that need to be emphasized. The first is 'chute and lobe', a term coined by Southard *et al.* (1984). In a study of channel processes in a small glacial outwash stream, Southard *et al.* (1984) noted that chutes and lobes are important elements of the braiding process. The chute and lobe mechanism shares similarities with the lobe dissection and the transverse bar conversion processes just described. The most distinctive characteristic is perhaps the braided environment within which they appear to predominate. As originally described, chutes and lobes are characteristic of relatively steep and shallow channels, and appear to be active during intermediate and high discharges (Southard *et al.*, 1984; Ashworth *et al.*, 1992a; Ferguson *et al.*, 1992). Generally speaking, they consist of a relatively straight and narrow channel with a lobe-shaped deposit at the downstream end. Chutes and lobes are relatively small features (e.g. a metre or less wide; Southard *et al.*, 1984), forming quickly and being active for relatively short periods of time. Ferguson *et al.* (1992) observed in the field (Sunwapta River, Canadian Rockies) that lobes form in a zone of divergent flow and sediment transport. Once formed, lobes frequently begin to be incised, and become partly exposed. Further incision may erode a significant part of the lobe and, commonly, one or more segments are left behind as small braid bars (Southard *et al.*, 1984).

The last major type of braiding mechanism can be simply summarized as avulsion. Avulsion can be defined as the relatively sudden switching of a river course from one channel to another (Ferguson, 1993). Avulsion processes discussed here refer to processes occurring at a spatial scale larger than the chute cutoff situation described earlier. Large-scale switching of the main flow occurs in braided rivers, and a number of scenarios of large-scale avulsion are mentioned, for instance by Ferguson (1993). An example stressed by Carson (1984b) and Ferguson (1993) is avulsion into an adjacent inactive channel induced by extensive bank erosion in a curved channel.

5.3.4 Flow and sediment transport

Relatively few extensive field studies of channel morphology, flow, and sediment transport processes have been conducted on braided rivers. This certainly stems, at least in part, from the considerable practical difficulties involved in conducting sampling and measurements in high-energy environments characterized by rapidly changing flow–sediment transport–

channel morphology conditions (Bridge, 1993). Nonetheless, glacial melt-water streams represent excellent natural laboratories because of the relatively small size and because of the periodic and highly predictable rising and falling stages and associated bedload transport events (e.g. Ashworth and Ferguson, 1986; Ashworth *et al.*, 1992a; Ferguson *et al.*, 1992). As emphasized before, hydraulic modelling of braided streams has also further enhanced understanding of processes in braided streams and related interactions between flow, bedload transfer and stream geometry.

Bridge and Gabel (1992), for instance, conducted a field investigation of channel geometry, flow and sediment transport associated with a single midstream bar in a low-sinuosity braided river (Calamus River, Nebraska, USA). The island along the middle portion of the studied reach was about 40 m in length, with a width of approximately 10 m. They observed that patterns of flow and sediment transport in the curved channels adjacent to

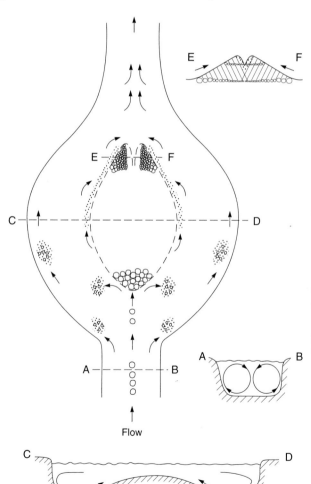

Figure 5.15 Schematic model of secondary circulation, sediment sorting, and downstream bar fining mechanisms in a simple, idealized, braided reach. After Ashworth *et al.* (1992a), figure 25.3 and Powell (1998). Arrows on the chute-bar diagram indicate the dominant direction of bedload transport for the sizes indicated, while arrows on the cross-sections indicate flow direction and secondary circulation. Reproduced with the permission of the publishers, John Wiley & Sons Ltd, Chichester, UK

the mid-channel bar were similar to those described before for individual curved channels (section 5.2.4; Dietrich *et al.*, 1979; Dietrich and Smith, 1983, 1984). As for meander bends in single-thread channels, transverse water slopes are observed, with super-elevation occurring on both left and right outer banks around the mid-channel bars and this controls the pattern of secondary circulation around the island (Figure 5.15). Similar observations on secondary circulation were reported by Richardson *et al.* (1996) on velocity fields around a large bar on one of the largest alluvial rivers (Brahmaputra River, Bangladesh). As illustrated in Figure 5.15, with two curved channels around a mid-channel bar, secondary circulation drives surface water outwards towards the banks, where it plunges, while slower near-bed water moves inwards towards the area of deposition in the vicinity of the mid-channel bar.

Spatial distributions of bed shear stress and average downstream velocity around the island (i.e. long individual anabranch segment) are also similar to the characteristic patterns of variation along meander bends (Figures 5.8 and 5.9). Similarly, local bedload transport rates and the mean grain size of the bedload are usually closely associated with the zones where local bed shear stress is maximized. In both channels around the island, the zone of maximum bedload transport rate crosses from the inner to the outer bank.

Ashmore (1991b) and Goff and Ashmore (1994) also addressed bedload transfer mechanisms in braided rivers, with a particular emphasis on the effects of bedload pulses on channel morphology. The effects of bedload sheets on braiding mechanisms and bar growth have already been described and summarized. Moreover, Ashmore (1991b) showed that sudden increases of bedload input (bedload pulses; see section 3.5.4 and Gomez (1983, 1991) and Hoey (1992)) were directly responsible for the formation of unit bars, as well as an increase in braiding intensity, anabranch avulsion, and eventually formation of more complex bar forms. Hence the variability over time of the morphology of braided streams is a direct response to increases in bedload input (Ashmore, 1991b). Pulses of bedload appear as waves of aggradation accompanied by migrating unit bars, and bedload pulses may lead to an increase in the frequency of avalanche-face bar forms which migrate downstream.

Goff and Ashmore (1994), in an extensive monitoring of bar evolution along a reach of the Sunwapta River (Alberta, Canada), observed that both bank scour and bed erosion are important sources of sediment for gravel transport in braided rivers, with the largest transport events recorded over a three-week period during the peak snow-melt season being almost completely the result of bed erosion and channel incision. As expected, periods of significant and rapid morphological changes (and therefore high bedload transport rates) coincided with periods of high stream power. Periods of peak discharges coincided with the greatest morphological changes (e.g. complete destruction and reformation of a large medial bar), during which net erosion was observed along the reach studied. Net erosion was also observed to be greatest during rising and peak stages, with deposition increasing on falling stages. Instances of morphological changes and significant bedload transport not directly matched to discharge fluctuations were also reported. For instance, rises in bedload transport during falling stages suggest adjustments independent of discharge, and may reflect incision taking place around newly deposited complex bar forms (Goff and Ashmore, 1994, p. 210).

Ashworth and Ferguson (1986), Ashworth *et al.* (1992a,b), Ferguson *et al.* (1992) and Davoren and Mosley (1986) also showed broad consistency between transport rates and hydraulic conditions. These field studies also illustrated the role played by non-uniform channel geometry and narrow chutes that concentrate bedload transport in discrete zones of locally high bed shear stresses. Davoren and Mosley (1986) and Ashworth and Ferguson. (1986) also showed the preponderant role played by the pattern of diverging decelerating flow and converging accelerating flow in explaining channel changes and bar formation. Bedload transport rates were shown to increase with flow intensity, but also to depend strongly on sediment supply conditions and mobility of sediment at the surface (Ashworth and Furguson, 1986; Davoren and Mosley, 1986).

Ferguson *et al.* (1992) were able to observe in the field the actual development of a new lobe (as described before for the chute and lobe mechanism). The lobe formed in a zone where both flow and bedload transport rates were divergent, with the non-uniform bed topography strongly influencing the spatial patterns of bed shear stresses and bedload transport rates. During phases of chute scour and lobe deposition, Ferguson *et al.* (1992) also observed that the volumes of erosion and deposition within the reach were very similar, and that mean transport rates estimated from Helley-Smith samplers were similar to those inferred from the scour zone. A series of interrelated measurements were reported by Ashworth *et al.* (1992a) on bedload transport characteristics (i.e. changing grain size distributions of bed, bedload and bar head deposition) on a chute-lobe unit. They observed that, although flow and bedload transport conditions were highly variable from day to day, the D_{50} of the bedload was remarkably consistent over space and over time in a chute-lobe unit. Bedload transport and bedload deposition were also almost always finer than the ambient bed grain size, with both factors suggesting overall selective transport. However, given the 'marginal' transport conditions observed in Ashworth *et al.* (1992a) and Ferguson *et al.* (1992) (i.e. relatively small transport rates and dimensionless bed shear stress rarely in excess of 0.06), the limited period for field measurements and sampling, and the complexity of sorting processes (e.g. the importance of changing sediment supply conditions, distance of travel of individual particles, etc.), the authors referred to the need for collaborative and intensive studies on flow, bedload transport, and channel morphology in braided river environments.

Finally, it is well known that there exists a general tendency for grain size to decrease longitudinally, i.e. in the downstream direction along bars

(Smith, 1974; Bluck, 1987; Bridge, 1993) and laterally across bars (e.g. Ferguson, 1993). In addition to local sorting due to selective entrainment of particles associated with local differences in bed shear stress, local sorting along and across bars may be due to a number of factors. One of the potential additional mechanisms leading to lateral sorting at the bar scale is the effect of a transverse slope, as described before for meander bends, i.e. the differential effect of lateral bed slope where coarse particles tend to migrate down the slope under the influence of gravity. Secondary circulation (e.g. Ashmore *et al.*, 1992) may also play a significant role in contributing to lateral sorting at the bar scale (Ashworth *et al.*, 1992b; Figure 5.15). Secondary circulation (presented in more detail below in section 5.4.3) in the context of confluent channels in braided rivers, is generally envisaged as a back-to-back version of what is usually observed in meander bends. As schematically illustrated in Figure 5.15 (upstream from the mid-channel bar), secondary circulation can contribute to sorting by moving the fine fraction of the bedload bankwards. Because of secondary circulation, the finer fraction of the bedload tends to be swept away towards one or both banks of the 'distributaries' (Ashworth *et al.*, 1992b; Powell, 1998), while the coarse fraction has sufficient momentum to move towards the bar head, where it may accumulate.

Bluck (1982, 1987) also emphasized sediment sorting during deposition, and the potential role played by a turbulence-controlled feedback mechanism (Clifford *et al.*, 1993b). That is, the differences in bed height created by the different clast sizes generate various turbulence intensity levels and scales, which, in turn, control the range of clast sizes observed at specific locations along a unit bar. In this inferred turbulence-controlled feedback mechanism, fine grains are firstly removed from an initially poorly sorted deposit, due to the relatively high turbulence intensity generated in the vicinity of the large clasts (e.g. Buffin-Bélanger and Roy, 1998; Lawless and Robert, 2001b). In turn, these zones characterized by higher turbulence intensity create conditions where only clasts large enough to 'tolerate' high turbulence levels can be deposited (Bluck, 1987; Clifford *et al.*, 1993b; Powell, 1998). Such a sorting mechanism may significantly contribute to the downstream fining illustrated in Figure 5.15, where settling of coarse particles in the vicinity of the large clasts is unlikely, due to increased turbulence. The fine fraction of the bedload may therefore be 'rejected' (Bluck, 1987) at the bar head and transported further downstream, where deposition may take place.

5.4 CHANNEL CONFLUENCES

The study of flow and sedimentary processes at channel confluences is relatively recent. Significant advances were made through laboratory work, where controlling variables can be easily manipulated and the emphasis placed on flow and sediment dynamics for confluences of various configurations and inflow conditions. Laboratory experiments (e.g. Best and Reid, 1984; Best, 1986; Best and Roy, 1991; Biron *et al.*, 1996a, b) provided insights into the main variables controlling bed morphology and flow processes at channel confluences that can then be tested in the field.

Confluences are obviously ubiquitous in drainage networks, but also dominate the physical environment in braided rivers. Confluences are among the most highly turbulent locations in fluvial systems (Sukhodolov and Rhoads, 2001) and many processes at river channel confluences have important implications for problems such as pollutant dispersal, navigation, and overall management of river systems (Gaudet and Roy, 1995).

5.4.1 Cross-sectional area and flow acceleration at river junctions

The average flow velocity usually increases at channel confluences as a result of changes in channel geometry taking place at river junctions (Roy and Roy, 1988). It has been shown that the total cross-section area above confluences usually differs from that below the confluence. At the confluence of two streams designated here as A and B, the summation of the cross-section area for stream A (A_a) and stream B (A_b) is usually greater than the cross-section area of the receiving stream (A_c). Since discharge of the receiving stream (Q_c) is the summation of the discharges of the two incoming streams ($Q_c = Q_a + Q_b$) and since discharge is the product of cross-section area and average flow velocity (e.g. $Q_c = A_cV_c$, where V_c is the average cross-sectional velocity at the confluence), it follows from continuity principles that the average flow velocity of the receiving stream must be somewhat larger than the average of the two incoming channels. When considering the average flow velocity across the channel, it is therefore common to observe flow acceleration at the confluence of natural rivers (Roy and Roy, 1988; Roy *et al.*, 1988). Roy *et al.* (1988), for instance, observed that at bankfull stage, the average velocity at the confluence was almost 1.5 times higher than on either tributary. If maximum velocity is used instead of average velocity, the differences are more pronounced, with the maximum velocity at the confluence being almost twice that on the tributaries under bankfull conditions (Roy *et al.*, 1988). They also observed that flow acceleration when the streams merge occurs for flow at or above intermediate stages.

It was also noted in Chapter 2 that a flow separation zone can be observed at the confluence of river channels, downstream from the junction corner. The presence or absence of a flow separation zone at a confluence is a function of planform geometry and bank alignment. The presence of a flow separation zone below a confluence reduces the cross-sectional area of the channel available for the incoming tributaries (Best and Reid, 1984). This, in turn, may also be responsible for the frequently observed acceleration at the confluence. Finally, as the flow exits the confluence zone itself and merges into a single receiving stream, flow deceleration is usually observed. Roy *et al.* (1988), for instance, observed that the ratio of average velocity of the receiving stream (about 10 metres downstream from the confluence) to that at the junction is constantly smaller than one (regardless of discharge).

5.4.2 Confluence bed morphology

Channel confluences are often characterized by the presence of a scour zone. A deep scour area often dominates the middle portion of the confluence. McLelland *et al.* (1996), for instance, reported a scour hole approximately four times deeper than the tributary depth (for the Sunwapta field site, Alberta, Canada). Relatively steep faces can therefore be observed at the mouth of each tributary, marking the entrance into the scour zone (Best and Reid, 1984). The two main factors controlling the size and location of the scour zone are junction angle and discharge ratio. Junction angle is simply defined as the angle between the incoming tributaries (which can vary between 5–10° and 90+°). The depth of scour increases with the discharge ratio of the two tributaries (Q_r) and the junction angle (α). Empirical results (from laboratory modelling) regarding the role played by junction angles and discharge ratios are illustrated in Figure 5.16. In this diagram, Q_r is defined as the ratio of the discharge of the minor tributary to that of the major tributary (or main channel; Best, 1988), while the depth of the scour zone (d_s) is expressed in dimensionless terms, i.e. the depth of the scour zone divided by the average flow depth of the two tributaries (Figure 5.16). The dimensionless scour depth increases gradually with an increase of the

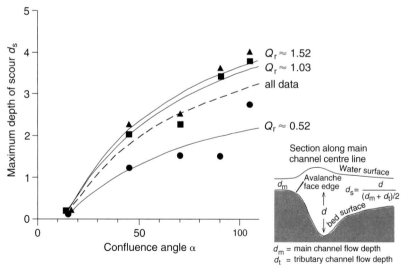

Figure 5.16 Empirical observations (from laboratory experiments) illustrating the relationship between maximum scour depth (d_s) and confluence angle (α), for three values of discharge ratio (Q_r). After Best (1988), figure 5. Reproduced with the permission of Blackwell Science Ltd, Oxford, UK.

junction angle. For a given angle α, the ratio of discharges for the two streams merging at the confluence also appears to be dominant, with the depth of scour increasing as the value of Q_r increases. At natural confluences, the scour depth is also to some extent a function of junction angle (Ashmore and Parker, 1983), although considerable variability is observed because of the numerous variables affecting field observations and measurements (Figure 5.17).

The avalanche faces at the mouth of each channel are more pronounced at higher junction angles, since their height is a direct function of the size or depth of the scour zone (Best, 1986). The location of the avalanche faces is also a function of the discharge ratio. At low confluence angles and low discharge ratios, the avalanche face of the main tributary penetrates well into the confluence, but as junction angle and discharge ratio increase, the flow deflection from the tributary becomes progressively greater, and that shifts the avalanche face of the main tributary further upstream. When the discharge of the minor tributary actually exceeds that of the main tributary, the avalanche face of the minor tributary begins to migrate into the confluence (Best, 1986).

The last major morphological elements commonly observed along chan-

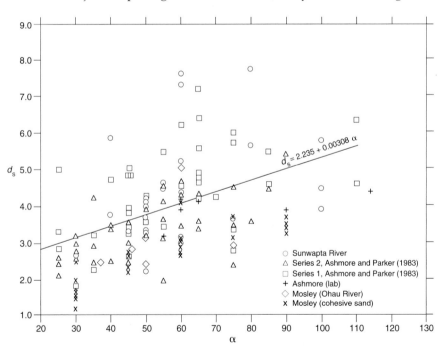

Figure 5.17 Diagram of the relationship between the dimensionless maximum scour depth (d_s) and confluence angle (α) for various empirical data sets (a combination of field measurements and laboratory observations). After Ashmore and Parker (1983), figure 9a. Reproduced by permission of the American Geophysical Union, Washington D.C., USA.

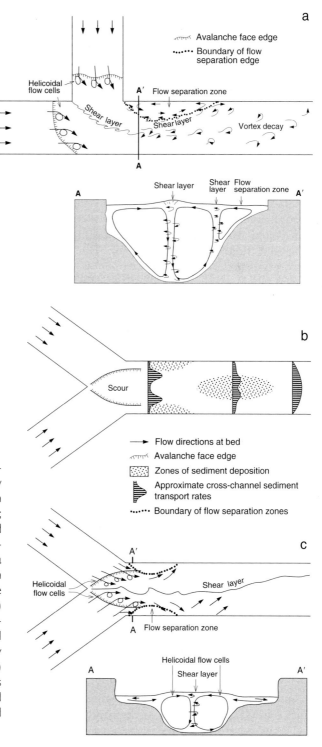

Figure 5.18 Bed morphology and main flow characteristics at: (a) an asymmetric confluence; (b) features of bed morphology and sediment transport at a symmetrical planform confluence (confluence angle about 50°); (c) features of flow dynamics at a symmetrical confluence. After Mosley (1976), Ashmore (1982) and Best (1986, figures 4 and 5). Reproduced by permission of Arnold Publishers, London, UK.

nel confluences are zones of sediment accumulations or bars (see Figure 5.1 and section 5.3.2 on bar classification). The location and type of bars at channel confluences vary as a function of planform geometry (Best, 1986). Along symmetrical confluences (where the angular deviation between each tributary and the receiving stream is roughly the same), a bar of sediment may form within the post-confluence channel (Mosley, 1976; Ashmore, 1982; Best, 1986). This mid-channel bar (transverse unit bar) is formed because of downstream accumulation of material eroded from the scour zone, as well as convergence of flows and sediment pathways at the confluence. At asymmetrical junctions, bars are frequently formed below the downstream junction corner. The formation of this bar is linked to the formation of a zone of flow separation (Figure 5.18a). The fluid from the tributary at the downstream junction corner cannot remain attached to the channel bank at this location, and a zone of flow separation is formed. This zone of low velocity and recirculation is therefore a favourable location for sediment deposition (Best and Reid, 1984; Best, 1986). The bar formed at the downstream junction corner also becomes larger as both the junction angle and the discharge ratio increase (Best, 1988). This in turn is due to the increase in size of the flow separation zone as junction angle and discharge ratio increase. The increasing size of the flow separation zone means a larger area into which sediment is entrained and deposited.

5.4.3 Flow characteristics

Also illustrated in Figure 5.18 is the presence of shear layers and helicoidal flow cells (secondary circulation). As mentioned before, shear layers develop at the interface of two flow zones characterized by different velocities. One such shear layer is therefore present at the margin of the flow separation zone, because of the low velocity in this area when compared with the main flow further away from the downstream junction corner (Figure 5.18a). A second shear layer is located near the middle of the channel, where the flows from the two tributaries merge. Significant vorticity can be observed along the shear layer formed by the two confluent flows. This vorticity can be well displayed when there is a difference in suspended sediment loads between each tributary (the vortices being highly visible when there is a difference in turbidity between the two merging flows; e.g. Biron *et al.*, 1993a, pp. 199–200). The exact location of the shear layer also varies as a function of the discharge ratio of the two tributaries and the junction angle. This is because the greater the junction angle and/or discharge ratio, the more significant will be the penetration of the flow coming from the tributary into the main channel (or major tributary). The location of the shear layer is a dynamic phenomenon, and it may well vary during the passage of a flood event as the discharge ratio changes.

As seen before in the context of bedforms, shear layers are areas of intense turbulence activity. At the confluence of two sand-bedded channels and from two-dimensional turbulence measurements (vertical and downstream flow components), Biron *et al.* (1993a), observed three scales of turbulent flow fluctuations associated with shear layer turbulence (see also Bradbrook *et al.*, 2000b): (a) variations of the location of the shear layer (>80 seconds); (b) large-scale eddies generated from the shear layer (3–15 s); and (c) short-term high-magnitude fluctuations within large-scale eddies (0.5–1 s). The temporal fluctuations in the position of the shear layer are essentially due to the varying momentum ratio between the two tributaries (the momentum of flowing water being the product of its mass and velocity; see equation 2.1). Their velocity records obtained from EMCMs also suggest that RMS values for downstream and vertical flow velocities (equation 2.52 and 2.53 respectively) within the mixing layer between the two confluent flows are up to five times the turbulence intensities observed in the ambient flow outside the shear layer. The increased turbulence intensities within the shear layer also suggest that the potential for bed erosion and sediment transport could be maximized under the shear layer (Biron *et al.*, 1993a, b).

Sukhodolov and Rhoads (2001) also recently investigated the three-dimensional flow structure at three stream confluences, from ADV measurements. They also observed higher turbulence kinetic energy (equation 2.55) within the shear layer, with values two to three times greater than the turbulence kinetic energy of the ambient flow. Their results show that the structure of turbulence within the shear layer is different from that of the ambient flow. They reported that shear layer turbulence is dominated by large-scale two-dimensional coherent structures, with the energy levels of downstream and lateral velocity components vastly exceeding the energy level of the vertical component (at low frequencies). They therefore describe the large-scale turbulence structure associated with the presence of the shear layer as being essentially two-dimensional and isotropic. The relatively low turbulence intensity of the vertical flow component (RMS_V) reported by Sukhodolov and Rhoads (2001) in the mixing layer is in contrast to those reported by Biron *et al.* (1993b) and De Serres *et al.* (1999). Sukhodolov and Rhoads (2001) also did not observe 'spikes' in velocity signals, i.e. very large, sudden and high-frequency oscillations in velocity signals. Differences in turbulent flow structures between these observations may be attributed, at least in part, to the fact that Sukhodolov and Rhoads' (2001) measurements were obtained at concordant junctions (where tributaries are of equal depth), while Biron *et al.* (1993b) and De Serres *et al.* (1999) reported measurements obtained at discordant confluences (where the difference in bed elevation between the confluence may significantly affect flow dynamics). This will be further discussed below in section 5.4.5. Finally, shear layer turbulence may play a significant role in shaping the bed and creating the scour zone observed at confluences. However, the turbulent flows measured by Sukhodolov and Rhoads (2001) were not responsible for the scouring of the bed at the junction investigated, and other factors such as flow acceleration within the central portion of the channel and helical flow could also contribute to bed erosion and creation of scour zones (Sukhodolov and Rhoads, 2001).

As initially observed by Mosley (1976), secondary flows can be very significant at confluences (Figure 5.18). Secondary circulation at channel confluences usually takes the form of two helicoidal flow cells merging near the water surface and diverging in the vicinity of the bed near the middle of the channel (Figure 5.18a, c). The cells therefore converge towards the bed in the centre of the scour zone, and move upwards along the avalanche faces. Above the scour zone, the water surface also stands at a somewhat higher elevation above the bed, because of the presence of helicoidal flow cells (as illustrated in Figure 5.18). The injection of dye into the flow revealed a circulation in which the flows from the two channels converge near the surface and near the upstream section of the scour zone, plunge downward and outward along the bed and the avalanche faces, and therefore create two flow cells with opposite sign of rotation (Ashmore, 1982). Secondary circulation was further reported in the field along confluences in braided rivers, in numerous studies. Among these are the investigations of Ashmore *et al.* (1992) and McLelland *et al.* (1996) in the Canadian Rockies. Two-dimensional flow measurements (Ashmore *et al.*, 1992) were made on symmetrical (Y-shaped) confluences along the Sunwapta River (D_{50} = 30 mm). Secondary flow cells such as those illustrated in Figure 5.18 were clearly observed. Ashmore *et al.* (1992) also reported that the strength of the secondary flow cells appears to decrease with distance downstream from the scour zone and laterally away from the thalweg area (the deepest portion of the channel) in each cross-section. Similar observations on helicoidal flow cells at natural confluences were also reported by Rhoads (1996) and Rhoads and Kenworthy (1998), who observed a consistent pattern of secondary circulation at a small asymmetrical confluence characterized by two surface convergent flow cells, one on each side of the mixing layer. Furthermore, in many studies it has been implicitly assumed that secondary flows (with a helical flow structure) observed above scour zones are responsible for the generation and maintenance of the bed morphology at concordant confluences (confluences where incoming tributaries are of equal depth; e.g. Ashmore, 1982; Best, 1988; Ashmore *et al.*, 1992; Rhoads and Kenworthy, 1995).

McLelland *et al.* (1996) also investigated coherent flow structures and helicoidal flow cells, both in the laboratory and in the field. In addition to confirming the presence of clearly defined helicoidal flow cells at confluences, their detailed three-dimensional data suggest that secondary flows are closely associated with flow separation phenomena being observed on the lee-side of avalanche faces at the mouth of each confluent channel. Several mechanisms have been suggested in the past to account for the formation of secondary flow cells, including 'streamline curvature' due to planform morphology, distortion of the shear layer (to be explained below) and flow separation associated with avalanche faces and the scour zone at confluences. In addition to being able to confirm the presence of counter-rotating flow cells from three-dimensional flow measurements, McLelland *et al.*'s field and laboratory observations suggest that, although streamline curvature may increase the intensity of secondary flow at confluences, the presence of channel-scale secondary flow structures is strongly influenced by avalanche-face flow separation phenomena taking place at the mouth of each confluent channel (McLelland *et al.*, 1996).

5.4.4 Conceptual model of flow and sediment transport

Best (1987) suggested a descriptive model of flow dynamics at junctions of rivers (Figure 5.19). Although limited to concordant junctions and a simplified configuration (an asymmetrical 90° confluence), the model presented in Figure 5.19 provides a useful summary of flow fields at confluences. These zones are dynamic, and their sizes and locations vary as a function of junction angle and momentum ratio. At the junction corner, a zone of flow stagnation can be created. Past the zone of stagnation, the flows from the tributaries are gradually merging (flow deflection zone in Figure 5.19). Flow from the tributary is deflected towards the outer bank. The presence of a flow separation zone at the downstream junction corner forces the flow into a narrower section of the receiving stream, where flow velocity is maximized. With distance from the confluence, the flows gradually mix, deceleration takes place, and 'flow recovery' is observed. Complete mixing of flows along concordant (equal depth) confluents can be expected to occur in the receiving stream only at distances from the confluences that are fairly large, ranging from about 25 channel widths to more than 100 channel widths (Gaudet and Roy, 1995). This will be further discussed later in the context of confluence of channels of different depths.

This conceptual model of flow zones at confluences can be linked to sedi-

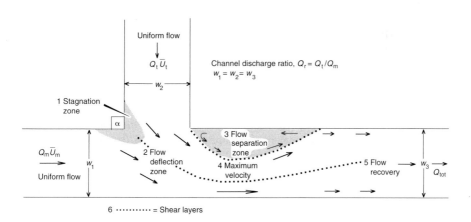

Figure 5.19 Conceptual model of flow dynamics at channel confluences (as derived from laboratory observations for an asymmetrical, 90° confluence with tributaries of equal depth). Subscript 'm' refers to the main channel and subscript 't' refers to the tributary (in Q_m, Q_t, U_m and U_t, where Q is discharge and U is average velocity). After Best (1987), figure 1. Reproduced with the permission of the publishers, the Society for Sedimentary Geology (SEPM), Oklahoma, USA.

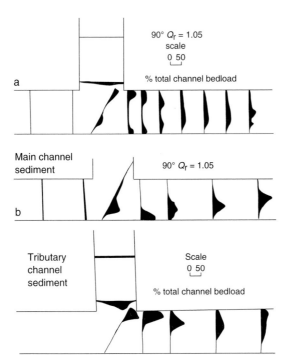

Figure 5.20 (a) Distribution of total sediment transport within a 90° confluence and for a discharge ratio of 1.05 (see the text for a definition of the discharge ratio). Sediment transport rates are expressed in relative terms, i.e. as a percentage of the total bedload measured at a given cross-section; (b) maps of bedload transport with each confluent channel (for the same discharge ratio, i.e. 1.05). After Best (1987), figure 8. Reproduced with the permission of the publishers, the Society for Sedimentary Geology (SEPM), Oklahoma, USA.

ment transport pathways and sediment transport distributions observed, for instance, at a 90° confluence (Figure 5.20). Patterns of flow and sediment transport illustrated in Figure 5.19 and 5.20 demonstrate that mutual deflection of flows and flow separation are the dominant flow dynamic features at concordant confluences (Best, 1987, 1988; Roy and De Serres, 1989). These factors lead to the segregation of sediment loads from each channel around the middle of the junction (Figure 5.20). The mutual deflection of flows clearly is responsible for the deflection of the sediment coming from the main channel towards the outer bank, and vice versa for the sediment load originating from the minor tributary (i.e. sediment load being pushed towards the inner bank). As junction angle increases, the mutual deflection of flows becomes greater, and the segregation of the sediment loads from each channel as they pass through the confluence becomes more pronounced (Best, 1988). This is due to a number of factors. Firstly, the flow from the main channel and its sediment load become progressively confined to a narrower section of the confluence as the junction angle increases and the flow from the tributary penetrates further into the main channel. Moreover, the progressively larger flow separation zone (below the downstream junction corner; Figure 5.19) also enhances sediment load segregation. That is, the large flow separation zone acts as a 'sink' for sediment transported through this area mostly from the tributary channel. The presence of helical flow cells in the scour zone, and the high levels of turbulence intensity, further promote sediment transport segregation around the scour zone. A confluence angle of 15–20° also appears to be a minimum value to generate flow and sediment deflection as well as large-scale flow separation (Best, 1988). The previous observations suggest a lack of sediment transport though the confluence scour, and the scour hole is therefore maintained by the sediment transport pathways around the confluence (as illustrated in Figure 5.20 for an asymmetrical 90° angle).

5.4.5 Bed discordance

The model for flow and sediment dynamics at channel confluences presented above corresponds with widespread field and laboratory observations at concordant open-channel confluences, i.e. when two channels of equal depth join. Many natural confluences, however, are characterized by channels with different depths (Kennedy, 1984), and these confluences are referred to as discordant confluences. When channels of different depth join, the bed elevation difference induces a number of additional phenomena, creating complex three-dimensional flow fields at confluences (Best and Roy, 1991).

The mixing of the two flows of different depth essentially involves interactions between the mixing layer that forms at the interface of the two merging flows and flow separation phenomena downstream from the mouth of the tributary. Insights from laboratory experiments were provided by the studies of Best and Roy (1991) and Biron et al. (1996a, b). Laboratory confluence models were created, with a tributary joining a main channel at a higher bed elevation. At the confluence, a sudden drop in bed elevation at the exit of the tributary was therefore introduced, and its effects on flow dynamics were analysed. A dominant characteristic of discordant confluences is the 'distortion' of the mixing layer (Best and Roy, 1991). As opposed to concordant confluences characterized by a vertical mixing layer (e.g. Rhoads and Kenworthy, 1998), a distortion of the shear layer at discordant junctions is created by the presence of a step downstream at the mouth of the tributary and, under these conditions, the vertical axis of the mixing layer is inclined towards the shallower tributary (Biron et al., 1996a). This mixing-layer distortion induces complex three-dimensional flow features at confluences, and it promotes vertical fluid upwelling. At discordant confluences, fluid (and its suspended sediment) may be transferred rapidly from the deeper channel across to the shallower tributary, upwelling downstream from the junction (Best and Roy, 1991). Moreover, fluid from the deeper channel can be entrained in the lee of the mouth of the shallower channel.

This process of mixing-layer distortion and fluid upwelling can be invoked to explain patterns of flow mixing at natural confluences. Gaudet and Roy (1995) showed that height discordance between confluent channels can significantly increase mixing rates, with complete mixing taking place at distances five to ten times shorter than those reported for concordant confluences. Mixing length appears to be inversely related to the level of bed discordance. When bed discordance is less important (and water levels are high), mixing lengths tend to be much longer, and the flows from each con-fluent channel tend to be segregated along their respective side of the receiving stream (Gaudet and Roy, 1995). Conversely, when water levels are relatively low and the level of bed discordance more significant, complete mixing of the two merging flows takes place over shorter distances. Under these conditions, the water from the shallower tributary tends to flow above the water from the deeper channel, therefore inducing mixing rapidly with-in the confluence. This 'overriding' effect causes a distortion of the mixing layer and enhances mixing.

Biron *et al.* (1996a) also suggested that helicoidal flow cells at discordant confluences can be modified or even destroyed by the enhanced mixing and the fluid upwelling generated by the discordance. The lateral motion of fluid may also be mistaken for secondary circulation, with velocity signa-tures similar to that corresponding with helicoidal flow cells. The role of bed discordance was further confirmed by De Serres *et al.* (1999) at a natural confluence of rivers, and by Bradbrook *et al.* (2001) from numerical model-ling. The field study of De Serres *et al.* (1999) emphasizes many of the points mentioned herein. Using field measurements, they showed the importance of bed discordance and momentum flux ratio in controlling turbulent flow structures at confluences and changing bed morphology. Finally, numerical modelling of three-dimensional flow structures at confluences represents a complementary approach to flume and field investigations (Bradbrook *et al.*, 2000a, b; Lane *et al.*, 2000). Although beyond the scope of this book, numeri-cal models allow further understanding of processes, and enhance our ability to understand coherent flow structures and related phenomena in river channel confluences (Lane *et al.*, 2000).

6

RIVER CHANNELS, AQUATIC HABITATS, AND THE HYPORHEIC ZONE

6.1 VEGETATION, SEDIMENTS, AND AQUATIC HABITATS

6.1.1 Introduction

Aquatic communities in alluvial channels are affected by and adjust to spatial and temporal variations in flow and sedimentary processes (Klingeman and MacArthur, 1990). Discharge variations, sediment supply conditions and related sediment transport processes can have considerable influence on the biology of invertebrate fauna and salmonid fishes (Milner *et al.*, 1981). The range of surface and subsurface particle sizes also plays a very significant role in controlling the density and diversity of both benthic organisms and fish populations.

The characteristics of the bed sediments determine porosity and permeability, which in turn affect burial depth of salmonid eggs, survival of embryos, susceptibility to scour under high-flow conditions, and habitat diversity for organisms preyed upon by fish. Porosity of bed sediments is important, because void spaces are used by many invertebrates as living space. Permeability is also crucial, in that it controls inter-gravel flow properties and other local subsurface environmental conditions (e.g. oxygen supply).

Bed stability is perhaps the most significant factor affecting aquatic habitats in alluvial channels. Aquatic vegetation patches promote a greater degree of bed stability, and introduce spatial diversity into flow and sedimentary processes. Bedload transport frequency and magnitude, depth of scour, and flow competence and capacity all affect benthic organisms living in the substrate, and salmonid fish populations. Sediment transport processes affect salmonid fish, because the depth of scour during significant bedload transport events may be sufficient to remove and wash away salmonid eggs embedded into the subsurface. Sediment transport processes also control the winnowing (or flushing) of fine particles from the interstices at or near the bed surface and subsequent deposition of a fine matrix within the open framework of coarse gravel (e.g. Milner *et al.*, 1981; ASCE, 1992; Parkinson *et al.*, 1999). The removal and/or deposition of fine material affects porosity and permeability and, in that respect, can limit the density and the diversity of organisms living or developing in the substrate, restrict inter-gravel flow, and affect overall survival rate (Lisle, 1989; Lisle and Lewis, 1992; Montgomery *et al.*, 1996).

The heterogeneous nature of bed material and the complexity of natural river bed surfaces not only affect sediment transport processes (and therefore aquatic habitat quality), but also influence local aquatic habitat characterizations and associations (Klingeman and MacArthur, 1990). That is, physical diversity is influential and contributes positively to habitat value. Local turbulent flow phenomena, turbulence intensity, bed relief features, textural variations, and bed structure arrangements (as described in Chapters 3 and 4) all influence local aquatic habitat diversity, heterogeneity and value (ASCE, 1992).

6.1.2 Aquatic vegetation

Submerged, rooted vegetation provides shelter for fish and forms a large substratum for macro-invertebrates (Sand-Jensen *et al.*, 1989). Submerged macrophytes (i.e. members of the macroscopic plant life in a body of water) significantly affect flow resistance and flow turbulence, as well as sediment transport and deposition (Nepf, 1999; Sand-Jensen and Pedersen, 1999). Lowland rivers characterized by fine bed material and relatively low velocity may provide a suitable environment for the presence of submerged vegetation growth. The range of discharges that may prevail along a given reach affect macrophyte growth, as does the availability of light. High discharges create mechanical stresses on plants that may limit the growth and abundance of submerged macrophytes. High discharges may also reduce light penetration because of the increasing turbidity levels with increasing flow stages. Light attenuation has the potential for reducing the biomass of submerged macrophytes (Sand-Jensen, 1998).

The rate of change of velocity (cross-sectional average) with increasing discharge is significantly controlled by the size and density of macrophyte patches. Frictional resistance is created by the presence of macrophyte stands, and a decrease in average flow velocity is usually observed with an increase in macrophyte biomass, especially during summer flows when biomass is high and discharges lower (Sand-Jensen *et al.*, 1989). The morphology and canopy structure of various species control the extent to which flow and sediment transport processes are affected by the presence of macrophyte patches on the bed. Stands of submerged vegetation with open canopies and streamlined leaves have little effect on flow velocity, turbulent flow structure, and sediment deposition within or in the vicinity of the macrophyte beds (Sand-Jensen, 1998). However, dense submerged macrophyte stands characterized by a closed canopy structure significantly control the turbulent flow characteristics in the vicinity of the stands and related sediment transport processes. The growth of macrophyte patches increases the spatial heterogeneity of flow and bed sediment composition and this, in turn, favours the formation of diversified aquatic habitats (Sand-Jensen, 1998).

The presence of macrophyte stands generates an environment conducive to sediment deposition. In dense patches where near-bed velocities are greatly reduced, sediment deposition takes place. The sediment surface within the patches is raised, because of the deposition of sediment within the submerged stands. The proportion of fine sediment at the surface increases, at least in the upstream portions of the vegetation patches (Sand-Jensen, 1998). Sediment particles deposited within the macrophyte stands originate from particles transported as bedload and/or in suspension. The front of the vegetation stands generates very low velocities (or zero velocities) that lead to sudden and significant deposition immediately inside the patches. Material transported in suspension may also contribute significantly to sediment deposition within the plant beds, as the flow decelerates and settling takes place (Sand-Jensen, 1998). The content of organic matter can also be significantly higher in the surface sediment of the submerged vegetation stands than in the unvegetated sediments (Sand-Jensen, 1998), and sediments are enriched within plant beds because of the retention of organic particles.

Flow measurements in natural streams (Sand-Jensen and Pedersen, 1999) and experiments in flumes (Nepf, 1999; Nepf and Vivoni, 2000) also showed the significant control exerted by aquatic vegetation on the turbulent flow structure. The turbulent flow characteristics within and above plant canopies vary with the physical characteristics and the density of the various plant species. Open stands, with long, streamlined and flexible leaves, for instance, allow the water to flow through the canopies, with minimal effects on both the mean and the turbulent flow structure. In turn, dense and relatively closed or 'sealed' canopies deflect the flow around and above the plant stands, and the overall effects on the turbulent flow are similar to those observed around and above solid obstacles (as described in section 2.5, for instance). In the presence of a relatively dense and sealed canopy structure, the turbulence intensity (RMS_u; equation 2.52) inside the plant canopy is significantly reduced to mean levels that are much lower than those observed immediately upstream of the macrophyte beds (Sand-Jensen and Pedersen, 1999).

Perhaps the most significant effect of sealed canopy structure on turbulent flow characteristics is the presence of a shear layer that forms immediately above the canopy surface (Sand-Jensen and Pedersen, 1999; Nepf and Vivoni, 2000). Very steep velocity gradients develop at the top of sealed canopies, and this is where turbulent intensity is maximized. In addition to differences in canopy architecture, the influence of aquatic vegetation on mean and turbulent flow structure varies with the areal cover and stem population density of the submerged vegetation stands (e.g. Nepf, 1999) and the ratio of plant stands to water depths (Sand-Jensen and Pedersen, 1999). More experimental work on the hydraulic resistance created by aquatic vegetation in natural streams and depth-limited flows is clearly needed, together with further studies on flow turbulence and sediment transport processes in the presence of aquatic plants in natural environments.

6.1.3 Benthic organisms and bed sediments

Benthic invertebrate species may be categorized as either attached types or burrowing types (ASCE, 1992). Benthic invertebrate populations can show considerable spatial and temporal variations in abundance and diversity. Many factors influence invertebrate populations, including stream hydraulics (Statzner and Higler, 1986), food availability, stream temperature, water quality, and predation (Hynes, 1970; Milner *et al.*, 1981). The most important factors in relation to flow and sedimentary processes, however, are the dynamic nature of the substratum, the near-bed flow characteristics, and the flow–bed interactions (i.e. associated sediment transport processes).

The heterogeneity of the substratum and the range of particle sizes may be the most important factors determining the distribution of benthic organisms. Heterogeneity is associated with a wide range of microhabitats, which in turn can support abundant and diverse fauna (Milner *et al.*, 1981). For instance, although few species appear to be restricted to either pools or riffles, differences in invertebrate densities and community structure within pools and riffles have been observed, and these differences appear to be primarily controlled by changes in bed material characteristics (rather than longitudinal variations in velocities and flow depth, for instance; Milner *et al.*, 1981). In addition to longitudinal variations and associated macrodistribution and sediment sorting patterns, vertical distributions of invertebrates within stream beds may be significant. Physical factors that may influence such a vertical distribution include the range of particle sizes and related void spaces, compaction, bed structure and therefore porosity and permeability. This in turn may affect the microdistribution of oxygen concentration, the amount of organic matter, inter-gravel flow and temperature, and therefore the abundance of interstitial fauna.

Generally speaking, coarse and poorly sorted sediments are associated with higher levels of species diversity. This is due to two main factors: (a) poorly sorted coarse sediments offer a wide range of void spaces that can be used by different species, and (b) bed stability conditions in coarse-grained channels are observed over much longer periods of time. Benthic community development requires bed stability over periods of time longer than a life cycle. The much lower threshold of initial motion associated with sand-bed channels, and the near-continual movement of the bed sediment, do eliminate most benthic organisms. Instead, sand-bed channels are often characterized by abundant and specialized species, often much smaller in size than those found in other sediment types.

6.1.4 Fish and bed sediments

Fish populations are also influenced strongly by bed sediment characteristics. As mentioned before – and most importantly – fish use sediments for spawning and cover. Moreover, fish move continuously and exploit zones of preferred turbulence and depth/velocity combinations (ASCE, 1992). Spawning sites for trout, for instance, frequently correspond with areas where the depth varies between 10 and 40 cm, where the velocity in the near-bed region is relatively high (e.g. between 40 and 60 cm s^{-1} at 10 cm above the bed surface), and where the bed material size is within the gravel-size range (i.e. between 2 and 64 mm; Parkinson *et al.*, 1999). Differences between species in the selection of sites with characteristic velocities and depths may also be an expression of variations in the size of the fish, with larger fish being able to sustain faster currents and relatively deeper flows (Milner *et al.*, 1981). Fish also use sediments for feeding, in the sense that fish species prey on specific benthic organisms that may specialize in living in certain bed sediments (ASCE, 1992).

It is frequently observed that salmonids spawn in the same areas year after year. This suggests that spawners detect some physical cues related to the environment (and the gravel-bed characteristics), which in turn stimulate spawning in a particular area. Spawning generally occurs in areas of relatively high inter-gravel flow and low silt content (Milner *et al.*, 1981). In addition to potential bed scouring at levels corresponding with egg burial depth, sediment movement may be detrimental to embryonic survival, since rolling, sliding, and saltation can cause physical damage from crushing and can wash away eggs in the vicinity of the bed surface.

Inter-gravel flow is also crucial when considering embryonic survival. Oxygen consumption by salmonid eggs and critical dissolved oxygen concentration vary during embryonic development (with the critical concentration increasing from about 1 to about 10 mg L^{-1} in the course of embryonic development; Milner *et al.*, 1981). Egg size and relative oxygen requirements also vary from species to species. Oxygen supply to salmonid embryos is determined by the velocity of the inter-gravel flow and its oxygen content. Inter-gravel flow velocity, in turn, varies with permeability (among other factors). Permeability for brown trout spawning nests, for instance, has been observed to vary between 160 and 6000 cm h^{-1} (Milner *et al.*, 1981).

6.1.5 Aquatic habitats and stream bed classification

Based on the previous broad considerations of bed sediments and their effects on invertebrates and fish populations, a bed material based classification of stream reaches can be established (ASCE, 1992). As emphasized in Chapters 1 and 3, bed material size decreases in the downstream direction in rivers, as a result of selective transport and abrasion. Longitudinal changes in bed material size at the scale of the drainage basin are also linked to changes in morphology and other physical factors in the downstream direction (width, depth, velocity, and slope). Gradual fining of bed material size, and its interaction with other stream channel characteristics therefore partially explain downstream changes in aquatic communities (ASCE, 1992).

The classification presented in Table 6.1 is based solely on inorganic sediment. Organic materials (e.g. leaf residues and other organic detritus) may represent a significant component of the matrix infiltrating gravel-bed surfaces and, under some circumstances, the coarse framework of gravel-bed surfaces is known to be an important temporary sink of organic materials in fluvial systems (Carling and Reader, 1982). Organic sediments provide the basic source of energy for many riverine ecosystems (ASCE, 1992), and sources of organic materials vary significantly within and between drainage basins (e.g. as a function of type and density of riparian vegetation).

Boulder–cobble channels are usually characterized by the 'cascade' system or the 'step-pool' bedforms described earlier in Chapters 1 and 4. Both the bed stability in the steep headwater segments of numerous drainage basins and the physical heterogeneity of the step-pool and cascade environments often provide the conditions for a dense and diversified invertebrate community. For instances, densities of 14 000 organisms per square metre have been reported in boulder–cobble reaches (ASCE, 1992). Benthic organisms can also be found at significant depth below the surface (e.g. 70 cm below bed level) in coarse beds with large voids.

Table 6.1 Bed material based stream reach classification of aquatic habitats (from ASCE, 1992)

Bed type	Range of particle sizes, mm	Relative frequency of bed movement	Density of benthic macro-invertebrates	Diversity of benthic macro-invertebrates	Fish use of bed sediments
Boulder–cobble	≥64	Rare	High	High	Cover, spawning, feeding
Gravel–pebble–cobble	2–64 64–256	Rare to periodic	Moderate	Moderate	Spawning, feeding
Sand	0.062–2	Continual	High	Low	Off-channel fine deposit used for feeding
Fine material	<0.062	Continual or rare	High	Low	Feeding

Gravel–cobble reaches (Table 6.1) also tend to have a gravel-bed frame-work that is occupied by densely populated and diversified benthic organisms. As discussed before, these streams are often characterized by riffle-pool sequences, and the physical heterogeneity provided by the riffle-pool sequences favours high density and high diversity. The framework of gravel–cobble streams is often well aerated and used by a range of invertebrates for living space. Seasonal variations in the frequency and magnitude of peak flows, and corresponding seasonal variations in the levels of sedimentation of fine material (i.e. the settling of silt transported in suspension during summer base flows and the winnowing of the fine matrix from the coarse framework following significant precipitation events) can also produce seasonal fluctuations in benthic communities (Milner *et al.*, 1981; ASCE, 1992).

As alluded to before, the embryo survival rate is a function essentially of three variables:

(a) interstitial voids and heterogeneity of framework, which affect the eggs buried below the surface;
(b) adequate permeability, to allow the transport of oxygen to the developing embryos; and
(c) the bed stability conditions during the time period between spawning and emergence.

Salmonid egg survival rates are severely affected by sedimentation levels. Survival rates are inversely related to the percentage of material finer than gravel in the bed framework, and are directly related to the ratio of mean particle diameter to egg diameter (Figure 6.1; ASCE, 1992). All three aforementioned factors are probably embedded into the variability illustrated, for instance, in Figure 6.1, where the percentage of salmonid embryo survival varies between 5 per cent and 95 per cent as the ratio of mean gravel diameter to egg diameter increases from 0.5 to 4.

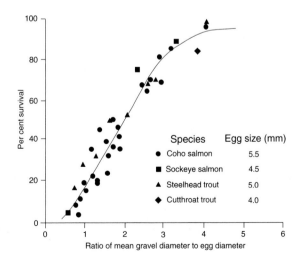

Figure 6.1 Variation of the salmonid embryo survival rate as a function of the ratio of geometric bed material size to egg diameter. After ASCE (1992), figure 2. Reproduced with the permission of the publishers, The American Society of Civil Engineers (ASCE).

In sand-bed rivers (Table 6.1), the frequent movement of the bed material provides harsh conditions for most benthic species, but is not usually detrimental to the density of benthic organisms. Recent work has pointed to very high densities (e.g. between 10^4 and 10^6 organisms per square metre; ASCE, 1992) of very small organisms (e.g. <0.2 mm) being observed in sand-bed channels. These small organisms exhibit various adaptations that allow them to survive within a frequently mobile sand-bedded stream channel. The density also usually declines rapidly with depth below the surface, and most organisms are found within the first 10 cm below the bed surface (ASCE, 1992). Natural flow obstructions (e.g. fallen trees and large woody debris) increase residence times for sediment and organic material within a reach and, as such, they provide important 'traps' for food and nutrients (ASCE, 1992, p. 678). Moreover, 'slack' water areas and zones of accumulation of fine sediment are often densely colonized by benthic organisms.

The last category in Table 6.1 refers to bed sediment finer than sand. As mentioned before, stream beds dominated by silty material are uncommon, and little information appears to be available on bed sediments and aquatic habitats in fine-bed material (ASCE, 1992).

6.2 SCOUR DEPTH AND SALMONID EGG BURIAL DEPTH

6.2.1 Salmonid redds

All salmonids create depressions in the gravel bed of freshwater streams in order to protect their eggs during the incubation period. Each female constructs a redd (or spawning nest), which typically consists of several egg pockets created at some depth below the bed surface. The female creates these 'pits' by turning on her side and using abrupt movements of her tail a few centimetres above the bed surface. This action is usually sufficient to lift a substantial amount of fine material into suspension – a component that is then washed away and transported further downstream (Kondolf *et al.*, 1993; Montgomery *et al.*, 1996). Once an appropriate pocket is excavated, the eggs are released by the female, immediately fertilized, and the female buries them, while at the same time excavating another pocket immediately upstream. It is generally agreed that a female salmonid may, in a given spawning season, construct one or more redds, and that the number of egg pockets per redd may vary substantially (Crisp and Carling, 1989).

Redds constructed by female salmonids form distinctive undulations on the bed surface, with an amplitude of 10 to 20 cm and an average spacing of the order of 2 metres (Montgomery *et al.*, 1996). These 'bedforms' created by the spawning process may persist on the bed surface until reworked during high-flow conditions. The bed undulations in turn increase flow resistance, and may represent a substantial component of form drag (see equation 2.47). This may further enhance the stability of the bed by increasing the critical shear stress at which the coarse fraction of the bed material will be entrained. Increased bed stability conditions may in turn favour salmonid populations and increase the survival rate of embryos (Montgomery et al., 1996; Parkinson et al., 1999).

6.2.2 Scour depth and depth of egg pockets

Montgomery et al. (1996) measured bed scour in relation to egg pocket depths (of salmonid embryos) in Pacific Northwest gravel-bedded streams. The results for Kennedy Creek are illustrated in Figure 6.2. The observations reported in Figure 6.2 were made during the time of peak flows and incubation of salmonid embryos within the interstitial voids of the stream bed (Montgomery et al., 1996). Scour depths ($n = 104$) ranged from 0 to 60 cm, with an average of 13.4 cm, while egg pocket depths ($n = 40$) ranged from 10 to 49 cm, with an average of 22.6 cm. Sixty-five per cent of the recorded scour depths were below 10 cm, while only 5 per cent of the egg pocket depths were less than 10 cm. Therefore, the distributions presented in Figure 6.2 show that only a small proportion of the bed scouring events were significant enough to affect spawning and disturb incubation. However, a close look at Figure 6.2 also suggests that a slight increase in the average scour depth would jeopardize a significant proportion of the egg pockets and affect salmon populations. Potential survival rates – as derived from Figure 6.2 – for Kennedy Creek as a function of scour depth are presented in Figure 6.3. It indicates clearly that an increase of the average scour depth to about 25 cm (from the current 13.4 cm) would, for instance, lead to a percentage of egg loss in excess of 60 per cent.

Figure 6.2 Histograms of (a) scour depths ($n = 104$) and (b) egg burial depths ($n = 40$) for Kennedy Creek in 1991–2. After Montgomery et al. (1996), figure 3. Reproduced with the permission of the publisher, NRC Research Press, Ottawa, Canada.

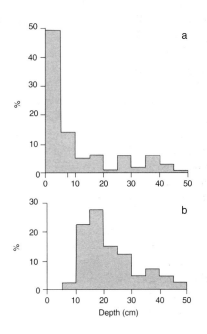

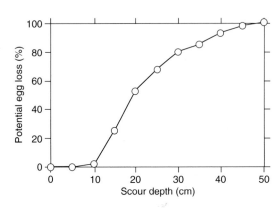

Figure 6.3 Estimated potential egg loss with changes in scour depth (as derived from Figure 6.2 for Kennedy Creek). After Montgomery et al. (1996), figure 4. Reproduced with the permission of the publisher, NRC Research Press, Ottawa, Canada.

The depth of scour in gravel-bed rivers reflects the bedload transport rate. As seen in equations 3.30 and 3.32, the rate of bedload transport in turn is a function of the transport stage or the difference between average bed shear stress and the critical value for initial motion (or the difference between stream power and the critical stream power at the initiation of sediment movement). The depth of scour can be estimated from the bedload transport rate and the bed sediment porosity and:

$$d_s = I_b/[U_b \, \rho_s \, (1 - p)] \tag{6.1}$$

where d_s is scour depth, I_b is bedload transport rate per unit width, U_b is average bedload velocity, ρ_s is sediment density, and p is porosity (Carling, 1987; Montgomery et al., 1996).

Changes therefore in the grain stress component and/or the critical stress for initial motion (e.g. coarsening or fining of bed surface material over time) can significantly affect bedload transport rates and scour depth (thereby affecting embryo survival rate). In armoured gravel-bed channels, mobilization of the coarser bed-surface material may clearly lead to a substantial and rapid increase in transport rate and scour depth because of the exposure of the finer subsurface material (Jackson and Beschta, 1982; Montgomery et al., 1996). Critical shear stresses and changes in bed surface sediment size can be significantly affected by variations in sediment supply conditions. Land-use activities and changes in watershed processes may also alter bedload fluxes and sediment supply conditions. Increased sediment supply and higher bedload transport rates resulting from the increased sediment yields may lead to bed surface fining (Dietrich et al., 1989), a decrease in the stability of the bed surface (a decrease of the critical shear stress for initial motion) and increased scour depth. Many land-use activities may lead to such an increase in peak flows and/or increase in sediment supply, both having the potential to increase scour depth and to affect embryo survival rates and the overall protection of salmonid habitats. At the drainage basin scale, recovery from a single large sediment input, for instance, may take several decades (Beechie, 2001). Recovery at a single point along the channel may take up to one decade, and the disturbance and its effects on aquatic habitats move gradually downstream (Beechie, 2001).

Burial depth also varies from one species to another. Inter-species variations in egg burial depth may have significant implications when assessing embryo survival rates (DeVries, 1997). Differences between species appear to be related to various physical and behavioural factors. Sources of variation include the size of the female (Crisp and Carling, 1989; DeVries, 1997), her spawning behaviour, and the physical characteristics of a particular environment in terms of combination of substrate size, flow depth (and distance from the banks; Heggberget et al., 1988), and flow velocity. Of these, fish size appears to be the most significant factor affecting burial depth, and this may be reflected in both inter- and intra-species variations (Crisp and Carling, 1989; DeVries, 1997). Numerous observations suggest a direct relationship between fish size and burial depth, with the larger females simply having greater strength and a physical advantage over the smaller ones. Data reported by Crisp and Carling (1989) also suggest a lower velocity limit of about 15–20 cm s^{-1}, below which salmonids of all sizes apparently prefer not to spawn, and an upper velocity limit related to fish size. A plot of mean flow depth in the vicinity of each redd and female fish length also shows considerable scatter, but clearly shows an increase in the minimum flow depth with an increase in fish size.

Larger fish (inter- and intra-species variations) can also spawn within a coarser gravel framework and sustain deeper and faster flow conditions. The gravel size of the spawning sites of Atlantic salmon and brown trout, for instance, differs significantly (DeVries, 1997), with the gravel size used for the spawning redds of Atlantic salmon usually being larger than the equivalent used by trout (sometimes more than twice the size of that for brown trout; Heggberget et al., 1988). The effects of bed armouring and the various degrees of vertical sorting of bed sediment may also be significant, contributing to both intra- and inter-species variations in egg burial depths (as a function of fish size).

6.2.3 Influence of spawning on bed sediment properties and bed mobility

As mentioned before, the process of redd construction by female salmonids involves the removal of interstitial fine sediment from the gravel framework. This repeated process in turn affects the overall fluvial gravel size and its sorting, and hence the mobility of the bed sediment and the embryo survival rates (Kondolf et al., 1993; Montgomery et al., 1996; Parkinson et al., 1999).

Montgomery et al. (1996) investigated the effects of spawning activity on the channel bed sediment. Their results indicate clearly that spawning and redd construction lead to coarser bed sediments (Table 6.2), with the increase in median surface grain size from unspawned to spawned sites varying roughly between 30 and 70 per cent. The coarsening of the bed

Table 6.2 Effects of spawning activity on median surface grain size (D_{50} in mm). From Montgomery *et al.* (1996)

Sample	Unspawned	Spawned	Per cent difference
			Kennedy Creek
1	23	32	+39
2	21	28	+33
			Montana Creek
1	12	20	+67
2	16	25	+56
3	15	26	+73
4	18	29	+61

surface along the spawned sites was also clearly accompanied by an increase in the degree of sorting of the surficial bed material (see Montgomery *et al.*, 1996 for numerical values of sorting coefficients). When the grain size distributions of spawned and unspawned sites are compared, the coarse end of the size distributions is somewhat similar, but the percentages corresponding with the fine fractions of the redd surfaces decrease significantly. Fine sediment removed from the spawning sites may also be deposited further downstream and deposited along the channel margins and the pool sections (Montgomery *et al.*, 1996).

Similarly, Kondolf *et al.* (1993) sampled redds and adjacent undisturbed gravels in an effort to document changes in grain size distributions due to spawning activities. In particular, they observed that the percentage of material finer than 1 mm in the spawning gravels, $P1_f$, is a fraction of the initial percentage of sediment finer than 1 mm ($P1_i$) and that:

$$P1_f = 0.63 \, P1_i \tag{6.2}$$

($R^2 = 0.93$). Interestingly, spawning-related bed modifications may positively influence embryo survival by increasing bed stability. The coarsening of the bed surface may lead to a significant increase of the critical shear stress needed to mobilize the bed. This reduction of the bed surface mobility due to spawning activities may correspond with periods during which embryos are more susceptible to scouring and disruption, possibly resulting in less-frequent bed scour to egg pocket depths. This process can be further enhanced by a greater offspring survival (Montgomery *et al.*, 1996), followed by a greater density of spawning nests and a further coarsening of the bed surface.

Conversely, a negative feedback mechanism may be at work if a mass-spawning population decline is observed in a particular area (due to land-use changes, for instance). Increased discharge and/or sediment supply to reaches where redd construction and spawning is significant can lead to a greater scour depth and a decrease in the spawning-related gravel modifications (such as those presented in Table 6.2). Decrease of mass-spawning gravel modifications may potentially lead to more frequent sediment transport events detrimental to redds and embryo survival during incubation, increased egg loss percentages, and further population decline (Montgomery *et al.*, 1996).

The percentage of fine sediment removed increases with higher initial fine sediment content (equation 6.2; Kondolf *et al.*, 1993). The effects of spawning on gravel texture may also lead to an increase of the porosity of the bed material, and potentially an increase in permeability and inter-gravel flow rates (Crisp and Carling, 1989; Kondolf *et al.*, 1993).

6.3 SEDIMENT TRANSPORT AND DEPOSITION IN SPAWNING GRAVELS

6.3.1 Depths and modes of accumulation and infiltration

The differences enumerated above, between redds and adjacent undis-turbed sites, can be at least partially erased fairly rapidly by infiltration of fine sediment into the interstices of an open gravel framework. Infiltration of fine material (Frostick *et al.*, 1984) takes place by gravitational settling of material in suspension, local bedload transport (Lisle, 1989), and near-bed turbulent flow phenomena (Carling, 1984), as well as local flow direction or 'downwelling' flow paths (see sections 6.4; Kondolf *et al.*, 1993). The rate of fine sediment infiltration is predominantly a function of the size characteris-tics of the infiltrating sediment in relation to those of the gravel, the local bed topography, and the near-bed suspended sediment concentrations. Significant infiltration of fine inorganic sediment into an open framework during the incubation period is detrimental to embryo survival, reducing the permeability, the inter-gravel flow rates, and therefore the transport of oxygen to the egg pockets.

In flume experiments, Carling (1984) observed that fine sediment filled the interstices of the open framework at a constant rate, with only a thin surface layer free of deposited fine material. Near-bed flow turbulence (i.e. at the sediment–water interface) prevented accumulation at the surface, and permanent deposition occurred below a level corresponding to approxi-mately one particle diameter below the bed surface. Lisle (1989) conducted experiments (on natural channels) that were designed for the investigation of sediment transport and deposition in spawning gravels, for three streams along the coast of North California. He observed that the level of penetra-tion of particles finer than the lower limit for gravel (i.e. <2 mm) and the increase in the percentage of fines with depth below the surface (if any) appears to be a direct function of the degree of sorting of the bed material. Sand is also commonly deposited near the surface of heterogeneous coarse-grained surfaces, and finer material tends to be deposited at greater depth.

6.3.2 Accumulation rates and formation of seals at the surface

Accumulation rates of fine sediments vary significantly across channels and from reach to reach (Lisle and Lewis, 1992). Using 'gravel cans' embedded into stream beds, Lisle (1989) observed rates of accumulation of sediment that vary by almost one order of magnitude. Moreover, vertical sorting of the material infiltrating the gravel cans was observed, and sediment tended (for the most part) to accumulate into two distinct portions of the containers, i.e. near the tops and the bottoms of the cans. Sediment accumulating at greater depths below the bed surface (near the bottom of the cans) was predominantly fine sand, silt, and organic matter, while at the surface, coarser sediment (sand and fine gravel) completely filled the voids of the top surface layers. This accumulation of relatively coarser sediment (when compared with material reaching greater depths below the surface) generally 'sealed' the surface of the gravel beds, forming deposits of several centimetres in thickness, which prevented deposition into the underlying layers. The plugging of surficial gravel interstices that prevents infiltration into deeper layers has also been reported elsewhere in various studies (e.g. Carling, 1984; Diplas and Parker, 1992).

The accumulation of coarser sediment at the surface (the sealing of surficial interstices) appears to be particularly important during significant storm-flow events. A sequence of processes of scour and fill may often dominate, leading to a high spatial and temporal variability of infiltration rates and depths of infiltration. The formation of a surface seal after a significant storm event, during which bed scouring took place and where the bed has been 'cleaned' of fine material in the surficial layers, appears to be inevitable (Lisle, 1989). The main component of the sediment infiltrating the bed in the experiments conducted by Lisle (1989) was fine bedload, not suspended sediment. Bedload particles move in frequent or continuous contacts with the bed surface, and fit readily into the surficial gravel interstices. On the other hand, accumulation of silt near the surface is inhibited by winnowing (e.g. by near-bed turbulent flow exchange) and by infrequent contacts with the bed surface (if any).

6.3.3 Bedload transport, scour and fill, and salmonid populations

These processes are important when assessing embryo survival and salmonid spawning in relation to the dynamic nature of sediment transport processes in natural channels with heterogeneous coarse sediments. The temporal and spatial variability in survival rates are highly dependent on the volume of fine sediment infiltrating a coarse framework and the size of material that accumulates in spawning gravels, and this depends, at least in part, on the flux of fine bedload in a given reach during the time of incubation (Lisle and Lewis, 1992).

Following Lisle (1989), a sequence of processes similar to that described below may be observed after spawning and redd construction in gravel-bed rivers (redd construction itself being associated with winnowing of fine material, coarsening of the surface layers and better-sorted surface sediment, as explained before). During the initial part of a subsequent storm event, part of the fine material transported in suspension (and the very fine fraction of the initial stages of bedload transport) may infiltrate into the coarse framework and reach levels corresponding with the egg pockets. As grain shear stress increases with an increase in flow stage, critical shear stress for initial motion of progressively larger grain sizes is reached, larger particles are transported and bedload transport rates increase. A seal of sand and fine gravel forms at the surface, prohibiting infiltration of fine sediment into the bed, despite the increase of suspended sediment concentration in the near-bed flow. As bedload transport increases in intensity, scouring of lower levels of the bed may take place, which may jeopardize the survival of egg pockets at some depth below the bed surface. Moreover, as bedload transport fluctuates during peak flow conditions, seals created in the vicinity of the bed surface by bedload deposition can therefore be formed at successively lower levels. Clogging of the near-surface pores may be detrimental to downwelling of water into gravel interstices, and may also prevent fry emergence at the end of the incubation period (commonly two to six months after spawning; Lisle, 1989). Although the formation of seals prevents further infiltration of fine sediment, the sealing of the surface may occur after enough fine sediment has infiltrated the surface to endanger the egg pockets' survival (Lisle, 1989).

During bedload transport events, changes in porosity, permeability and inter-gravel flow velocity are all dynamic phenomena resulting predominantly from changes in bedload fluxes, erosion of heterogeneous sediments, and subsequent depositional processes. These changes, in turn, control variables affecting salmonid populations and survival rates, i.e. the concentration of oxygen available to the embryos, the stability of the bed sediment at the level of the spawning nests, and the ability of fry to emerge through the bed surface at the end of the incubation period. A better understanding of the factors affecting the population dynamics of stream fishes has been achieved through a selected number of empirical studies. More progress could be made by establishing the more general relationships between the appropriate conditions for embryos to develop in heterogeneous gravel-beds, the sediment transport processes, and depth and grain size of fine-sediment infiltration (Lisle and Lewis, 1992).

6.4 THE HYPORHEIC ZONE

6.4.1 Definition and significance

In addition to providing habitats for invertebrates, and being central to the reproduction and development of various fish species, the bed of alluvial rivers provides a 'filter-layer' influencing the exchange processes occurring between stream flow and groundwater flow (Schälchli, 1992). A growing and relatively recent body of research attests to the importance of the exchange zone underneath stream channels. Subsurface flow paths, fluxes, and associated fluvial processes are often neglected in studies of geomorphology and hydrology. From an ecological perspective, this zone within which flow exchanges take place provides the links between the aquatic and terrestrial components of stream ecosystems (Stanford and Ward, 1988, 1993; Boulton *et al.*, 1998; Wondzell and Swanson, 1999).

Groundwater and stream water have traditionally been treated separately in most ecological studies (Brunke and Gonser, 1997). The hyporheic zone (HZ) represents a transition zone between streams and groundwater. Various definitions of the hyporheic zone have been suggested. Following White (1993) and Brunke and Gonser (1997), the HZ can be referred to as being the saturated zone beneath the stream bed, and into the stream banks, that contains some proportion of channel water, or that has been altered by surface water infiltration (Brunke and Gonser, 1997, p. 3). A diagram showing vertical and longitudinal exchanges of water between the open channel

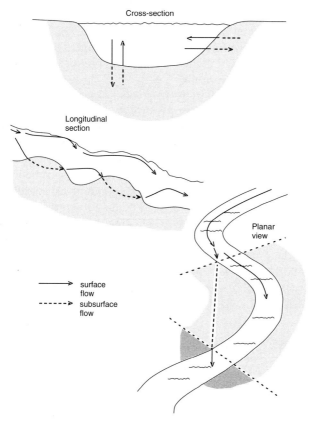

Figure 6.4 Illustration of the vertical and lateral exchanges of water between the stream channel and the surrounding hyporheic zone (shaded region). After Findlay (1995), figure 1. Reproduced with the permission of the publisher, the American Society of Limnology & Oceanography, Waco, Texas, USA.

and the hyporheic zone is presented in Figure 6.4 (Findlay, 1995). Subsurface regions are categorized as either groundwater or hyporheic zone, based on the level of hydrologic exchange with surface waters (Jones and Holmes, 1996). Specific criteria can be used therefore to define the lower boundary of the HZ and the transition to the underlying phreatic groundwater zone. One such definition proposes that the transition from the HZ to the groundwater zone occurs where less than 10 per cent of the subsurface water originated from the stream channel (Jones and Holmes, 1996, p. 239; see also Brunke and Gonser, 1997). Similarly, different layers within the HZ characterized by different mixing ratios of surface and subsurface water can be established, with a distinction being made between a thin surface HZ containing more than 98 per cent of advected surface water, and an underlying interactive HZ containing between 10 per cent and 98 per cent of advected surface water (i.e. water originating from the stream channel).

6.4.2 Environmental characteristics of the HZ, and factors controlling interchange

An important characteristic controlling the nature and the spatial extent of the HZ is clearly the type of substrate forming the stream bed (Williams, 1984). Porosity varies significantly with the degree of sorting of the bed material and the packing density. The interchange of water between stream channels and subsurface flows in natural streams is complex, in part because of the heterogeneity of bed porosity under natural conditions, and its spatial and temporal variability.

As illustrated in Figure 6.4, flow through the interstices of the hyperheic zone in streams includes a vertical and a longitudinal (or lateral) component. A very substantial reduction of the velocity usually occurs within the top portion of the hyperheic zone. Natural stream gravels, for instance, have permeabilities ranging from a few mm per second to about 25–30 mm s^{-1} (Williams, 1984). Permeability of the HZ depends on the hydraulic conductivity of the sediment layer (Brunke and Gonser, 1997). More specifically, the interchange of water between the surface and the HZ is the product of the hydraulic gradient and the hydraulic conductivity (Darcy's Law). Hydraulic gradient is the difference in water pressure between two bodies of water, while hydraulic conductivity refers to a measure of the resistance to flow imposed by a porous substrate (e.g. Jones and Holmes, 1996, p. 239). This can be expressed mathematically as:

$$U_0 = -K/\mu \; dp/dx \qquad (6.3)$$

where U_0 is pore-water velocity, K is intrinsic permeability (a function only of the porous medium; Dingman, 1984), μ is pore-water (dynamic) viscosity, p is pressure and x is distance downstream (Thibodeaux and Boyle, 1987).

The discharge of water in the HZ can be compared with that in the channel. The volume of water (per unit time) flowing into the HZ can be determined from the cross-sectional area of the HZ times the average velocity of the flow through the interstices. The ratio of the cross-sectional area of the HZ (A_h) to that of the stream channel (A) may be highly variable. For example, Boulton *et al.*, (1998) showed that A_h/A varies from almost zero (bedrock channels) to as much as five. The small interstitial flow velocities (when compared with stream velocities), combined with the characteristic small ratio of A_h/A, lead to stream discharge that may be up to three or four orders of magnitude greater than the hyporheic flow discharge (Boulton *et al.*, 1998).

The pore-water velocity also depends significantly on water temperature (equation 6.3). In the hyporheic zone, the temperature is generally lower than stream temperature in the summer, and vice versa in the winter, with the difference usually increasing with depth below the surface (Williams, 1984). Light penetration into the interstices also varies somewhat with substrate particle size. However, light commonly fails to penetrate the sediment below a depth of about four to five times the average particle diameter (Brunke and Gonser, 1997). In natural channels with heterogeneous bed sediments, light penetration can be further reduced to shallower depths, and therefore most of the HZ is usually in total darkness. Gradients of light intensity are therefore very pronounced at the sediment – stream water interface, and the absence of light penetration precludes photosynthesis (Williams, 1984). Finally, in general, the oxygen content of the interstitial water declines with increasing depth below the surface, until it reaches the more stable conditions of the groundwater (Brunke and Gonser, 1997).

6.4.3 Spatial scales and flow paths

Frequent water flow exchanges will take place (back and forth) between the channel itself and the subsurface (hyporheic flow paths). The length of the subsurface flow path, from the point where it leaves the channel and enters the hyporheic zone, to the point where it re-enters the stream, can vary from a few centimetres to hundreds of metres (Harvey and Wagner, 2000). In addition to variations in hydraulic conductivity (and related sediment types), the length and direction of flow paths are strongly affected by changes in stream channel morphology, i.e. variations in stream bed slope, bed undulations (bedforms) of different magnitude and scale, and channel curvature (Figure 6.4).

More specifically, three broad scales of hyporheic flow paths can be defined (Figure 6.5; Boulton *et al.*, 1998). Some of the key processes associated with fine-scale flow paths and corresponding granulometric features have already been discussed at length in relation to invertebrates and spawning in gravels. Key fluvial processes at the sediment-scale level include those that modify the size or amount of pore spaces (particle size, shape, sorting, packing density, etc.), clogging of surficial interstices by fine sediment transport and deposition, oxygen availability, and the significance of organic-matter deposition into interstitial voids (Boulton *et al.*, 1998).

Reach-scale processes and flow paths have to some extent dominated the

Figure 6.5 Lateral view of the hyporheic zone at three spatial scales. (a) Catchment scale and the hyporheic corridor concept; (b) reach scale and alternation of upwelling and downwelling flow zones; (c) sediment scale (microscale gradients). Arrows indicate water flow paths. After Boulton _et al._ (1998), figure 2. Reproduced with permission from the Annual Reviews, California, USA.

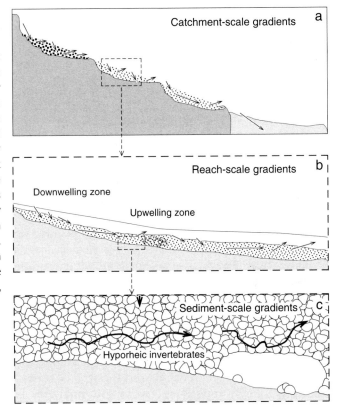

research on hyporheic exchanges. Geomorphic features play a dominant role in the exchange processes at this spatial scale, controlling in part the localization and the spatial extent of the downwelling and upwelling areas (Figures 6.4 and 6.5) in response to discontinuities in channel morphology (Harvey and Bencala, 1993). The presence of bedforms such as pools and riffles, sand dunes, macro-scale gravel bars, obstacles of various origins (e.g. the accumulation of large woody debris) and channel planform characteristics, all affect subsurface flow pathways. At the end of a pool section, for instance, or along the stoss side of a sand bedform, the increasing bed elevation (decreasing flow depth) forces surface water down into the bed sediments (downwelling). This infiltration of stream water into the bed surface therefore is displacing interstitial water some distance before upwelling again into the stream channel further downstream (Boulton _et al._, 1998). Similarly, flows entering and leaving stream banks can be considered equivalent to the downwelling and upwelling processes described above for bedforms (Boulton _et al._, 1998). The characteristics (e.g. temperature, nutrient content) of upwelling and downwelling water along a stream channel may be significantly different, and the broad ecological patterns may be correlated with the location of specific upwelling or downwelling zones (upwelling water, for instance, being rich in nutrients thereby affecting productivity in surface streams; Boulton *et al.*, 1998).

An estimate of the interstitial flow velocity due to the presence of bed-forms can be obtained from stream flow and bedform properties. More specifically:

$$U_0 = K/v \, (C_d \, U^2/l + g \, S) \tag{6.4}$$

where U_0 is pore-water velocity, K is intrinsic permeability, v is kinematic viscosity, C_d is a drag coefficient (as defined for form roughness; see equations 2.46 to 2.48), U is average stream velocity, l is bedform spacing, g is gravitational acceleration, and S is average water surface slope (Thibodeaux and Boyle, 1987). The dimensional character of intrinsic permeability (K) is $[L^2]$. It is a function of porous medium itself, and its value varies with porosity of the bed sediment and the square of the median diameter of the subsurface bed material (Dingman, 1984, p. 299).

Upwelling flows may also exert significant influences on flow and sediment transport processes in channels (Keller *et al.*, 1990). Emerging subsurface flows may, for instance, affect sediment entrainment (the seepage force reducing the effective weight of the bed material and therefore potentially facilitating sediment entrainment; Keller *et al.*, 1990). The role of upwelling flows on sediment transport remains, however, essentially unknown; it is usually assumed that the seepage force associated with emerging groundwater is very small compared with the drag force involved in the initial motion process, and therefore it can be neglected (Keller *et al.*, 1990). During major flood events, geomorphic processes can also reshape the channel significantly, thereby modifying the longitudinal and lateral pattern of bed undulations (e.g. Wondzell and Swanson, 1999). Changes in channel morphology following major bedload transport events affect significantly the hyporheic flow paths and the extent of the hyporheic zone. In channels prone to such occurrences, changes to the hyperheic zone at the reach scale can also be induced by the formation and destruction of large woody debris jams (Wondzell and Swanson, 1999).

Finally, the third major scale for the investigation of subsurface hyporheic flow paths is the drainage basin scale. This approach has led to the elaboration of the concept of a 'hyporheic corridor' (e.g. Stanford and Ward, 1993), in which connections and interactions between the HZ and the drainage basin are emphasized (Boulton *et al.*, 1998). Fluctuating groundwater levels, for instance, can have significant effects on channel banks and their stability. During the rising limb of a major precipitation event, bank materials may be relatively dry and may absorb water from the increased flow level (Keller *et al.*, 1990). The process is reversed during the falling limb, where the saturated banks lose water as the flow level recedes. Dewatering of the saturated banks as the flow level decreases following peak flow conditions can produce significant bank failure (Keller *et al.*, 1990). Riparian vegetation can also be affected significantly by fluctuating groundwater levels in the bank. Loss of riparian vegetation due to the lowering of the groundwater level, for instance, may greatly affect bank stability and lead to massive bank erosion

(Keller *et al.*, 1990).

The need for an interdisciplinary approach to the study of stream ecosystems has been advocated frequently in the recent past (e.g. Statzner *et al.*, 1988; Findlay, 1995; Jones and Holmes, 1996, Montgomery, 2001). Flow and sediment transport processes in alluvial channels, hydrological processes and hyporheic water flows, biogeochemical processes and surface–subsurface exchange mechanisms, and the ecology of subsurface organisms, are all interconnected. Understanding these interactions in alluvial channels presents unique challenges that require an interdisciplinary approach (Jones and Holmes, 1996).

REFERENCES

Abbott, J.E. and Francis, J.R.D. 1977: Saltation and suspension trajectories of solid grains in a water stream. *Philosophical Transactions of the Royal Society of London* **284,** 225–54.

Abrahams, A.D., Li, G. and Atkinson, J.F. 1995: Step-pool streams: adjustment to maximum flow resistance. *Water Resources Research* **31,** 2593–602.

Acarlar, M.S. and Smith, C.R. 1987: A study of hairpin vortices in a laminar boundary layer. Part I. Hairpin vortices generated by a hemisphere protuberance. *Journal of Fluid Mechanics* **175,** 1–41.

Allen, J.R.L. 1968: *Current ripples: their relation to patterns of water and sediment motion.* Amsterdam: North Holland, 433 pp.

Allen, J.R.L. 1982: *Sedimentary structures: their character and physical basis.* Amsterdam: Elsevier, 593 pp.

Allen, J.R.L. 1983: River bedforms: progress and problems. In Collinson, J.D. and Lewin, J. (eds), *Modern and ancient fluvial systems.* Special Publication No. 6 of the International Association of Sedimentologists, Oxford: Blackwell Scientific Publications, 19–33.

Allen, J.R.L. 1985: *Principles of physical sedimentology.* London: Allen & Unwin, 272 pp.

Allen, J.R.L. 1994: Fundamental properties of fluids and their relation to sediment transport processes. In Pye, K. (ed.), *Sediment transport and depositional processes.* Oxford: Blackwell Scientific Publications, 51–60.

Anderson, R.S. 1990: Eolian ripples as examples of self-organization in geomorphological systems. *Earth-Science Reviews* **29,** 77–96.

Andrews, E.D. 1983: Entrainment of gravel from naturally sorted riverbed material. *Geological Society of America Bulletin* **94,** 1225–31.

Antonia, R.A. and Luxton, R.E. 1971: The response of a turbulent boundary layer to a step change in surface roughness. Part I. Smooth to rough. *Journal of Fluid Mechanics* **48,** 721–61.

Antonia, R.A. and Luxton, R.E. 1972: The response of a turbulent boundary layer to a step change in surface roughness. Part 2. Rough to smooth. *Journal of Fluid Mechanics* **53,** 737–57.

ASCE, 1992: Sediment and aquatic habitat in river systems. *Journal of Hydraulic Engineering, American Society of Civil Engineers* **118,** 669–87.

Ashley, G. 1990: Classification of large-scale sub-aqueous bedforms: a new look at an old problem. *Journal of Sedimentary Petrology* **60,** 160–72.

Ashmore, P.E. 1982: Laboratory modeling of gravel braided stream morphology. *Earth Surface Processes and Landforms* **7,** 201–25.

Ashmore, P.E. 1991a: How do gravel-bed rivers braid? *Canadian Journal of Earth Sciences* **28,** 326–41.

Ashmore, P.E. 1991b: Channel morphology and bed load pulses in braided, gravel-bed streams. *Geografiska Annaler* **73A,** 37–52.

Ashmore, P.E. 1993: Contemporary erosion of the Canadian landscape. *Progress in Physical Geography* **17,** 190–204.

Ashmore, P.E. and Church, M. 1998: Sediment transport and river morphology: a paradigm for study. In Klingeman, P.C., Beschta, R.L., Komar, P.D. and Bradley, J.B. (eds), *Gravel-bed rivers in the environment.* Highlands Ranch, Colorado: Water Resources Publication, 115–48.

Ashmore, P.E. and Parker, G. 1983: Confluence scour in coarse braided streams. *Water Resources Research* **19,** 392–402.

Ashmore, P.E., Ferguson, R.I., Prestegaard, K.L., Ashworth, P.J., and Paola, C. 1992: Secondary flow in anabranch confluences of a braided, gravel-bed stream. *Earth Surface Processes and Landforms* **17,** 299–311.

Ashmore, P.E., Conly, F.M., deBoer, D., Martin, Y., Petticrew, E. and Roy, A.G. 2000: Recent (1995–1998) Canadian research on contemporary processes of river erosion and sedimentation, and river mechanics. *Hydrological Processes* **14,** 1687–706.

Ashworth, P.J., Bennett, S., Best, J.L. and McLelland, S. (eds) 1996: *Coherent flow structures in open channels.* Chichester: Wiley, 733 pp.

Ashworth, P.J. and Ferguson, R.I. 1986: Interrelationships of channel processes, changes and sediments in a proglacial braided river. *Geografiska Annaler,* **68A,** 361–71.

Ashworth, P.J. and Ferguson, R.I. 1989: Size-selective entrainment of bed load in gravel-bed streams. *Water Resources Research* **25,** 627–34.

Ashworth, P.J., Ferguson, R.I., Ashmore, P.E., Paola, C., Powell, D.M. and Prestegaard, K.L. 1992a: Measurements in a braided river chute and lobe. 2. Sorting of bedload during entrainment, transport and deposition. *Water Resources Research* **28,** 1887–96.

Ashworth, P.J., Ferguson, R.I. and Powell, D.M. 1992b: Bedload transport and sorting in braided channels. In Billi, P., Hey, R.D., Thorne, C.R. and Taconni, P. (eds), *Dynamics of gravel-bed rivers.* Chichester: Wiley, 497–513.

Baas, J.H. 1994: A flume study on the development and equilibrium morphology of small-scale bedforms in very fine sand. *Sedimentology* **41,** 185–209.

Baas, J.H. 1999. An empirical model for the development and equilibrium morphology of current ripples in fine sand. *Sedimentology* **46,** 123–38.

Babakaiff, C.S. and Hickin, E.J. 1996: Coherent flow structures in Squamish River Estuary, British Columbia, Canada. In Ashworth, P.J., Bennett, S.J., Best, J.L. and McLelland, S. J. (eds), *Coherent flow structures in open channels.* Chichester: Wiley, 321–42.

Bagnold, R.A. 1977: Bed load transport by natural rivers. *Water Resources Research* **13,** 303–12.

Bagnold, R.A. 1980: An empirical correlation of bedload transport rates in flumes and natural rivers. *Proceedings of the Royal Society of London, Series A* **372,** 453–73.

Bagnold, R.A. 1986: Transport of solids by natural water flow: evidence for a world-wide correlation. *Proceedings of the Royal Society of London, Series A* **405,** 369–74.

Bathurst, J.C., Graf, W.H. and Cao, H.H. 1982: Bedforms and flow resistance in steep gravel-bed channels. In Mutlu, S.B. and Mueller, A. (eds), *Mechanics of sediment transport.* Rotterdam: A.A. Balkema, 215–21.

Beechie, T.J. 2001: Empirical predictors of annual bed load travel distance, and implications for salmonid habitat restoration and protection. *Earth Surface Processes and Landforms* **26,** 1025–34.

Bennett, S.J. and Best, J.L. 1994: Structure of turbulence over two-dimensional dunes. In Béloggey, M., Rajaona, R.D. and Sleath, J.F.A. (eds), *Sediment transport mechanisms in coastal environments and rivers.* Singapore: World Scientific, 3–13.

Bennett, S.J. and Best, J.L. 1995: Mean flow and turbulence structure over fixed, two dimensional ripples: implications for sediment transport and bedform stability. *Sedimentology* **42,** 491–513.

Bennett, S.J. and Best, J.L. 1996: Mean flow and turbulence structure over fixed ripples and the ripple–dune transition. In Ashworth, P., Bennett , S.J., Best, J.L. and McLelland, S. (eds), *Coherent flow structures in open channels.* Chichester: Wiley, 281–304.

Bennett, S.J. and Bridge, J.S. 1995: The geometry and dynamics of flow-relief bed forms in heterogeneous sediment in a laboratory channel, and their relationship to water flow and sediment transport. *Journal of Sedimentary Research* **A65,** 29–39.

Bergeron, N.E. and Abrahams, A.D. 1992: Estimating shear velocity and roughness length from velocity profiles. *Water Resources Research* **28,** 2155–8.

Best, J.L. 1986: The morphology of river channel confluences. *Progress in Physical Geography* **10,** 157–74.

Best, J.L. 1987: Flow dynamics at river channel confluences: implications for sediment transport and bed morphology. In Ethridge, F.G., Flores, R.M. and Harvey, D. (eds), *Recent developments in fluvial sedimentology,* The Society of Economic Paleontologists and Mineralogists, 27–35.

Best, J.L. 1988: Sediment transport and bed morphology at river channel confluences. *Sedimentology* **35,** 481–98.

Best, J.L. 1992: On the entrainment of sediment and initiation of bed defects: insights from recent developments within turbulent boundary layer research. *Sedimentology* **39,** 797–811.

Best, J.L. 1993: On the interactions between turbulent flow structure, sediment transport and bedform development. In Clifford, N.J., French, J. and Hardisty, J. (eds). *Turbulence: perspectives on flow and sediment transport.* Chichester: Wiley, 61–92.

Best, J.L. 1996: The fluid dynamics of small-scale alluvial bedforms. In Carling, P.A. and Dawson, M. (eds) *Advances in fluvial dynamics and stratigraphy.* Chichester: Wiley, 67–125.

Best, J.L. and Kostaschuk, R. 2002: An experimental study of turbulent flow over a low-angle dune. *Journal of Geophysical Research Oceans* **107,** 3135–54.

Best, J.L. and Reid, I. 1984: Separation zone at open-channel junctions. *Journal of Hydraulic Engineering, American Society of Civil Engineers* **110,** 1588–94.

Best, J.L. and Roy, A.G. 1991: Mixing-layer distortion at the confluence of channels of different depth. *Nature* **350,** 411–13.

Billi, P. 1988: A note on cluster bedform behaviour in a gravel-bed river. *Catena* **15,** 473–81.

Biron, P., DeSerres, B. and Best, J.L. 1993a: Shear layer turbulence at unequal depth channel confluence. In Clifford, N.J., French, J.R. and Hardisty, J. (eds), *Turbulence: perspectives on flow and sediment transport.* Chichester: Wiley, 197–213.

Biron, P., Roy, A.G., Best, J.L. and Boyer, C.J. 1993b: Bed morphology and sedimentology at the confluence of unequal depth channels. *Geomorphology* **8,** 115–29.

Biron, P., Roy, A.G. and Best, J.L. 1995: A scheme for resampling, filtering and sub-sampling unevenly spaced laser Doppler Anemometer data. *Mathematical Geology* **27,** 731–48.

Biron, P., Best, J.L. and Roy, A.G. 1996a: Effects of bed discordance on flow dynamics at open channel confluences. *Journal of Hydraulic Engineering, American Society of Civil Engineers* **122,** 676–82.

Biron, P., Roy, A.G. and Best, J.L. 1996b: Turbulent flow structure at concordant and discordant open-channel confluences. *Experiments in Fluids* **21,** 437–46.

Biron, P.M., Lane, S.N., Roy, A.G., Bradbrock, K.F. and Richards, K.S. 1998: Sensitivity of bed shear stress estimated from vertical velocity profiles: the problem of sampling resolution. *Earth Surface Processes and Landforms* **23,** 133–9.

Bluck, B.J. 1982: Texture and gravel bars in braided streams. In Hey, R.D., Bathurst, J.C. and Thorne, C.R. (eds), *Gravel-bed rivers.* Chichester: Wiley, 339–55.

Bluck, B.J. 1987: Bed forms and clast size changes in gravel-bed rivers. In Richards, K.S. (ed.), *River channels: environment and process.* Oxford: Blackwell, 159–78.

Boothroyd, J.C. and Ashley, G. 1975: Process, bar morphology, and sedimentary structures on braided outwash fans, north-eastern Gulf of Alaska. In Jopling, A.V. and McDonald, B.C. (eds), *Glaciofluvial and glaciolacustrine sedimentation.* Society of Economic Palaeontologists and Mineralogists Special Publication **23,** 193–222.

Boulton, A.J., Findlay. S., Marmonier, P., Stanley, E.H. and Vallet, H.M. 1998: The functional significance of the hyporheic zone in streams and rivers. *Annual Review of Ecology and Systematics* **29,** 59–81.

Bradbrook, K.F., Lane, S.N. and Richards, K.S. 2000a: Numerical simulation of three-dimensional, time-averaged flow structure at river channel confluences. *Water Resources Research* **36,** 2731–46.

Bradbrook, K.F., Lane, S.N., Richards, K.S., Biron, P.M. and Roy, A.G. 2000b: Large eddy simulation of periodic flow characteristics at river channel confluences. *Journal of Hydraulic Research* **38,** 207–15.

Bradbrook, K.F., Lane, S.N., Richards, K.S., Biron, P.M. and Roy, A.G. 2001: Role of bed discordance at asymmetrical river confluences. *Journal of Hydraulic Engineering, American Society of Civil Engineers* **127,** 351–68.

Bradley, E.F. 1968: A micrometeorological study of velocity profiles and surface drag in the region modified by a change in surface roughness. *Quarterly Journal of the Royal Meteorological Society* **94,** 361–79.

Bradshaw, P. 1985: *An introduction to turbulence and its measurement.* Oxford: Pergamon Press, 218 pp.

Bray, D.I. 1982: Flow resistance in gravel-bed rivers. In Hey, R.D., Bathurst, J.C. and Thorne, C.R. (eds), *Gravel-bed rivers.* Chichester: Wiley, 109–33.

Brayshaw, A.C. 1983: *Bed microtopography and bedload transport in coarse-grained alluvial channels.* Unpublished Ph.D. thesis, University of London.

Brayshaw, A.C. 1984: The characteristics and origin of cluster bedforms in coarse-grained alluvial channels. In Koster, C.H. and Stell, R.H. (eds), *Sedimentology of gravels and conglomerates.* Canadian Society of Petroleum Geologists Memoir **10,** 77–85.

Brayshaw, A.C. 1985: Bed microtopography and entrainment thresholds in gravel-bed rivers. *Geological Society of America Bulletin* **96,** 218–23.

Brayshaw, A.C., Frostick, L.E. and Reid, I. 1983: The hydrodynamics of particle clusters and sediment entrainment in coarse alluvial channels. *Sedimentology* **30,** 137–43.

Bridge, J.S. 1993: The interaction between channel geometry, water flow, sediment transport and deposition in braided rivers. In Best, J.L. and Bristow, C.S. (eds), *Braided rivers*, Geological Society of London Special Publication No. 75, 13–71.

Bridge, J.S. and Best, J.L. 1988: Flow, sediment transport and bedform dynamics over the transition from dunes to upper-stage plane beds: implications for the formation of planar laminae. *Sedimentology* **35**, 753–63.

Bridge, J.S. and Gabel, S.L. 1992: Flow and sediment dynamics in a low sinuosity, braided river: Calamus River, Nebraska Sandhills. *Sedimentology* **39**, 125–42.

Bridge, J.S. and Jarvis, J. 1982: The dynamics of a river bend: a study in flow and sedimentary processes. *Sedimentology* **29**, 499–541.

Brierley, G.J. 1991: Bar sedimentology of the Squamish River, British Columbia: definition and application of morphostratigraphic units. *Journal of Sedimentary Petrology* **61**, 211–25.

Brierley, G.J. and Hickin, E.J. 1985: The downstream gradation of particle sizes in the Squamish River, British Columbia. *Earth Surface Processes and Landforms* **10**, 597–606.

Bristow, C.S. and Best, J.L. 1993: Braided rivers: perspectives and problems. In Best, J.L. and Bristow, C.S. (eds), *Braided rivers*. Geological Society of London Special Publication No. 75, 1–11.

Brunke, M. and Gonser, T. 1997: The ecological significance of exchange processes between rivers and groundwater. *Freshwater Biology* **37**, 1–33.

Buffin-Bélanger, T. and Roy, A.G. 1998: Effects of a pebble cluster on the turbulence structure of a depth-limited flow in a gravel-bed river. *Geomorphology* **25**, 249–67.

Buffin-Bélanger, T., Roy, A.G. and Kirkbride, A.D. 2000: On large-scale flow structures in a gravel-bed river. *Geomorphology* **32**, 417–35.

Buffington, J.M. 1999: The legend of A. F. Shields. *Journal of Hydraulic Engineering, American Society of Civil Engineers* **125**, 376–87.

Buffington, J.M. and Montgomery, D.R. 1997: A systematic analysis of eight decades of incipient motion studies, with special reference to gravel-bedded rivers. *Water Resources Research* **33**, 1993–2029.

Buffington, J.M. and Montgomery, D.R. 1999: Effects of sediment supply on surface textures of gravel-bed rivers. *Water Resources Research* **35**, 3523–30.

Butler, J.B., Lane, S.N. and Chandler, J.H. 1998: Assessment of DEM quality for characterizing surface roughness using close range digital photogrammetry. *Photogrammetric Record* **16** (92), 271–91.

Butler, J.B., Lane, S.N. and Chandler, J.H. 2001: Characterization of the structure of river-bed gravels using two-dimensional fractal analysis. *Mathematical Geology* **33**, 301–30.

Carbonneau, P.E. and Bergeron, N.E. 2000: The effects of bedload transport on mean and turbulent flow properties. *Geomorphology* **35**, 267–78.

Carling, P.A. 1983: Threshold of coarse sediment transport in broad and narrow natural streams. *Earth Surface Processes and Landforms* **8**, 1–18.

Carling, P.A. 1984: Deposition of fine and coarse sand in an open-work gravel bed. *Canadian Journal of Fisheries and Aquatic Sciences* **41**, 263–70.

Carling, P.A. 1987: Bed stability in gravel streams, with reference to stream regulation and ecology. In Richards, K.S. (ed.), *River channels. Environment and process*. Oxford: Basil Blackwell, 321–47.

Carling, P.A. 1991: An appraisal of the velocity-reversal hypothesis for stable pools–riffle sequences in the River Severn. *Earth Surface Processes and Landforms* **16**, 19–31.

Carling, P.A. 1999: Subaqueous gravel dunes *Journal of Sedimentary Research* **69**, 534–45.

Carling, P.A. and Orr, G.H. 2000: Morphology of riffle-pool sequences in the River Severn, England. *Earth Surface Processes and Landforms* **25**, 369–84.

Carling, P.A. and Reader, N.A. 1982: Structure, composition and bulk properties of upland stream gravels. *Earth Surface Processes and Landforms* **7**, 349–65.

Carling, P.A., Golz, E., Orr, H.G. and Radecki-Pawlik, A. 2000a: The morphodynamics of fluvial sand dunes in the River Rhine, near Mainz, Germany. I. Sedimentology and morphology. *Sedimentology* **47**, 227–52.

Carling, P.A., Williams, J.J., Golz, E. and Kelsey, A.D. 2000b: The morphodynamics of fluvial sand dunes in the River Rhine, near Mainz, Germany. II. Hydrodynamics and sediment transport. *Sedimentology* **47**, 253–78.

Carson, M.A. 1984a: The meandering–braided river threshold: a reappraisal. *Journal of Hydrology* **73**, 315–34.

Carson, M.A. 1984b: Observations on the meandering–braided river transition, the Canterbury Plains, New Zealand: part one. *New Zealand Geographer* **40**, 12–17.

Carson, M.A 1986: Characteristics of high-energy 'meandering' rivers: the Canterbury Plains, New Zealand. *Geological Society of America Bulletin* **97**, 886–95.

Carson, M.A. 1987: Measures of flow intensity as predictors of bedload. *Journal of Hydraulic Engineering, American Society of Civil Engineers* **113**, 1402–21.

Carson, M.A. and Griffiths, G.A. 1987: Bedload transport in gravel channels. *Journal of Hydrology (New Zealand)* **26**, 1–151.

Carson, M.A. and Lapointe, M.F. 1983: The inherent asymmetry of river meander planform. *Journal of Geology* **91**, 41–55

Chanson, H. 1999: *The hydraulics of open channel flow. An introduction.* London: Arnold, 495 pp.

Chin, A. 1989: Step-pools in stream channels. *Progress in Physical Geography* **13**, 391–408.

Chin, A. 1999a: On the origin of step-pool sequences in mountain streams. *Geophysical Research Letters* **26**, 231–4.

Chin, A. 1999b: The morphologic structure of step-pools in mountain streams. *Geomorphology* **27**, 191–204.

Church M. 1992: Channel morphology and typology. In Calow, P. and Petts, G.E. (eds), *The river handbook.* vol. 1. Oxford: Blackwell Scientific Publications, 126–43.

Church, M. and Hassan, M.A. 1992: Size and distance of travel of unconstrained clasts on a streambed. *Water Resources Research* **28**, 299–303.

Church, M. and Jones, D. 1982: Channel bars in gravel-bed rivers. In Hey, R.D., Bathurst, J.C. and Thorne, C.R. (eds), *Gravel-Bed Rivers.* Chichester: Wiley, 291–324.

Church, M. and Mark, D.M. 1980: On size and scale in geomorphology. *Progress in Physical Geography* **4**, 342–90.

Church, M., McLean, D.G. and Wolcott, J.F. 1987: River bed gravels: sampling and analysis. In Thorne, C.R., Bathurst, J.C. and Hey, R.D. (eds), *Sediment transport in gravel-bed rivers.* Chichester: Wiley, 43–87.

Church, M., Wolcott, J.F. and Fletcher, W.K. 1991: A test of equal mobility in fluvial sediment transport: behavior of the sand fraction. *Water Resources Research* **27**, 2941–51.

Clifford, N.J. 1993a: Differential bed sedimentology and the maintenance of riffle-pool sequences. *Catena* **20**, 447–68.

Clifford, N.J. 1993b: Formation of riffle-pool sequences: field evidence for an autogenic process. *Sedimentary Geology* **85**, 39–51.

Clifford, N.J. 1996: Morphology and stage-dependent flow structure in a gravel-bed river. In Ashworth, P.J., Bennett, S.J., Best, J.L. and McLelland, S.J. (eds), *Coherent flow structures in open channels*. Chichester: Wiley, 545–66.

Clifford, N.J. and French, J.R. 1993a: Monitoring and modeling turbulent flows: Historical and contemporary perspectives. In Clifford, N.J., French, J.R. and Hardistry, J. (eds), *Turbulence: perspectives on flow and sediment transport*. Chichester: Wiley, 1–34.

Clifford, N.J. and French, J.R. 1993b: Monitoring and analysis of turbulence in geophysical boundaries: Some analytical and conceptual issues. In Clifford, N.J., French, J.R and Hardisty (eds), *Turbulence: perspectives on flow and sediment transport*. Chichester: Wiley, 93–120.

Clifford, N.J. and Richards, K.S. 1992: The reversal hypothesis and the maintenance of riffle-pool sequences. In Carling, P.A. and Petts, G.E. (eds), *Lowland rivers: geomorphological perspectives*. Chichester: Wiley, 43–70.

Clifford, N.J., Richards, K.S. and Robert, A. 1992a: The influence of microform bed roughness elements on flow and sediment transport in gravel bed rivers: comment on a paper by M.A. Hassan and I. Reid. *Earth Surface Processes and Landforms* **17,** 529–34.

Clifford, N.J, Robert, A. and Richards, K.S. 1992b: Estimation of flow resistance in gravel-bedded rivers: a physical explanation of the multiplier of roughness length. *Earth Surface Processes and Landforms* **17,** 111–26.

Clifford, N.J., French, J.R. and Hardisty, J. (eds) 1993a: *Turbulence: perspectives on flow and sediment transport*. Chichester: Wiley, 360 pp.

Clifford, N.J., Hardisty, J., French, J.R. and Hart, S. 1993b: Downstream variation in bed material characteristics: a turbulence-controlled form-process feedback mechanism. In Best, J.L. and Bristow, C.S. (eds), *Braided Rivers*. Geological Society of London Special Publication No. 75, 89–104.

Clifford, N.J., Richards, K.S., Brown, R.A. and Lane, S.N. 1995: Scales of variation of suspended sediment concentration and turbidity in a glacial meltwater stream. *Geografiska Annaler* **77A,** 45–65.

Costello, W.R. and Southard, J.B. 1980: Flume experiments on lower-flow regime bed forms in coarse sand. *Journal of Sedimentary Petrology* **51,** 849–64.

Crisp, D.T. and Carling, P. 1989: Observations on siting, dimensions and structure of salmonid redds. *Journal of Fish Biology* **34,** 119–34.

Davies, T.R.H. 1982: Lower flow regime bedforms: rational classification. *Journal of the Hydraulics Division, American Society of Civil Engineers* **108,** 343–60.

Davies, T.R.H. and Sutherland, A.J. 1980: Resistance to flow past deformable boundaries. *Earth Surface Processes and Landforms* **5,** 175–9.

Davies, T.R.H. and Tinker, C.C. 1984: Fundamental characteristics of stream meanders. *Geological Society of America Bulletin* **95,** 505–12.

Davoren, A. and Mosley, M.P. 1986: Observations of bedload movement, bar development and sediment supply in the braided Ohau River. *Earth Surface Processes and Landforms* **11,** 643–52.

Dawson, M.D. 1988: Sediment size variation in a braided reach of the Sunwapta River, Alberta, Canada. *Earth Surface Processes and Landforms* **13,** 599–618.

Day, T.J. 1980: A study of initial motion characteristics of particles in graded bed material. *Geological Survey of Canada, Current Research, Part A, Paper 80-1A*, 281–6.

De Serres, B., Roy, A.G., Biron, P.M. and Best, J.L. 1999: Three-dimensional structure of flow at a confluence of river channels with discordant beds. *Geomorphology*, **26,** 313–35.

Desloges, J.R. and Church, M.A. 1989: Wandering gravel-bed rivers. *Canadian Geographer* **33,** 360–4.

DeVries, P. 1997: Riverine salmonid egg burial depths: review of published data and implications for scour studies. *Canadian Journal of Fisheries and Aquatic Sciences* **54,** 1685–98.

Dietrich, W.E. 1987: Mechanics of flow and sediment transport in river bends. In Richards, K.S. (ed.), *River channels: environment and process*, Oxford: Basil Blackwell, 179–227.

Dietrich, W.E. and Smith, J.D. 1983: Influence of a point bar on flow through curved channels. *Water Resources Research* **19,** 1173–92.

Dietrich, W.E. and Smith, J.D. 1984: Bedload transport in a river meander. *Water Resources Research* **20,** 1355–80.

Dietrich, W.E., Smith, J.D. and Dunne, T. 1979: Flow and sediment transport in a sand bedded meander. *Journal of Geology* **87,** 305–15.

Dietrich, W.E., Kirchner, J.W., Ikeda, H. and Iseya, F. 1989: Sediment supply and the development of the coarse surface layer in gravel-bedded rivers. *Nature* **340,** 215–17.

Dinehart, R.L. 1992: Evolution of coarse gravel bed forms: field measurements at flood stage. *Water Resources Research* **28,** 2667–89.

Dingman, S.L. 1984: *Fluvial hydrology.* New York: Freeman, 383 pp.

Diplas, P. and Parker, G. 1992: Deposition and removal of fines in gravel-bed streams. In Billi, P., Hey, R.D., Thorne, C.R. and Tacconi, P. (eds), *Dynamics of gravel-bed rivers.* Chichester: Wiley, 313–29.

Drake, T.G., Shreve, R.L., Dietrich, W.E., Whiting, P.J. and Leopold, L.B. 1988: Bedload transport of fine gravel observed by motion-picture photography. *Journal of Fluid Mechanics* **192,** 193–217.

Dyer, K.R. 1986: *Coastal and estuarine sediment dynamics.* Chichester: Wiley, 342 pp.

Easterbrook, D.J. 1999: *Surface Processes and Landforms* (2nd edn). Prentice Hall, New Jersey, 546 pp.

Einstein, H.A. and Banks, R.B. 1950: Fluid resistance of composite roughness. *Transactions, American Geophysical Union* **31,** 603–10.

Einstein, H.A. and Barbarossa, N.L. 1952: River channel roughness. *Transactions, American Society of Civil Engineers* **117,** 1121–32.

Emmett, W.W. 1980: A field calibration of the sediment-trapping characteristics of the Helley-Smith bedload samplers. *United States Geological Survey Professional Paper* **113a,** 44 pp.

Fenton, J.D. and Abbott, J.E. 1977: Initial movement of grains in a stream bed: the effects of relative protrusion. *Proceedings of the Royal Society of London, Series A,* **352,** 532–7.

Ferguson, R.I. 1981: Channel form and channel changes. In Lewin, J. (ed.), *British Rivers.* London: Allen & Unwin, 90–125.

Ferguson, R.I. 1986: Hydraulics and hydraulic geometry. *Progress in Physical Geography,* **10,** 1–31.

Ferguson, R.I. 1987: Hydraulic and sedimentary controls of channel pattern. In Richards, K.S. (ed.), *River channels: environment and process.* Oxford: Basil Blackwell, 129–58.

Ferguson, R.I. 1993: Understanding braiding processes in gravel-bed rivers: progress and unsolved problems. In Best, J.L. and Bristow, C.S. (eds), *Braided rivers.* Geological Society of London Special Publication No. 75, 73–87.

Ferguson, R.I., Ashmore, P.E., Ashworth, P.J., Paola, C. and Prestegaard, K.L. 1992:

Measurements in a braided river chute and lobe. 1. Flow pattern, sediment transport and channel change. *Water Resources Research*, **28**, 1877–86.

Ferguson, R.I., Hoey, T., Wathen, S. and Werritty, A. 1996a: Field evidence for rapid downstream fining of river gravels through selective transport. *Geology*, **24**, 179–82.

Ferguson, R.I., Kirkbride, A.D. and Roy, A.G. 1996b: Markov analysis of velocity fluctuations in gravel-bed rivers. In Ashworth, P., Best, J.L., Bennett, S.J., and McLelland, S.J. (eds), *Coherent flow structures in open channels*. Chichester: Wiley, 165–83.

Ferguson, R.I., Prestegaard, K.L. and Ashworth, P.J. 1989: Influence of sand on hydraulics and gravel transport in a braided gravel bed river. *Water Resources Research* **25**, 635–43.

Findlay, S. 1995: Importance of surface–subsurface exchange in stream ecosystems. *Limnology and Oceanography* **40**, 159–64.

Francis, J.R.D. 1973: Experiments on the motion of solitary grains along the bed of a water-stream. *Proceedings of the Royal Society of London* **A332**, 443–71.

Frostick, L.E., Lucas, P.M. and Reid, I. 1984: The infiltration of fines matrices into coarse-grained alluvial sediments and its implications for stratigraphical interpretation. *Journal of the Geological Society of London* **141**, 955–65.

Gaudet, J.M. and Roy, A.G. 1995: Effects of bed morphology on flow mixing length at river confluences. *Nature* **373**, 138–9.

Goff, J.R. and Ashmore, P. 1994: Gravel transport and morphological change in braided Sunwapta River, Alberta, Canada. *Earth Surface Processes and Landforms* **19**, 195–212.

Gomez, B. 1983: Temporal variations in bedload transport rates: the effect of progressing bed armouring. *Earth Surface Processes and Landforms* **8**, 41–54.

Gomez, B. 1991: Bedload transport. *Earth-Science Reviews* **31**, 89–132.

Gomez, B. 1993: Roughness of stable, armored gravel beds. *Water Resources Research* **29**, 3631–42

Gomez, B. and Church, M. 1989: An assessment of bed load sediment transport formulae for gravel bed rivers. *Water Resources Research* **25**, 1161–86.

Gomez, B., Naff, R.L., and Hubbell, D.W. 1989: Temporal variations in bedload transport rates associated with the migration of bedforms. *Earth Surface Processes and Landforms* **14**, 135–56.

Gordon, C.M. 1974: Intermittent momentum transport in a geophysical boundary layer. *Nature* **248**, 392–4.

Goudie, A. 1994: *Geomorphological techniques* (2nd edn). London: Routledge, 570 pp.

Grass, A.J. 1970: Initial instability of fine sand bed. *Journal of the Hydraulics Division, American Society of Civil Engineers* **96**, 619–32.

Grass, A.J. 1971: Structural features of turbulent flow over smooth and rough boundaries. *Journal of Fluid Mechanics* **50**, 233–55.

Grass, A.J. 1983: The influence of boundary layer turbulence on the mechanics of sediment transport. *Euromech 156; Mechanics of Sediment Transport*, Rotterdam, 3–17.

Grass, A.J., Stuart, R.J. and Mansour-Tehrani, M. 1991: Vortical structures and coherent motion in turbulent flow over smooth and rough boundaries. *Philosophical Transactions of the Royal Society of London, Series A* **336**, 35–65.

Griffiths, G.A. 1989: Form resistance in gravel channels with mobile beds. *Journal of Hydraulic Engineering, American Society of Civil Engineers* **115**, 340–55.

Hammond, F.D.C., Heathershaw, A.D. and Langhorne, D.N. 1984: A comparison between Shields' threshold criterion and the movement of loosely packed gravel in a tidal channel. *Sedimentology* **31**, 51–62.

Hardisty, J. 1993: Monitoring and modeling sediment transport at turbulent frequencies. In Clifford, N.J., French, J.R. and Hardisty, J. (eds), *Turbulence: perspectives on flow and sediment transport*. Chichester: Wiley, 35–59.

Harris, T. and Richards, K.S. 1995: Design and calibration of a recording bedload trap. *Earth Surface Processes and Landforms* **20**, 711–20.

Harvey, J.W. and Bencala, K.E. 1993: The effect of streambed topography on surface–subsurface water exchange in mountain catchments. *Water Resources Research* **29**, 89–98.

Harvey, J.W. and Wagner, B.J. 2000: Quantifying hydrologic interactions between streams and their subsurface hyporheic zones. In Jones, J.B and Mulholland, P.J. (eds), *Streams and ground waters*. New York: Academic Press, 3–44.

Hassan, M.A., Church, M. and Schick, A.P. 1991: Distance of movement of coarse particles in gravel bed streams. *Water Resources Research* **27**, 503–11.

Hassan, M.A. and Church, M. 1992a: The movement of individual grains on the streambed. In Billi, P., Hey, R.D., Thorne, C.R. and Taconni, P. (eds), *Dynamics of gravel-bed rivers*. Chichester: Wiley, 159–75.

Hassan, M.A., Church, M., and Ashworth, P.J. 1992b: Virtual rate and mean distance of travel of individual clasts in gravel-bed channels. *Earth Surface Processes and Landforms* **17**, 617–27.

Hassan, M.A. and Reid, I. 1990: The influence of microform bed roughness elements on flow and sediment transport in gravel bed rivers. *Earth Surface Processes and Landforms* **15**, 739–50.

Head, M.R. and Bandyopadhyay, P. 1981: New aspects of turbulent boundary layer structure. *Journal of Fluid Mechanics* **107**, 297–338.

Heathershaw, A.D. and Langhorne, D.N. 1988: Observations of near-bed velocity profiles and seabed roughness in tidal currents flowing over sandy gravels. *Estuarine and Coastal Shelf Science* **26**, 459–82.

Heggberget, T.G., Haukebo, T., Mork, J. and Stahl., G. 1988: Temporal and spatial segregation of spawning in sympatric populations of Atlantic salmon, *Salmo salar L.*, and brown trout, *Salmo trutta L. Journal of Fish Biology* **33**, 347–56.

Hey. R.D. 1988: Bar form resistance in gravel-bed rivers. *Journal of Hydraulic Engineering, American Society of Civil Engineers* **114**, 1498–1508.

Hey, R.D. and Thorne, C.R. 1983: Accuracy of surface samples from gravel bed material. *Journal of Hydraulic Engineering, American Society of Civil Engineers* **109**, 842–51.

Hey, R.D. and Thorne, C. R. 1986: Stable channels with mobile gravel beds. *Journal of Hydraulic Engineering, American Society of Civil Engineers* **112**, 671–89.

Hickin, E.J. 1978: Mean flow structure in meanders of the Squamish River, British Columbia. *Canadian Journal of Earth Sciences* **15**, 1833–49.

Hickin, E.J. 1984: Vegetation and river channel dynamics. *The Canadian Geographer* **28**, 111–126.

Hickin, E.J. and Nanson, G.C. 1984: Lateral migration rates of river bends. *Journal of Hydraulic Engineering, American Society of Civil Engineers* **110**, 1557–67.

Hoey, T.B. 1992: Temporal variations in bedload transport rates and sediment storage in gravel-bed rivers. *Progress in Physical Geography* **16**, 319–38.

Hoey, T.B. and Sutherland, A.J. 1991: Channel morphology and bedload pulses in braided rivers: a laboratory investigation. *Earth Surface Processes and Landforms* **16**, 447–62.

Hooke, R. Le B. 1975: Distribution of sediment transport and shear stress in a meander bend. *Journal of Geology* **83**, 543–65.

Horton, J.K 2001: *Flow and bedform dynamics of a bimodal sand–gravel mixture.* Unpublished Ph.D. Thesis, School of Earth Sciences, University of Leeds, UK.

Hynes, H.B.N. 1970: *The ecology of running waters.* Toronto: University of Toronto Press, 555 pp.

Iseya, F. and Ikeda, H. 1987: Pulsations in bedload transport rates induced by a longitudinal sediment sorting: a flume study using sand and gravel mixtures. *Geografiska Annaler* **69A**, 15–27.

Jackson, N.A. 1976: The propagation of a modified flow downstream of a change of roughness. *Quarterly Journal of the Royal Meteorological Society* **102**, 924–33.

Jackson, R.G. 1976: Sedimentological and fluid-dynamic implications of the turbulent bursting phenomenon in geophysical flows. *Journal of Fluid Mechanics* **77**, 531–60.

Jackson, W.L. and Beschta, R.L. 1982: A model of two-phase bedload transport in an Oregon coast range stream. *Earth Surface Processes and Landforms* **7**, 517–28.

Jain, S.C. and Kennedy, J.F 1974: The spectral evolution of sedimentary bedforms. *Journal of Fluid Mechanics* **63(2)**, 301–14.

Jones, J.B. and Holmes, R.M. 1996: Surface–subsurface interactions in stream ecosystems. *Trends in Ecology and Evolution* **11**, 239–43.

Julien, P. and Klassen, G. 1995: Sand-dune geometry of large rivers during floods. *Journal of Hydraulic Engineering, American Society of Civil Engineers* **121**, 657–63.

Keller, E.A. 1971: Areal sorting of bed load material; the hypothesis of velocity reversal. *Geological Society of America Bulletin* **82**, 753–56.

Keller, E.A. and Melhorn, N. 1978: Rhythmic spacing and origin of pools and riffles. *Geological Society America Bulletin* **89**, 723–30.

Keller, E.A., Knodolf, G.M., and Hagerty, D.J. 1990: Groundwater and fluvial processes; selected observations. In Higgins, C.G. and Coates, D.R. (eds), *Groundwater geomorphology; the role of subsurface water in earth-surface processes and landforms.* Geological Society of America Special Paper 252, 319–40

Kellerhals, R. and Church, M. 1989: The morphology of large rivers: characterization and management. In Dodge, D.P. (ed.), *Proceedings of the International Large River Symposium, Canadian Special Publication of Fisheries and Aquatic Sciences* **106**, 31–48.

Kennedy, B.A. 1984: On Playfair's law of accordant junctions. *Earth Surface Processes and Landforms* **9**, 153–73.

Kirchner, J.W., Dietrich, W.E., Iseya, F. and Ikeda, H. 1990: The variability of critical shear stress, friction angle, and grain protrusion in water-worked sediments. *Sedimentology* **37**, 647–72.

Kirkbride, A. 1993: Observations of the influence of bed roughness on turbulence structure in depth limited flow over gravel beds. In Clifford, N.J., French, J.R. and Hardisty, J. (eds), *Turbulence: perspectives on flow and sediment transport.* Chichester: Wiley, 185–96.

Kirkbride, A.D. 1994: Visualization of the turbulent flow structure in a gravel-bed river. *Earth Surface Processes and Landforms* **19**, 819–25.

Kirkgöz, M.S. 1989: Turbulent velocity profiles for smooth and rough open channel flow. *Journal of Hydraulic Engineering, American Society of Civil Engineers* **115**, 1543–61.

Kline, S.J., Reynolds, W.C., Schraub, F.A. and Runstadler, P.W. 1967: The structure of turbulent boundary layers. *Journal of Fluid Mechanics* **30**, 741–73.

Klingeman, P. and MacArthur, R. 1990: Sediment transport and aquatic habitat in gravel-bed rivers. *Hydraulic Engineering: Proceedings of the National Conference,* American Society of Civil Engineers, 1116–1121.

Knighton, A.D. 1998: *Fluvial forms and processes. A new perspective.* London: Arnold, 383 pp.

Knighton, A.D. and Nanson, G.C. 1993: Anastomosis and the continuum of channel pattern. *Earth Surface Processes and Landforms* **18,** 613–25.

Komar, P.D. 1987a: Selective grain entrainment by a current from a bed of mixed sizes: a reanalysis. *Journal of Sedimentary Petrology* **57,** 203–11.

Komar, P.D. 1987b: Selective gravel entrainment and the empirical evaluation of flow competence. *Sedimentology* **34,** 1165–76.

Komar, P.D. 1996: Entrainment of sediment from deposits of mixed grain sizes and densities. In Carling, P.A. and Dawson, M.R. (eds), *Advances in fluvial dynamics and stratigraphy,* Chichester: Wiley, 127–81.

Komar, P.D. and Carling, P.A. 1991: Grain sorting in gravel-bed streams and the choice of particle sizes for flow-competence evaluations. *Sedimentology* **38,** 489–502.

Komar, P.D. and Li, Z. 1986: Pivoting analyses of the selective entrainment of sediments by shape and size with application to gravel threshold. *Sedimentology* **33,** 425–36.

Komar, P.D. and Li, Z. 1988: Applications of grain-pivoting and sliding analysis to selective entrainment of gravel and flow competence evaluations. *Sedimentology* **35,** 681–95.

Kondolf, G.M., Sale, M.J. and Wolman, M.G. 1993: Modification of fluvial gravel size by spawning salmonids. *Water Resources Research* **29,** 2265–74.

Kostaschuk, R. 2000: A field study of turbulence and sediment dynamics over subaqueous dunes with flow separation. *Sedimentology* **47,** 519–31.

Kostaschuk, R. and Church, M. 1993: Macroturbulence generated by dunes: Fraser River, Canada. *Sedimentary Geology* **85,** 25–37.

Kostaschuk, R. and Ilersich, S.A. 1995: Dune geometry and sediment transport, Fraser River, British Columbia. In Hickin, E.J. (ed.), *River geomorphology.* Chichester: Wiley, 19–36.

Kostaschuk, R. and Villard, P. 1996: Flow and sediment transport over large subaqueous dunes: Fraser River, Canada. *Sedimentology* **43,** 849–63.

Kostaschuk, R.A., Church, M.A. and Luternauer, J.L. 1989: Bedforms, bed material, and bedload transport in a salt-wedge estuary: Fraser River, British Columbia. *Canadian Journal of Earth Sciences* **26,** 1440–52.

Koster, E.H. 1978: Transverse ribs: their characteristics, origin and paleohydraulic significance. In Miall, A.D. (ed.), *Fluvial sedimentology.* Memoir 5, Canadian Society of Petroleum Geologists, Calgary, Canada.

Lane, S.N., Richards, K.S. and Warburton, J. 1993: Comparison between high frequency velocity records obtained with spherical and discoidal electromagnetic current meters. In Clifford, N.J., French, J.R. and Hardisty, J. (eds), *Turbulence: perspectives on flow and sediment transport.* Chichester: Wiley, 121–64.

Lane, S.N. 2000: The measurement of river channel morphology using digital photogrammetry. *Photogrammetric Record* **16** (96), 937–61.

Lane, S.N., Biron, P., Bradbrook, K.F., Buttler, J.B, Chandler, J.H. Crowell, M.D., McLelland, S.J., Richards, K.S. and Roy, A.G. 1998: Three-dimensional measurements of river channel flow processes using acoustic Doppler velocimetry. *Earth Surface Processes and Landforms* **23,** 1247–67.

Lane, S.L., Bradbrook, K.F., Richards, K.S., Biron, P.M. and Roy, A.G. 2000: Secondary circulation cells in river channel confluences: measurement artifacts or coherent flow structures. *Hydrological Processes* **14,** 2047–71.

Lapointe, M.F. 1992: Burst-like sediment suspension events in a sand bed river. *Earth Surface Processes and Landforms* **17,** 253–70.

Lapointe, M.F. 1996: Frequency spectra and intermittency of the turbulent suspension process in a sand-bed river. *Sedimentology* **43,** 439–49.

Laronne, J.B. and Carson, M.A. 1976: Interrelationships between bed morphology and bed material transport for a small, gravel-bed channel. *Sedimentology* **23,** 67–85.

Lawler, D.M. 1992: Process dominance in bank erosion systems. In Carling, P.A. and Petts, G.E. (eds) *Lowland floodplain rivers: geomorphological perspectives.* Chichester: Wiley, 117–43.

Lawless, M. and Robert, A. 2001a: Scales of boundary resistance in coarse-grained channels. *Geomorphology* **39,** 221–38.

Lawless, M. and Robert, A. 2001b: Three-dimensional flow structure around small-scale bedforms in a simulated gravel-bed environment. *Earth Surface Processes and Landforms* **26,** 507–22.

Leeder, M.R. 1983: On the interactions between turbulent flow, sediment transport and bedform mechanics in channelized flows. In Collinson, J.D. and Lewin, J. (eds), *Modern and ancient fluvial systems.* Internal Association of Sedimentologists Special Publication **6,** 5–18

Leopold, L.B. 1997: *Water, rivers and creeks.* Sausalito: University Science Books, 185 pp.

Leopold, L.B. and Emmett, W.W. 1976: Bedload measurements, East Fork River, Wyoming. *Proceedings of the National Academy of Science (USA)*, **73,** 1000–4.

Leopold, L.B. and Maddock, T. 1953: The hydraulic geometry of stream channels and some physiographic implications. *United States Geological Survey Professional Paper* **252,** 57 pp.

Leopold, L.B. and Wolman, M.G. 1957: River channel patterns: braided, meandering, and straight. *United States Geological Survey Professional Paper* **282-B,** 85 pp.

Leopold, L.B., Wolman, M.G. and Miller, J.P. 1964: *Fluvial Processes in Geomorphology.* San Francisco: Freeman, 522 pp.

Levi, E. 1991: Vortices in hydraulics. *Journal of Hydraulic Engineering, American Society of Civil Engineers* **117,** 399–413.

Li, M.Z. 1994: Direct skin friction measurements and stress partitioning over movable sand ripples. *Journal of Geophysical Research* **99,** 791–9.

Li, Z. and Komar, P.D. 1986: Laboratory measurements of pivoting angles for applications to selective entrainment of gravel in a current. *Sedimentology* **33,** 413–23.

Limerinos, J.T. 1970: Determination of the Manning coefficient from measured bed roughness in natural channels. *United States Geological Survey Water-Supply Paper*, **1898-B.**

Lisle, T.E. 1979: A sorting mechanism for a riffle-pool sequence. *Geological Society of America Bulletin* **90,** 1142–57.

Lisle, T.E. 1989: Sediment transport and resulting deposition in spawning gravels, North Coastal California. *Water Resources Research* **25,** 1303–19.

Lisle, T.E. and Hilton, S. 1999. Fine bed material in pools of natural gravel bed channels. *Water Resources Research* **35,** 1291–1304.

Lisle, T.E. and Lewis, J. 1992. Effects of sediment transport on survival of salmonid embryos in a natural stream: a simulation approach. *Canadian Journal of Fisheries and Aquatic Sciences* **49,** 2337–44.

Lu, S.S. and Willmarth, W.W. 1973. Measurements of the structure of the Reynolds stress in a turbulent boundary layer. *Journal of Fluid Mechanics* **60,** 481–511.

Luchik, T.S. and Tiederman, W.G. 1987. Timescales and structure of ejections and bursts in turbulent channel flows. *Journal of Fluid Mechanics* **174,** 529–52.

McDonald, B.C. and Banerjee, I. 1971: Sediments and bed forms on a braided outwash plain. *Canadian Journal of Earth Sciences* **8,** 1282–301.

McLean, S.R., Nelson, J.M. and Wolfe, S.R. 1994: Turbulence structure over two-dimensional bedforms: implications for sediment transport. *Journal of Geophysical Research* **99,** 12 729–47.

McLean, S.R., Nelson, J.M. and Shreve, R.L. 1996: Flow–sediment interactions in separating flows over bedforms. In Ashworth, P., Bennett, S., Best, J. and McLelland, S. (eds), *Coherent flow structures in open channels.* Chichester: Wiley, 203–26.

McLean, S.R., Wolfe, S.R. and Nelson, J.M. 1999: Spatially averaged flow over a wavy boundary revisited. *Journal of Geophysical Research* **104,** 15 743–53.

McLean, D.G., Church, M. and Tassone, B. 1999: Sediment transport along lower Fraser River 1. Measurements and hydraulic computations. *Water Resources Research* **35,** 2533–48.

McLelland, S.J. and Nicholas, A.P. 2000: A new method for evaluating errors in high-frequency ADV measurements. *Hydrological Processes* **14,** 351–66.

McLelland, S.J., Ashworth, P.J. and Best, J.L. 1996: The origin and downstream development of coherent flow structures at channel junctions. In Ashworth, P.J., Bennett, S.J., Best, J.L and McLelland, S.J. (eds), *Coherent flow structures in open channels.* Chichester: Wiley, 459–89.

Meyer-Peter, E. and Muller, R. 1948: Formulas for bed-load transport. In *International Association for Hydraulic Research Proceedings, 2nd Congress,* Stockholm, 39–65.

Miall, A.D. 1977: A review of the braided-river depositional environment. *Earth-Science Reviews* **13,** 1–62.

Middleton, G. and Southard, J.B. 1984: *Mechanics of sediment movement.* SEPM. Short Course number 3.

Milne, J.A. 1982: Bed forms and bend-arc spacings of some coarse-bedload channels in Upland Britain. *Earth Surface Processes and Landforms* **7,** 227–40.

Milner, N.J, Scullion, J., Carling, P.A. and Crisp, D.T. 1981: The effects of discharge on sediment dynamics and consequent effects on invertebrates and salmonids in upland rivers. *Advances in Applied Biology* **6,** 153–220.

Montgomery, D.R. 2001: Geomorphology, river ecology, and ecosystem management. In Dorava, J.M., Montgomery, D.R., Palcsak, B.B. and Fitzpatrick, F.A. (eds), *Geomorphic processes and riverine habitat,* Water Science and Application 4, Washington DC: American Geophysical Union, 247–53.

Montgomery, D.R. and Buffington, J.M. 1997: Channel-reach morphology in mountain drainage basins. *Geological Society of America Bulletin* **109,** 596–611.

Montgomery, D.R. and Buffington, J.M. 1998: Channel processes, classification, and response. In Naiman, R. and Bilby, R. (eds), *River ecology and management.* New York: Springer-Verlag, 13–42.

Montgomery, D.R., Buffington, J.M., Smith, R.D., Schmidt, K.M. and Pess, G. 1995: Pool spacing in forest channels. *Water Resources Research* **31,** 1097–105.

Montgomery, D.R., Buffington, J.M., Peterson, N.P., Schuett-Hames, D. and Quinn, T.P. 1996: Stream-bed scour, egg burial depths, and the influence of salmonid spawning on bed surface mobility and embryo survival. *Canadian Journal of Fisheries and Aquatic Sciences* **53,** 1061–70.

Mosley, M.P. 1976: An experimental study of channel confluences. *Journal of Geology* **107,** 1713–33.

Mosley, M.P. and Tindale, D.S. 1985: Sediment variability and bed material sampling in gravel-bed rivers. *Earth Surface Processes and Landforms* **10**, 465–82.

Mulhearn, P.J. 1978: A wind-tunnel boundary-layer study of the effects of a surface roughness change: rough to smooth. *Boundary-Layer Meteorology* **15**, 3–30.

Naden, P.S. and Brayshaw, A.C. 1987: Small- and medium-scale bedforms in gravel-bed rivers. In Richards, K.S. (ed.), *River channels: environment and process*. Oxford: Basil Blackwell, 249–71.

Nelson, J. and Smith, J.D. 1989: Mechanics of flow over ripples and dunes. *Journal of Geophysical Research* **94**, 8146–62.

Nelson, J., McLean, S. and Wolfe, S. 1993: Mean flow turbulence over two-dimensional bed forms. *Water Resources Research* **29**, 3935–53.

Nelson, J.M., Shreve, R.L., McLean, S.R. and Drake, T.G. 1995: Role of near-bed turbulence structure in bed load transport and bed form mechanics. *Water Resources Research* **31**, 2071–86.

Nepf, H.M. 1999: Drag, turbulence, and diffusion in flow through emergent vegetation. *Water Resources Research* **35**, 479–89.

Nepf, H.M. and Vivoni, E.R. 2000: Flow structure in depth-limited, vegetated flow. *Journal of Geophysical Research* **105**, C12, 28 547–57.

Nezu, I. and Nakagawa, H. 1993: *Turbulence in open-channel flows*. IAHR Monograph Series. Rotterdam: A.A. Balkema, 281 pp.

Nikora, V.I. and Goring, D.G. 1998: ADV measurements of turbulence: can we improve their interpretation? *Journal of Hydraulic Engineering, American Society of Civil Engineers* **124**, 630–4.

Nikora, V.I. and Smart, G.M. 1997: Turbulence characteristics of New Zealand gravel-bed rivers. *Journal of Hydraulic Engineering, American Society of Civil Engineers* **123**, 764–73.

Nikora, V.I., Goring, D.G. and Biggs, B.J.F. 1998: On gravel-bed roughness characterization. *Water Resources Research* **34**, 517–27.

Nowell, A.R.M. and Church, M. 1979: Turbulent flow in a depth-limited boundary layer. *Journal of Geophysical Research* **84**, 4816–24.

Oliver, M.A. and Webster, R. 1986: Semi-variogram for modelling the spatial pattern of landform and soil properties. *Earth Surface Processes and Landforms* **11**, 491–504.

Paola, C., Gust, G. and Southard, J.B. 1986: Skin friction behind isolated hemispheres and the formation of obstacles marks. *Sedimentology* **33**, 279–93.

Paola, C., Parker, G., Seal, R., Sinha, S.K., Southard, J.B. and Wilcock, P.R. 1992: Downstream fining by selective deposition in a laboratory flume. *Science* **258**, 1757–60.

Parker, G. and Klingeman, P.C. 1982: On why gravel bed streams are paved. *Water Resources Research* **18**, 1409–23.

Parker, G. and Peterson, A.W. 1980: Bar resistance of gravel bed rivers. *Journal of the Hydraulics Division, American Society of Civil Engineers* **106**, 1559–75.

Parker, G., Klingeman, P.C. and McLean, D.G. 1982: Bedload and size distribution in paved gravel-bed streams. *Journal of the Hydraulics Division, American Society of Civil Engineers* **108**, 544–71.

Parker, G., Diplas, P. and Akiyama, J. 1983: Meander bends of high amplitude. *Journal of Hydraulic Engineering, American Society of Civil Engineers* **109**, 1323–37.

Parkinson, D., Petit, F., Perpinien, G. and Phillipart, J.-C. 1999: Habitats de reproduction des poisons et processus géomorphologiques dans des rivières a fond caillouteux. Essai de synthèse et applications a quelques rivières du basin de la Meuse.

Bulletin de la Société Géographique de Liège **36,** 31–52.

Petit, F. 1987: The relationship between shear stress and the shaping of the bed of a pebble-loaded river, La Rulles, Ardennes. *Catena* **14,** 453–68.

Petit, F. 1989: The evaluation of grain shear stress from experiments in a pebble-bedded flume. *Earth Surface Processes and Landforms* **14,** 499–508.

Petit, F. 1994: Dimensionless critical shear stress evaluations from flume experiments using different gravel beds. *Earth Surface Processes and Landforms* **19,** 565–76.

Powell, D.M. 1998: Patterns and processes of sediment sorting in gravel-bed rivers. *Progress in Physical Geography* **22,** 1–32.

Prent, M.T.H. and Hickin, E.J. 2001: Annual regime of bedforms, roughness and flow resistance, Lillooet River, British Columbia, BC. *Geomorphology* **41,** 369–90.

Prestegaard, K.L. 1983: Bar resistance in gravel bed streams at bankfull stage. *Water Resources Research* **19,** 472–6.

Pye, K. 1994: Properties of sediment particles. In Pye, K. (ed.), *Sediment transport and depositional processes.* Oxford: Blackwell Scientific Publications, 1–24.

Rao, K.N., Narasimha, R. and Badri Narayanan, M.A. 1971: The 'bursting' phenomenon in a turbulent boundary layer. *Journal of Fluid Mechanics* **48,** 339–52.

Raudkivi, J. 1997: Ripples on stream beds. *Journal of Hydraulic Engineering, American Society of Civil Engineers* **123,** 58–63.

Raupach, M. 1992: Drag and drag partition on rough surfaces. *Boundary Layer Meteorology* **60,** 375–95.

Reid, I. and Frostick, L.E. 1986: Dynamics of bedload transport in Turkey Brook. *Earth Surface Processes and Landforms* **11,** 143–55.

Reid, I. and Frostick, L.E. 1987: Towards a better understanding of bedload transport. In Ethridge, F. (ed.), *Recent developments in fluvial sedimentology.* The Society of Economic Paleontologists and Mineralogists, 13–19.

Reid, I. and Frostick, L.E. 1994: Fluvial sediment transport and deposition. In Pye, K. (ed.), *Sediment transport and depositional processes.* Oxford: Blackwell Scientific Publications, 94–109.

Reid, I., Frostick, L.E. and Brayshaw, A.C. 1992: Microform roughness elements and the selective entrainment and entrapment of particles in gravel-bed rivers. In Billi, P., Hey, R.D., Thorne, C.R. and Taconni, P. (eds), *Dynamics of gravel-bed rivers,* Chichester: Wiley, 253–66.

Rhoads, B.L. 1996: Mean structure of transport-effective flows at an asymmetrical confluence when the main stream is dominant. In Ashworth, P.J., Bennett, S.J., Best, J.L. and McLelland, S.J. (eds), *Coherent flow structures in open channels.* Chichester: Wiley, 491–517.

Rhoads, B.L. and Kenworthy, S.T. 1995: Flow structure in an asymmetrical stream confluence. *Geomorphology* **11,** 273–93.

Rhoads, B.L. and Kenworthy, S.T. 1998: Time-averaged flow structure in the central region of a stream confluence. *Earth Surface Processes and Landforms* **23,** 171–91.

Rice, S. 1998: Which tributaries disrupt downstream fining along gravel-bed rivers? *Geomorphology* **22,** 39–56.

Rice, S. and Church, M. 1996a: Sampling surficial fluvial gravels: the precision of size distribution percentile estimates. *Journal of Sedimentary Research* **66,** 654–65.

Rice, S. and Church, M. 1996b: Bed material texture in low order streams on the Queen Charlotte Islands, British Columbia. *Earth Surface Processes and Landforms* **21,** 1–18.

Rice, S. and Church, M. 1998: Grain size along two gravel-bed rivers: statistical variation, spatial pattern and sedimentary links. *Earth Surface Processes and Landforms*

23, 345–63.

Richards, K.S. 1976: The morphology of riffle-pool sequences. *Earth Surface Processes and Landforms* **1,** 71–88.

Richards, K.S. 1982: *Rivers. Form and process in alluvial channels.* London: Methuen, 358 pp.

Richards, K.S. 1988: Fluvial geomorphology. *Progress in Physical Geography* **12,** 435–56.

Richardson, W.R.R., Thorne, C.R. and Mahmood, S. 1996: Secondary flow and channel changes around a bar in the Brahmaputra River, Bangladesh. In Ashworth, P.J., Bennett, S.J., Best, J.L. and McLelland, S.J. (eds), *Coherent flow structures in open channels.* Chichester: Wiley, 519–44.

Ritter, D.F., Kochel, R.C. and Miller, J.R. 1995: *Process geomorphology* (3rd edn). Dubuque, Iowa: Wm. C. Brown Publishers, 544 pp.

Robert, A. 1988: Statistical properties of sediment bed profiles in alluvial channels. *Mathematical Geology* **20,** 205–25.

Robert, A. 1990: Boundary roughness in coarse-grained channels. *Progress in Physical Geography* **14,** 42–70.

Robert, A. 1993: Microscale processes in alluvial channels. *Progress in Physical Geography* **17,** 123–36.

Robert, A. 1997: Characteristics of velocity profiles along riffle-pool sequences and estimates of bed shear stress, *Geomorphology* **19,** 89–98.

Robert, A. and Richards, K.S. 1988: On the modelling of sand bedforms using the semivariogram. *Earth Surface Processes and Landforms* **13,** 459–73.

Robert, A. and Uhlman, W. 2001: An experimental study on the ripple–dune transition. *Earth Surface Processes and Landforms* **26,** 615–29.

Robert, A., Roy, A.G. and De Serres, B. 1992: Changes in velocity profiles at roughness transitions in coarse-grained channels. *Sedimentology* **39,** 725–35.

Robert, A., Roy, A.G. and De Serres, B. 1993: Space–time correlations of velocity measurements at a roughness transition in a gravel-bed river. In Clifford, N.J., French, J.R. and Hardisty, J. (eds), *Turbulence: perspectives on flow and sediment transport.* Chichester: Wiley, 165–83.

Robert, A., Roy, A.G. and De Serres, B. 1996: Turbulence at a roughness transition in a depth limited flow over a gravel bed. *Geomorphology* **16,** 175–87.

Robinson, E.G. and Beschta, R.L. 1990: Coarse woody debris and channel morphology interactions for undisturbed streams in southeastern Alaska, USA. *Earth Surface Processes and Landforms* **15,** 149–56.

Robinson, S.K. 1991: Coherent motions in the turbulent boundary layers. *Annual Review of Fluid Mechanics* **23,** 601–39.

Rood, K.M. and Hickin, E.J. 1989: Suspended sediment concentration in relation to surface-flow structure in Squamish River estuary, southwestern British Columbia. *Canadian Journal of Earth Sciences* **26,** 2172–6.

Rosgen, D.L. 1994: A classification of natural rivers. *Catena* **22,** 169–99.

Roy, A.G. and De Serres, B. 1989: Morphologie du lit et dynamique des confluents de cours d'eau. *Bulletin de la Société Géographique de Liège* **25,** 113–27.

Roy, A.G. and Roy, R. 1988: Changes in channel size at river confluences with coarse bed material. *Earth Surface Processes and Landforms* **13,** 77–84.

Roy, A.G., Roy, R. and Bergeron, N. 1988: Hydraulic geometry and changes in flow velocity at a river confluence with coarse bed material. *Earth Surface Processes and Landforms* **13,** 583–98.

Roy, A.G., Biron, P. and Lapointe, M. 1997: Implications of low-pass filtering on power spectra and autocorrelation functions of turbulent velocity signals. *Mathematical Geology* **29,** 653–68.

Roy, A.G., Biron, P., Buffin-Bélanger, T. and Levasseur, M. 1999: Combined visual and quantitative techniques in the study of natural turbulent flows. *Water Resources Research* **35,** 871–7.

Rundle, A. 1985a: The mechanism of braiding. *Zeitschrift für Geomorphologie, Supplement-Band* **55,** 1–13.

Rundle, A. 1985b. Braid morphology and the formation of multiple channels: The Rakaia, New Zealand. *Zeitschrift für Geomorphologie, Supplement-Band* **55,** 15–37.

Saint-Laurent, D. and Guimont, P. 1999. Dynamique fluviale et évolution des berges du cours supérieur des rivières Nottoway, Broadback et de Rupert, en Jamésie (Québec). *Géographie Physique et Quaternaire* **53,** 389–99.

Sand-Jensen, K. 1998: Influence of submerged macrophytes on sediment composition and near-bed flow in lowland streams. *Freshwater Biology* **39,** 663–79.

Sand-Jensen, K. and Pedersen, O. 1999: Velocity gradients and turbulence around macrophyte stands in streams. *Freshwater Biology* **42,** 315–28.

Sand-Jensen, K., Jeppesen, E., Nielsen, K., Bijl, L. van der, Hjermind, L., Nielsen, L.W. and Iversen, T.M. 1989: Growth of macrophytes and ecosystem consequences in a lowland Danish stream. *Freshwater Biology* **22,** 15–32.

Schälchli, U. 1992: The clogging of coarse gravel river beds by fine sediment. *Hydrobiologia* **235/236,** 189–97.

Schmidt, K-H. and Ergenzinger, P. 1992: Bedload entrainment, travel lengths, step lengths, rest periods – studied with passive (iron, magnetic) and active (radio) tracer techniques. *Earth Surface Processes and Landforms* **17,** 147–65.

Schumm, S.A. 1977: *The fluvial system.* New York: Wiley, 338 pp.

Sear, D.A. 1996: Sediment transport processes in pool–riffle sequences. *Earth Surface Processes and Landforms* **21,** 241–62.

Smith, C.R. 1996: Coherent flow structures in smooth-wall turbulent boundary layers: facts, mechanisms and speculation. In Ashworth, P., Bennett, S., Best, J.L. and McLelland, S. (eds), *Coherent flow structures in open channels*, Chichester: Wiley, 1–39.

Smith, C.R. and Metzler, S.P. 1983: The characteristics of low speed streaks in the near-wall region of a turbulent boundary layer. *Journal of Fluid Mechanics* **129,** 27–54.

Smith, C.R., Walker, J.D.A., Haidara, A.H. and Sobrun, U. 1991: On the dynamics of near-wall turbulence. *Philosophical Transactions of the Royal Society of London, Series A* **336,** 131–75.

Smith, J.D. and McLean, S.R. 1977: Spatially averaged flow over a wavy surface. *Journal of Geophysical Research* **82,** 1735–46.

Smith, N.D. 1974: Sedimentology and bar formation in the Upper Kicking Horse River, a braided outwash stream. *Journal of Geology* **82,** 205–23.

Sontek Inc. 1997: *Acoustic Doppler Velocimeter Technical Documentation.* Sontek Inc.

Soulsby, R.L. 1980: Selecting record length and digitisation rate for near-bed measurements. *Journal of Physical Oceanography* **10,** 208–19.

Southard, J.B and Boguchwal, AL.A. 1990: Bed configurations in steady unidirectional water flows. Part 2. Synthesis of flume data. *Journal of Sedimentary Petrology* **60,** 658–79.

Southard, J.B., Smith, N.D. and Kuhnle, R.A. 1984: Chutes and lobes: newly identified elements of braiding in shallow gravelly streams. In Koster, E.H and Steel, R.J. (eds), *Sedimentology of gravels and conglomerates.* Canadian Society of Petroleum Geologists, Memoir 10, 51–9.

Stanford, J.A. and Ward, J.V. 1988: The hyporheic habitat of river ecosystems. *Nature* **335,** 64–6.

Stanford, J.A and Ward, J.V. 1993: An ecosystem perspective of alluvial rivers: connectivity and the hyporheic corridor. *Journal of the North American Benthological Society* **12,** 48–60.

Statzner, B. and Higler, B. 1986: Stream hydraulics as a major determinant of benthic invertebrate zonation patterns. *Freshwater Biology* **16,** 127–39.

Statzner, B., Gore, J.A. and Resh, V.R. 1988: Hydraulic stream ecology: observed patterns and potential applications. *Journal of the North American Benthological Society* **7,** 307–60.

Sukhodolov, A.N. and Rhoads, B.L. 2001: Field investigation of three-dimensional flow structure at stream confluences. 2. Turbulence. *Water Resources Research* **37,** 2411–24.

Thibodeaux, L.J. and Boyle, J.D. 1987: Bedform-generated convective transport in bottom sediment. *Nature* **325,** 341–3.

Thomas, D.S.G. and Goudie, A. (eds) 2000: *The dictionary of physical geography* (3rd edn). Oxford: Blackwell, 610 pp.

Thompson, D.M. 2001: Random controls on semi-rhythmic spacing of pools and riffles in constriction-dominated rivers. *Earth Surface Processes and Landforms* **26,** 1195–212.

Thompson, D.M. and Hoffman, K.S. 2001: Equilibrium pool dimensions and sediment-sorting patterns in coarse-grained, New England channels. *Geomorphology* **38,** 301–16.

Thompson, D.M., Wohl, E.E. and Jarrett, R.D. 1999: Velocity reversals and sediment sorting in pools and riffles controlled by channel constrictions. *Geomorphology* **27,** 229–41.

Thorne, C.R. 1982: Processes and mechanisms of river bank erosion. In Hey, R.D., Bathurst, J.C. and Thorne, C.R. (eds), *Gravel-bed rivers*. Chichester: Wiley, 227–71.

Thorne, C.R. 1998: River width adjustment. I: Processes and mechanisms (ASCE Task Committee on Hydraulics, Bank Mechanics, and Modelling of River Width Adjustment). *Journal of Hydraulic Engineering, American Society of Civil Engineers* **124,** 881–902.

Thorne, P.D., Williams, J.J. and Heathershaw, A.D. 1989: In situ acoustic measurements of marine gravel threshold and transport. *Sedimentology* **36,** 61–74.

van den Berg, J.H. 1987: Bedform migration and bed-load transport in some rivers and tidal environments. *Sedimentology* **34,** 681–98.

Vanoni, V.A. and Hwang, L-S. 1967: Relation between bed forms and friction in streams. *Journal of the Hydraulics Division, American Society of Civil Engineers* **93,** 121–44.

Vittal, N., Ranga Raju, K.G. and Garde, R.J. 1977: Resistance of two dimensional triangular roughness. *Journal of Hydraulic Research* **15,** 19–36.

Walling, D.E. and Webb, B.W. 1992: Water quality. I. Physical characteristics. In Calow, P. and Petts, G.E. (eds), *The river handbook*. vol. 1. Oxford: Blackwell, 48–71.

White, D.S. 1993: Perspectives on defining and delineating hyporheic zones. *Journal of the North American Benthological Society* **12,** 61–9.

Whiting, P.J. 1996: Sediment sorting over bed topography. In Carling, P.A. and Dawson, M.R. (eds), *Advances in Fluvial Dynamics and Stratigraphy*. Chichester: Wiley, 204–28.

Whiting, P.J. and Bradley, J.B.1993: A process-based classification system for headwater streams. *Earth Surface Processes and Landforms* **18,** 603–12.

Whiting, P.J. and Dietrich, W.E. 1990: Boundary shear stress and roughness over mobile alluvial beds. *Journal of Hydraulic Engineering, American Society of Civil Engineers* **116**, 1495–511.

Whiting, P.J., Dietrich, W.E., Leopold, L.B., Drake, T.G. and Shreve, R.L. 1988: Bedload sheets in heterogeneous sediment. *Geology* **16**, 105–8.

Whittaker, J.G. and Jaeggi, M.N.R. 1982: Origin of step-pool systems in mountain streams. *Journal of the Hydraulics Division, American Society of Civil Engineers* **108**, 758–73.

Wiberg, P.L. and Nelson, J.M. 1992: Unidirectional flow over asymmetric and symmetric ripples. *Journal of Geophysical Research* **97**, 12 745–61.

Wiberg, P.L. and Smith, J.D. 1987: Calculations of the critical shear stress for motion of uniform and heterogeneous sediments. *Water Resources Research* **23**, 1471–80.

Wiberg, P.L. and Smith, J.D. 1991: Velocity distribution and bed roughness. in high-gradient streams. *Water Resources Research* **27**, 825–38.

Wilcock, P.R. 1988: Methods for estimating the critical shear stress of individual fractions in mixed-size sediment. *Water Resources Research* **24**, 1127–35.

Wilcock, P.R. 1993: Critical shear stress of natural sediments. *Journal of Hydraulic Engineering, American Society of Civil Engineers* **119**, 491–505.

Wilcock, P.R. 1996: Estimating local shear stress from velocity observations. *Water Resources Research* **32**, 3361–6.

Wilcock, P.R. 1997: Entrainment, displacement and transport of tracer gravels. *Earth Surface Processes and Landforms* **22**, 1125–38.

Wilcock, P.R. and Southard, J.B. 1988: Experimental study of incipient motion in mixed-size sediment. *Water Resources Research* **24**, 1137–51.

Wilcock, P.R. and Southard, J.B. 1989: Bed load transport of mixed size sediment: fractional transport rates, bed forms, and the development of a coarse bed surface layer. *Water Resources Research* **25**, 1629–41.

Wilcock, P.R., Barta, A.F., Shea, C.C., Kondolf, G.M., Matthews, W.V.G. and Pitlick, J. 1996: Observations of flow and sediment entrainment on a large gravel-bed river. *Water Resources Research* **32**, 2897–909.

Wilkinson, R.H. 1984: A method for evaluating statistical errors associated with logarithmic velocity profiles. *Geo-Marine Letters* **3**, 49–52.

Williams, D.D. 1984: The hyporheic zone as a habitat for aquatic insects and associated arthropods. In Resh, V.H. and Rosenberg, D.M. (eds), *The ecology of aquatic insects*. New York: Praeger, 430–55.

Williams, G.P. 1970: Flume width and water depth effects in sediment transport experiments. *United States Geological Survey Professional Paper* **562-H**.

Williams, G.P. 1986: River meanders and channel size. *Journal of Hydrology* **88**, 147–64.

Williams, G.P. 1989: Sediment concentration versus water discharge during single hydrologic events in rivers. *Journal of Hydrology* **111**, 89–106.

Williams, J.J. 1996: Turbulent flow in rivers. In Carling, P.A. and Dawson, M.R. (eds), *Advances in fluvial dynamics and stratigraphy*. Wiley: Chichester, 1–32.

Williams, J.J., Thorne, P.D. and Heathershaw, A.D. 1989: Measurements of turbulence in the benthic boundary layer over a gravel bed. *Sedimentology* **36**, 959–79.

Wohl, E.E. 2000: *Mountain Rivers*. Washington, D.C.: American Geophysical Union, 320 pp.

Wohl, E.E. and Thompson, D.M. 2000: Velocity characteristics along a small step-pool channel. *Earth Surface Process and Landforms* **25**, 353–67.

Wohl, E.E., Masden, S. and MacDonald, L. 1997: Characteristics of log and clast bedsteps in step-pool streams of Northwestern Montana, USA. *Geomorphology* **20,** 1–10.

Wohl, E.E., Vincent, K.R. and Merritts, D. 1993: Pool and riffle characteristics in relation to channel gradient. *Geomorphology* **6,** 99–110.

Wolman, M.G. 1954: A method for sampling coarse bed material. *Transactions, American Geophysical Union* **35,** 951–6.

Wondzell, S.M. and Swanson, F.J. 1999: Floods, channel change, and the hyporheic zone. *Water Resources Research* **35,** 555–67.

Wooldridge, C.L. and Hickin, E.J. 2002: Step-pool and cascade morphology, Mosquito Creek, British Columbia: a test of four analytical techniques. *Canadian Journal of Earth Sciences* **39,** 493–503.

Yalin, M.S. 1977: *Mechanics of sediment transport* (2nd edn). Oxford: Pergamon Press, 298 pp.

Yalin, M.S. 1992: *River mechanics*. Oxford: Pergamon Press, 219 pp.

Yalin, M.S. and Karahan, E. 1979: Inception of sediment transport. *Journal of the Hydraulics Division, American Society of Civil Engineers* **105,** 1433–43.

Zimmerman, A. and Church, M. 2001: Channel morphology, gradient profiles and bed stresses during flood in a step-pool channel. *Geomorphology* **40,** 311–27.

INDEX